YOUR DREAM HOME

How To Build It For Less Than $3500

The Dream House That Grows

YOUR DREAM HOME

How To Build It For Less Than $3500

by

Hubbard Cobb

Sigman - Ward

Illustrators and
Architectural Consultants

New York
WM. H. WISE & CO., INC.
1950

ACKNOWLEDGEMENTS

WE WISH to acknowledge our appreciation for the assistance and information received from the following: Chase Brass and Copper Co., New York, N. Y.; James F. Coley, Westport, Conn.; Double-Kaye Plumbing Supply Co., New York, N. Y.; General Electric Co., Cleveland, Ohio; Holland Furnace Co., Holland, Mich.; National Electric Manufacturers Association, New York, N. Y.; National Gypsum Co., Buffalo, N. Y.; National Lumber Manufacturers Association, Washington, D. C.; Owens-Illinois Glass Corp., Chicago, Ill.; Portland Cement Association, Chicago, Ill.; United States Plywood Corp., New York, N. Y.; Westport Bank & Trust Co., Westport, Conn.; Westport Lumber Co., Westport, Conn.; Federal Housing Administration, Washington, D. C.; Housing and Home Finance Agency, Washington, D. C.; National Housing Agency, Washington, D. C.; Office of the Housing Expediter, Washington, D. C.; U. S. Department of Agriculture, Washington, D. C.; U. S. Department of Commerce, Washington, D. C.; U. S. Office of Education, Washington, D. C.; Veterans' Administration, Washington, D. C.; Victor Civkin, A.I.A.

We wish also to express our thanks to the illustrators of this book: Carl T. Sigman; William J. Ward, Jr.; William A. Patrick; Fergus Retrum; Carl R. Kinscherf; Jane Vincil; Walter J. Karl; Walter Freundel.

TABLE OF CONTENTS

YOUR DREAM HOME

How To Build It For Less Than $3500

Chapter 1

BUILDING YOUR OWN HOME

SINCE the end of World War II, over 90,000 families in this country have moved into homes that they have built entirely or partly by themselves. Twenty-five years ago, the idea of building your own home was almost unheard of—it was so much of a novelty, in fact, that it was sure to make the feature section of the Sunday paper. Today, more and more young couples, and some not so young, are getting tired of waiting for high costs to go down and are going out to build their own homes by themselves. It is, of course, the obvious solution for anyone with good health, a small income and a strong desire for a home of his own.

There seems little chance that the cost of either building materials or building labor will go down much in the immediate future. As there is no way to reduce the cost of the materials that go into a house without using inferior products, the solution is rather obvious—cut out, or at least cut down, the labor cost, which is over 60 per cent of the total construction cost. Of course, someone has to do the work, but that someone can be *you*—the only

person in the world willing to work for nothing to get your home.

Building a House by Yourself

The first question that naturally comes up is just how much of a job it is to build a house by yourself. Well, it's a big job. On the other hand, there is nothing too complicated or difficult about it. You will find that the great majority of the work consists of measuring a piece of wood, sawing it to size and then nailing it in place. When you know what the measurement should be, where the piece is to go and the size and number of nails to use, this work will not be difficult. If you can do just these three steps—measure, cut and nail—and almost anyone can, then you can build most of the house yourself.

The next big question is just how much of the entire house the average person can build by himself. That is going to depend on how much skill he has with his hands and how well he can follow directions. Each step in the construction of a house—and that includes installing the plumbing, heating and electrical systems, as well as the masonry and other jobs—is discussed in this book fully. Therefore, if you can follow simple directions and illustrations and have a modest amount of skill, you can do the entire house from basement to attic without having to call in any professional assistance. This does not mean that you will not need some help now and then. There are some jobs—such as getting the roof rafters in place—that will require two men, but that second man does not have to be an expert carpenter. He can be an unskilled laborer or just a good friend. We might better say a *very* good friend.

Professional Help

Probably only a few persons will decide to build a complete house by themselves. There are various arrangements that can be made with local contractors and builders, and such arrangements are especially helpful if you do not mind spending a little extra money to get the house up in the shortest possible time. For example, you may feel that it would be better to have the foundations dug and the house frame put up by a professional. After this has been done, you can go ahead and do the semi-skilled work, such as installing the sub-flooring, the sheathing, the roofing and the insulation. After the house is weathertight, an electrician, a plumber and a heating contractor can be employed to install the utilities. When they are finished, you go to work again and install the interior walls, the flooring, the trim and the thousand and one

other jobs that must be done before the house is finished. Now, this may not seem much like building your own home by yourself, but you will be surprised at just how much of the total building costs you save by doing only the rough and semi-skilled work yourself.

A very satisfactory arrangement that has been used frequently is for the owner-builder to work along with professional labor and do as much of the work as the professional feels that he is capable of doing. For example, why pay a plumber twenty dollars or more a day to uncrate and place plumbing fixtures in the various rooms when you can do this work yourself. Or why should a skilled electrician waste his talents and your money drilling holes through studding for **BX** cable when you can do the job just as well as he? This arrangement of working with skilled labor will save you a good deal of money, it will reduce the time that a job requires and it will also insure you of getting a satisfactory finished system.

In some communities, you may find it impossible to make this arrangement for various reasons, and in some cases, you will find that the professional builder will not be willing to take the job if you are going to help him out. The best thing to do here is to go to someone else. It is not surprising that the really top men in their trades are glad to have you help them out, because they are not interested in making a job last any longer than necessary.

Their services are always in demand and the quicker they get through one job the sooner they can take on another. Also, top-quality building men are enough interested in their trade that they are only too glad to teach you all that they can and all that you can absorb. An interesting example of such a set-up is a young veteran who built his own home by himself. Each evening, after his working day was over, a plumber would come around, check over the work that the owner-builder had done that day, and then explain how the next job should be done. The owner-builder completed his house with a perfect plumbing system, a good working knowledge of plumbing and a bill for practically nothing from the plumber. Find craftsmen of that type and you will not have any trouble building your own home.

If you feel that you are capable of doing the entire job of building the house yourself with the aid of a little unskilled help now and then, pick a person who can follow your directions and who can do simple jobs like sawing and hammering. Watch out for friends with good intentions and nothing else. They can often cause more trouble than they are worth.

Building Codes

No matter how much of the building you feel that you can do by yourself, there is another point that must be considered and that is the various local codes. Some communities have codes that insist that the electrical system be installed only by a licensed electrician. If you are building where such codes exist, the problem of whether or not you will install your own electrical system is solved for you—you don't. The same may hold true for plumbing and heating. So before you even start thinking about building your own home by yourself, check over these codes and see how much of the work the community building laws and codes will permit you to do yourself.

The Time to Build

Another important factor to remember always in building your own home is *not* to become discouraged. Once the foundations are in, the frame, roof and sheathing will go rather fast. But after that, your work will apparently slow down and it may seem that you can work all day and not make any noticeable progress at all. Don't let this get you down. Every piece of wood you saw, every nail you drive, is getting your house that much nearer to completion—it is just unfortunate that the last half seems to go so much slower than the first.

It is assumed that anyone building his own home wants a complete home in a hurry, and, therefore, it is important to plan your affairs so that you will be able to devote as much time as possible to active work on the place and also so that you will be able to move in just as soon as feasible. The best procedure to follow here is to get the house weathertight and the utilities installed as fast as you can. Once this has been done, you can move in and actually live in the house while you go ahead with the rest of the work.

The best time to start construction is in the spring as soon as the frost is out of the ground and the earth is sufficiently dry for the excavation work to get underway. By getting an early start, you will have ample time to get the house weathertight during the warm months when working outdoors is a pleasure. With luck, by fall your house will be near enough to completion so that you can move in and, with a heating system installed, do the interior work.

Living on the Site

An owner-builder is a hardy soul and many a family has pitched tents right on the building site as soon as the weather permitted and lived there during the summer or until the shell of the house was complete. When the utilities were installed, they then moved right into the house. If you have tight walls and a roof, a half-completed house makes a good summer camp. If you have utilities, it is almost a country club.

Another method, preferred by many builders, is to put up the garage first and use this for temporary living quarters until the house is far enough along to be lived in. This is a good arrangement, especially if you get a late start and need a place to live during the first winter or part of it.

The advantage of living right on the site is, first of all, that you can order larger quantities of building materials and have them on hand when you need them—and without the risk of someone walking off with them during the night. Midnight requisitioning of building materials is, unfortunately, much too common a practice.

Another advantage of living on the site is that it gives you more frequent opportunities to work on the house during your leisure moments. Holding down a nine-to-five job and then working on your home for three or four hours each night is probably the best cure for insomnia that exists. But those few hours of work each evening will get you into that house months before you would be able to move in if you confined your work merely to weekends and vacations.

WHAT YOU GAIN BY BUILDING YOUR HOUSE YOURSELF

The obvious answer to the question of what you gain by doing your own building is that you gain a saving of over 60 per cent of the total cost of your house. That should be a sufficient inducement for most of us, but there are a great many other advantages in building your own house yourself. One of the most important of these advantages is that you get just the sort of house you want and not one that has had to be trimmed down here and there so that it will fit into your budget. Almost everyone is familiar with the story of the couple who started out to see an architect with a beautiful vision of their dream house and finally ended up—after they had seen the architect, the real estate dealer, the contractor, and the banker—with a small one-story cottage, which they did not particularly want. Well, that can't happen to the man who builds his house himself, because if he wants an added feature here or there, he puts it in and the only cost is the relatively slight one for the materials. No matter how well you plan and how carefully these plans are drawn up, as the work progresses you will always find ways to improve on things. If the building is being done by hired help and you decide, after a wall is in place, that it would be nice to have a doorway at that point, you may find that, by the time you have paid for the extra labor, the door has cost you as much as several doors. But when you are doing the work yourself, you can put in doors or take out doors without adding much to your original cost.

One of the great complaints you hear from people that have just moved into new homes that were designed for them is, "Well, it's nice but we had to leave out a lot of things that we had our hearts set on having." This is a very sad state of affairs because few of us ever get a chance to build more than one house, and when you spend so much time and money, the final result should be perfect.

Another advantage of building your own house is that you can be absolutely certain that it is a good house. When you yourself have selected each piece of wood, cut it to size and nailed it in place, you can be certain that there were no short-cuts taken that would produce an inferior-grade construction. You don't have to worry about sagging floors caused by under-size joists or lack of bridging because you put the joists in and nailed the bridging between them yourself. No one can kid you into believing that the pipes in the plumbing system are something they aren't because you bought the pipes yourself and hooked them up.

And still another advantage in building your own house is the satisfaction you get when the job is finished; the feeling that this is yours, built with your own two hands and the sweat of your brow. This can be a mighty nice feeling and this in itself can be worth all the time and effort you spent on the place.

In this day and age, the creative urge that most of us have is more or less frustrated. Some people take this out in hobbies of one sort or another, but there is no hobby in the world that can compete with building your own house yourself.

THE BASIC HOUSE

If you will study the plans for the basic house described in this book, you will see that they have been carefully designed to give you the most house possible for your time and money. It is an attractive house and one that you can be proud to live in, to own, and to have built yourself.

One reason for its attractiveness is the simplicity of design, and you will thank your stars for this simplicity as you go ahead with the work, because there is nothing that wastes more time, money and temper than having to do a lot of fancy and tricky work that, rather than adding to the beauty of the house, may detract from it.

Variations

The basic house can be built in many ways and with many different materials. It can be built with or without a basement. It can be built with or without dormer windows, or they can be installed later on, after the house has been completed. The house can be built with any one of several different types of foundation. It can be built out of wood or with masonry blocks. Each method of building has been covered in the text and your only problem will be to decide which one you will select.

If you are building your own house, the time factor plays an important part. You want to get into the house just as soon as possible and yet you probably do not want to live in a half-completed house any longer than is absolutely necessary. At the same time, you do not want to have to do any jobs more than once. In view of these needs, the construction plans for the basic house have been worked out so that certain items can be done at any of various

stages of construction without involving any considerable amount of extra work.

For example, the attic can be converted into two bedrooms and a bath at some future date. We have run the water pipes for this extra bathroom up to the second floor and capped them so that additional plumbing, other than fixtures, will not be required. The ceiling joists in the attic have been framed so that a stairway can be put in, but if you do not care to install the stairway at this time, it can be left until later. The opening in the attic floor is left temporarily covered and the space on the first floor reserved for the stairs can be used as storage area for the time being. If the house is to have a basement, the inside basement stairs may also be omitted. Access to the basement is provided by the outside basement stairs and there is no positive, immediate need of inside stairs.

The same procedure has been followed with the attic dormer windows. You may find that installing these three windows during initial construction will require too much time or too much money. What you can do, however, is install the necessary rafter framing so that later on, when you are ready to finish off the attic, the only thing to be done as far as the existing roof is concerned, is to remove some of the roofing material and roofing boards. The time and money required for the additional roof framing for the dormer windows are almost nothing. Of course, if you prefer, you can install

all the stairs as well as the dormers and other items of this nature as you build. The choice is up to you, depending on your time, money, energy and desires.

The breezeway and garage can be constructed as the house is built or you can leave them out for the present. If you decide to omit them, the construction plans are such that adding the breezeway and garage later will not be difficult.

You will find that the time-consuming jobs are those that involve finished work, such as interior trim. Work of this sort can be done after you have moved in without much personal inconvenience.

Cost

It is, of course, almost impossible to make generalities about prices for a country as large as the United States. However, the materials list for the basic house—built on a concrete slab, with an expansion attic, and without the garage and breezeway—was submitted to a building supply firm in four sections of the country, the east coast, middle west, Rocky Mountain area, and Pacific coast. The total cost in each case came within the limit of $3500 which had been set. Likewise, the Vacation Hideaway came within a $1500 limit, and the Cape Cod Cottage totaled approximately $2700.

In warm sections of the country, where a central heating system is not required, or where a house may be built on piles, the cost will be reduced. Likewise a certain amount of insulation will not be required. On the other hand, in sections where an excavated cellar is necessary, this will add to the cost. But this will be a matter of several hundred dollars, and still adds up to an economical house.

Basic Assumptions

The only basic assumption in this book is that you know the nature of such woodworking tools as the saw, hammer, plane and square. Practically everybody knows that a nail driven through the end of a board that has split will not hold well, if at all, and that, once a nail has been used, to bend it back and use it again is not only a waste of time but also makes for a weak joint. It is also taken for granted that all cuts will be square unless an angular cut is specified and that all measurements will be made accurately. When, for example, the text mentions that a piece of studding must be plumb, it should be plumbed from *both* sides so that it will be absolutely upright and not leaning at a slight angle. Be sure that your cutting tools are kept sharp. It is impossible for the best craftsman to do good work with dull tools.

Chapter 2

SELECTING THE SITE AND BUYING THE PLOT

Your first step toward building a home of your own is to find the plot of ground on which to build. This sounds as if it should be easy, but actually it is going to take a considerable amount of time and investigation to make sure the plot is suited to your needs.

Finding the right site for a house means much more than locating a piece of land that is suitable for building at the price you can afford to pay. You not only must find a plot that has the necessary topographical requirements to make it a good building site, but you must also make sure that once the house has been built, it will be a comfortable place in which to live. This means that the site must be located in a pleasant neighborhood, with the desired facilities. And, quite as important, you will want to make sure that the land and the house you build on it will not decline in value rapidly.

As an owner-builder, there are several special things to keep in mind when you go looking for building sites. In your particular case, one of the most important of these points is whether or not, after you have purchased a piece of land, you will be allowed to build the house, or at least a good portion of it, yourself.

There are several types of restrictions that may prevent your doing the job yourself and, therefore, plots under such restrictions are not suitable.

BUILDING CODES

You will find that most well settled communities have various restrictive building codes. The main purpose of these codes is to insure that each building put up will be a safe place in which to live. The codes are enforced by local building inspectors, who come around while the job is under way to see that the codes are being followed.

Sensible building codes are good for every community to have. They eliminate the danger that a dishonest builder will cut his costs by using inferior materials, or materials that are too small or otherwise unsuited to the job. The code may insist that foundations in certain soil conditions be set a certain number of feet below the surface to insure that the building will have a good solid base. Unfortunately, however, some building codes go far beyond insuring the safety of construction. Some codes are so strict that they dictate the kind of materials to be used as well as the kind of workmanship that goes into the house. For example, some insist that all interior walls be made of plaster, despite the fact that plaster board can do the job just as well. Others insist that each house have a full basement, or, if the house has a second story, that there be two means of access to it. Certain codes state that all the actual construction work must be done by a licensed workman. In the latter case, if you do not have a license, you will not be able to obtain a building permit. Of course, some codes insist

only that certain jobs, such as electrical wiring or the plumbing system, be installed by a licensed workman. But even this can add substantially to the cost of a house you had originally planned to build entirely by means of your own labor.

So before you do anything else, check with the local building authorities, or building engineer, and obtain a copy of the codes. A short conversation with any of the local building officials will probably help clear up any questions you may have as to how much of the actual work you can do yourself and what, if any, special building materials must be used. When you get around to building, be sure to follow these codes at all times. And while you are with the local building officials, get a copy of the zoning map and zoning regulations, for these contain certain other restrictions about which you must be informed.

ZONING

Zoning regulations are local laws, like the building codes, which govern the type of building that can be erected in certain areas. Their over-all purpose is to protect the investment of the home-owner. A town or city may be divided into a number of areas or zones. Certain zones are given over to industrial purposes. Other zones are set aside for commercial enterprises, while still others are devoted exclusively to residential building.

If you build your home in a section that is zoned for residential development only, there is no chance that a factory, a store, or a gasoline filling station will be erected on a lot adjoining yours. In communities where there is no zoning, you do not have this sort of protection. The lots around you are open to any buyer for any purpose. Having a factory put up right next door to your house can reduce the value of your property for residential purposes to almost nothing, besides making your home uninhabitable.

While the intended purpose of zoning regulations is to protect the value of property, in some communities the regulations are of no more value to you than the paper on which they are written, because they can be changed any time the officials at the city hall feel like changing them. The best type of zoning regulations are those that can be altered only by the residents of the particular zone when they feel that adjustments of one sort or another are necessary for the general welfare of their zone and the community as a whole. This type of regulation gives you, as a home- and property-owner, a definite part in regulating the development of your zone and community.

Some zoning regulations go only so far as to set aside various areas for the exclusive use of residential building. This means that apartments, hotels, and two-family homes can be put up as well as private one-family dwellings. Other regulations go one step further and set aside certain zones for multi-family dwellings, and other zones for private dwellings. Lastly, some local regulations even state what the minimum cost of a house in a particular area must be—and perhaps the style of the house. This means that if you want to build a $10,000 Cape Cod cottage in an area that is zoned for $15,000 Tudor houses, you are out of luck. You will not be able to get a permit. Or you may find that you cannot build a detached garage. Highly restrictive zoning regulations should be studied very carefully, especially if you build in an area that contains expensive homes.

DEED RESTRICTIONS

There is one more type of restriction that you may encounter when it comes time to build your home, and that is a deed restriction. This is a restriction on the type of construction, style of building, cost, etc., that is written into the deed to the plot of land by the seller. It may have originated several generations back, and be continued through successive sales. Any such restriction is binding on you as the buyer, and while it cannot replace the zoning regulations, it can add to them to make them even more strict.

COUNTRY PROPERTY

These are the three main kinds of restriction that can prevent your building your home in certain areas. At this point you may very easily feel that if building your home in an already well built-up community is going to be that difficult, you will just by-pass all the fuss and get a piece of property out in the country where there are no laws and regulations and you can build anything you want in any way you want.

This is certainly a way to avoid restrictive building codes, but you may find that if you move way out into the country, it is going to be hard to get financing for your venture. Home-loan agencies often do not care to underwrite construction in areas that are not developed. Of course, this does not mean that you will not be able to get someone to finance a house just because it is out in the country, but it does mean that if you build in a section where there is no main thoroughfare maintained by the state or town, or where there is no chance of getting electric power or telephone service, it may prove difficult to obtain financial aid. And, even if you do get funds to

start construction, you may discover that having to dig a well, bring in a private road and maintain it, or run in power lines and telephone wires will be too costly.

If you feel that you would prefer to build some distance out of town, it is a simple matter to find out in advance if there is going to be any trouble in getting a lending agency to lend you the money to do the job. Drop in at a local bank, FHA agency, or any private home-finance company and frankly ask them whether it is advisable to purchase a home or land in the particular section you are considering. If they say, "no," better think twice before you go ahead and buy the land in question.

Of course, if you have all the ready cash you need, and do not have to depend on outside financing, the world is yours and you can build anywhere you please.

PICKING THE PROPERTY

Once you have found out in which areas the codes and restrictions allow you to build the house you have in mind by yourself, or at least a good part of it by yourself, your next job is to go to these areas and look them over critically.

A house and a piece of ground are an investment — a long-term investment for most of us. You certainly do not want the value of your property to drop suddenly. If it does, you will be

losing money just as certainly as if you bought an item for a dollar and sold it the next day for eighty cents. And nothing can be more distressing than having to pay installments on a $10,000 mortgage when the house is no longer worth half that amount, due to a sudden decrease in property value.

The best insurance you can have that the value of your dream property will not decline overnight is adequate zoning regulations, a good local government, and the right kind of people living in your prospective community.

If the area is not properly zoned, industrial or commercial enterprises that may reduce the value of the land in that section can be erected. If the local government is not honest, high taxes and numerous assessments on property may drive out prospective buyers and the value of the property will drop. And if the home-owners themselves do not keep their properties in good condition, their houses painted, and their lawns cut, they will drag down the appearance of the community, and the property values will be dragged down also.

Appearance of the Area

After you have found an area in which you want to build and checked that it is adequately protected by laws, explore it and do some further checking. The first thing to look for is the style and the condition of the houses. If they are all in the same general style and price range as yours is to be, it is a good sign. It seems that areas in which the families are more or less in the same general income bracket, with the same general taste in style of dwelling, change less rapidly than those where different levels of income and various costs and styles of houses are all mixed up together. If most of the homes are relatively new, in style as well as appearance, you can assume that this area is on the up-grade. Do not be too upset if you run into an occasional corner grocery store or gaso-

Fig. 1. Observe the general appearance of the neighborhood carefully. If old homes are being turned into rooming houses or undesirable features are beginning to intrude, the process will probably continue and property values will decline.

line filling station. If the section has been developed only lately, these may have been built before it was zoned, and you may find a few commercial enterprises of this type a great convenience. Be careful, however, of a section where there are numerous, large, old-fashioned homes. These are usually a sign that at one time the section was for the higher income brackets, but has now gone down a few pegs. Once a section begins to decline, it can decline very rapidly. It probably will not be too much longer before the large homes are made into apartments and, a few years later, the apartments cut up for roomers.

You will be able to discover a great deal about a section by observing the appearance of the houses and grounds. Homes that are kept freshly painted, lawns that are cut, and pleasant gardens are all signs that the people in this community are interested in making and keeping their homes attractive. When you find houses in need of paint or repair, rickety fences, and outbuildings that are falling apart, you should be careful.

Fig. 3. A near-by school suitable for the children is a point to keep in mind.

Fig. 2. A shopping center not too far distant from your home is a very desirable feature.

Convenience

Once you are satisfied that an area is a good place in which to live, go on to find out if it is a convenient place as well. There are many items on the convenience-list to look into. First, there should be good local schools and some means of transportation to take the children back and forth. There should be a good shopping center, not too far distant, and a church of your denom-

Check and talk with some of the people living in the particular area to see what they think of it. Do they find it a pleasant place to live? Do they have some of the same interests you do? Is there a nice community spirit that makes itself felt in various civic activities? You can also find out from the residents if there are any serious nuisances—such as heavy traffic on the roads at night, smoke and dust from distant factories that only appears when the wind is in a certain direction, or other unfavorable points of this sort.

You will also want to check the local tax assessment valuation and tax rate.

Fig. 4. While looking over the neighborhood; do not forget to find out whether there is a church of your denomination near-by.

Fig. 5. Transportation is important — transportation to school, to shopping centers, to your place of work, to business or commercial centers.

Fig. 6. Good fire and police departments are a protection to your home and may result in lower insurance rates.

ination. If you are far out of the main business and commercial center, there should be some near-by transportation connecting you with it. In sections that are heavily settled, there should be parks and playgrounds for children to give them a place to play other than the streets or vacant lots. Protection for the home and property in the form of a good police department, a good

fire department, street lights, and fire hydrants is also important.

If you have particular hobbies or pastimes, you may want to investigate the local facilities for them.

PUBLIC UTILITIES

Roads

Once you are satisfied that the neighborhood is suitable, you can start investigating the actual site where you plan to build. First of all, find out if the site is on a public or private road. If the development is rather new, it may still be a private road rather than a town or city road. This means that the town will not do any maintenance work or snow removal, and the original owner may not do anything either after

he has sold off all the lots. Towns usually will take over a private road when a certain number of homes have been built along it, but they may be particular about the construction of the road and not assume responsibility for it until it meets their specifications. If the road is not properly built, you, as one of the property owners along it, may be assessed for the necessary improvements.

Water Supply

The next point to check is whether you will be supplied with city water or must drill your own well. If there is city water, find out by asking around if the supply and pressure are adequate. Developments far away from the water supply may be troubled with low pressure, and this can be corrected only by increasing the size of the water mains, which will cost you money, or by installing additional pumping equipment in the house. Some local water systems are fine, except that they dry up during droughts, in which case the water may be turned on only during certain periods of the day.

Water from city water mains is tested, and treated if necessary, so that it is pure to drink, but, in some cases, the water contains a good many mineral salts that make it unpleasant to the taste. Hard water, as water containing a high percentage of minerals is called, will also be difficult to use for cooking or laundry purposes. And, in time, the minerals will coat the inside of pipes so they will have to be replaced. The hardness can be removed by installing water-softening equipment, but this is rather expensive. An adequate supply of soft water is a very important thing to remember in selecting a building site.

The water rate is another, if minor, point to keep in mind.

Power; Telephone

In regard to utilities, check to see if electric power is easily available to your lot, and if there will be a charge for additional poles and service wires to bring in the power. Electric power companies usually bring in power on public roads for a nominal service fee, but if you are building on a private road, you may find that you will have to pay for each pole required to bring the line from the public road to your house as well as for the necessary wires. This can run into several hundred dollars. The same thing holds true for telephone service. See Fig. 7.

Sewers

The size and location of the street sewer, if there is one, is another point on which to check. Some sewer lines are large enough to handle not only the waste from the plumbing fixtures but the discharge from the roof gutters as well. Sewers for plumbing fixtures only are called sanitary sewers, while those intended for rainfall disposal are called storm sewers. The advantage of having both types is that you will not have to build dry wells or some other type of well to take care of rain water. The position of the sewer line in relation to the house is also important. If the house is higher than the sewer line, there will be no difficulty with the waste flowing from the house to the sewer. However, when the house and sewer line are on the same level, you may have to install a special valve in the line to prevent filth from backing up from the sewer main into the house system. For best results, the sewer main should be situated lower

Fig. 7. In choosing the location for your house, be sure to check on the availability of the various public utilities, such as water supply, power and telephone service.

than the basement floor. This allows the plumbing fixtures to be installed in the basement.

If there is no main sewer line, you are going to have to install some private means of sewage disposal, such as a septic tank. This in turn means that you are going to require a fairly large lot, because the drainage field for the tank may have to be over 200 square feet. In most built-up communities, cesspools are prohibited, and, even if they are allowed, they are not as satisfactory as a septic tank.

THE INDIVIDUAL SITE

After you are completely satisfied that the community is all right, and that you can get the necessary services required for modern living, inspect the individual building sites.

Here you will be interested in the topography of the ground, the condition of the soil, and drainage. So far as topography goes, the least expensive plot to build on is one that is perfectly flat. A flat site will require a minimum amount of grading and excavation, and there will be no extras, such as retaining walls and terraces, to eat up your time and funds. On the other hand, a flat building site is the least

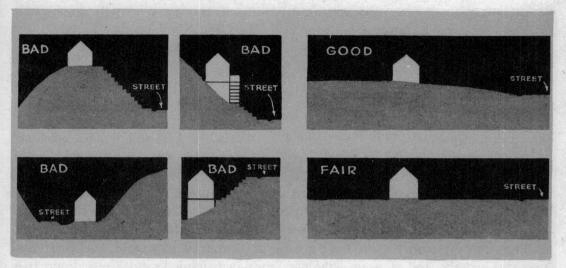

Fig. 8. Some good and bad sites for the home. Note that the best site is one where the land has a little slope. The perfectly flat site is adequate but uninteresting.

interesting. Also, it may not be very well drained or suited to homes with concrete-slab floors.

An ideal site is one where the house will be located on a slight rise in the ground. This will insure an adequate view, and there will be enough slope to allow surface water to drain away from the house. It will also render it a simple matter to make connections between the house sewer line and the sewer main, and there will be no possibility of the sewage's backing up into the house. Be careful, however, of a site with too much slope, for here you will run into considerable excavation, fill, and retaining walls. It is all well and good to have an interesting plot of ground that requires imagination to make it suitable for a house, but work of this kind requires money, because excavating and hauling fill is not easily done by the average home-builder.

If you have a site high above the street level or grade, you will need a steep driveway to get to the garage, and a front walk with steps. A garage at the top of a steep slope is all right in summer, but you may find it impossible to get up the driveway in slippery weather. And there is the added hazard, on drives of this type, of the car brakes' failing, with the car backing down across the thoroughfare.

If you should be wary of sites that are high above the street level, you want to be doubly careful of those far below the street. In the first place, sites like this have a bad habit of becoming extremely wet during heavy rain storms, especially if the street gutters cannot carry the load. In addition, you are still going to have trouble with the driveway and walk.

Beware especially of sites at the bottom of a gully. These are invariably damp, and trying to keep the basement dry may require a pumping system. Sites of this type usually have little or no view. See Fig. 8.

SOIL CONDITIONS

The type of soil on which you build is extremely important. The best soil, from the standpoint of economy, is probably natural soil. You will have a foot or so of topsoil and under it a base of gravel or clay. Having the top soil at hand eliminates the expense of hauling it in later on for landscaping. You can usually tell if your site has natural soil by the presence of some fairly large trees. Sometimes, however, someone has come in and removed most of the topsoil, leaving only a thin layer. Topsoil less than six inches deep is really not suitable for lawns and gardening. See Fig. 9.

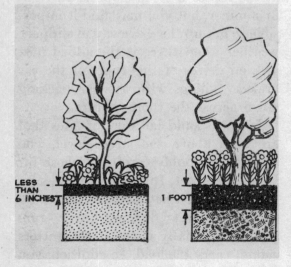

Fig. 9. Watch out for a plot where much of the natural topsoil has been removed. Lawns and gardens will require at least 6 inches of topsoil if they are to prosper.

Base Soil

As for the base soil, gravel, compact sand, and clay are all suitable for home construction. Wet sand is not satisfactory because if too much water mixes with the sand, the result is quick-sand —impossible for building unless you are prepared to spend the time and money to sink foundations down to a solid base. Rock makes a good base for any type of construction, but the cost of excavating it makes it impractical so far as small homes are concerned. It costs a great deal more money to blast and remove rock than it does to dig out gravel and clay, so think twice before you purchase a rocky plot. You will, of course, encounter small rocks from time to time, but if these can be handled by a power shovel, they should not cause any trouble and can often be used to advantage for footings, foundation walls, and similar purposes.

Fill

A great many of the sites found in new developments are built up on fill. Perhaps this particular site was once the town dump, where trash and ashes were placed. In time, these were leveled off and covered with a few feet of gravel and soil. This makes a very tricky base on which to build, because it will be many years before the fill has really become a compact mass. If you build on the fill as it exists now, your house will settle and cracks will appear in the walls, windows and doors will fail to work properly, and you may find it necessary to invest many hundreds of dollars in additional foundations. The only satisfactory way to build on filled ground is to sink the foundations far enough down so that they rest on a solid base of gravel, clay, or rock. This means, however, that the cost of your excavation is going to be way up. Sometimes fill is dumped over a low-lying or swampy area. This may appear to be a perfectly sound base, but actually you will be building on a mat of soil that is almost floating on a semi-liquid mass. The weight of the house upon this mat may cause it to sink.

See Fig. 10.

Checking the Soil

You can tell a good deal about the soil conditions just by observation. For example, many large trees are a good sign that the soil is natural and that you will not have to worry about bringing in topsoil or the possibility of fill. Out-croppings of rock are a warning that perhaps the entire site is very rocky. Soft spots in the ground, depressions, and wet spots after a rain are all indications that the fill may not be solid, and therefore not suitable for the building.

The best and surest way to find out about the nature of the soil is to dig

Fig. 10. Be careful about sites that have been built up on fill. In many cases the fill will settle in time and when it does your house will settle with it.

into it, and this it is advisable to do before the final papers are signed. Be sure, however, to obtain permission from the present owner before you undertake this operation.

Do not make the mistake of purchasing a plot of ground on the basis of just one visit. Go back again after a rain and see how it is standing up. If the soil seems dry and well drained, that is a good sign. Many low-lying lots can become extremely wet after even a light rain. Almost everyone is familiar with stories about building lots, sold during the Florida real-estate boom, that disappeared under water during the wet season. Don't be foolish enough to believe that this happens only in Florida. It has happened in lots of other places as well.

An ounce of precaution here, as in other matters, will pay off.

THE SIZE OF THE PLOT

The size of the plot may be taken out of your hands by zoning regulations that insist that each plot in the area be of a minimum size. If the choice is up to you, do not skimp too much at this point. The basic house with breezeway and garage can be built on a plot 50' by 75', but this is the bare minimum and will leave very little space for lawns, garden, etc. See Fig. 11.

Part of the joy of owning your own home is to have a decent-size lawn and garden, a space in back for an outdoor fireplace, perhaps a badminton court, and other recreational devices. You will also want a place where you can get a degree of privacy, and when houses are built one right up close against the other, there is precious little privacy for all concerned.

CHECKLIST FOR CHOOSING THE SITE

Neighborhood

Consider each of the following to determine whether the location of the property will satisfy your personal needs and preferences:

Convenience of public transportation

Stores conveniently located

Elementary school conveniently located

Absence of excessive traffic noise

Absence of smoke and unpleasant odors

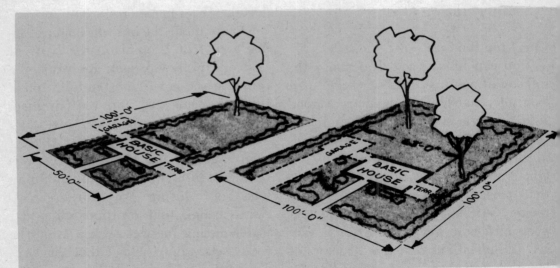

Fig. 11. Keep in mind the size of the completed house when you go looking for a plot. The house placed on a lot with a 50-foot front will have to do without the breezeway, the garage and the terrace. The house on a lot 100 feet by 100 feet will have room for future expansion and ample grounds for lawns and gardens.

Play area available for children
Fire and police protection provided
Residential usage safeguarded by adequate zoning

Existing Homes

Observe the exterior detail of neighboring houses and determine whether they are up to your standards in the following details:
Porches
Terraces
Garages
Gutters
Storm sash and screens
Weather stripping

Gardens
Size and style of house

The Lot

Consider each of the following to determine whether the lot is sufficiently large and can be properly improved:
Size of front yard satisfactory
Size of rear and side yards satisfactory
Walks will provide access to front and service entrances
Drive will provide easy access to the garage
Lot appears to drain satisfactorily
Soil condition satisfactory

BUYING THE PLOT

Once you have found a plot of land that appears to be satisfactory for your purpose, you can get down to brass tacks and start talking about buying it. At this point you will hear a good deal about contracts, title search, easements, survey, quitclaim deeds, etc. These unfamiliar terms may tend to confuse you and make you wonder if owning a piece of land is really worth all this trouble. Actually, it is not quite so bad as it may appear. Let us examine the various steps that you will have to go through before you assume title to the ground.

Agreement to Buy

The first thing you sign is a contract or agreement with the seller. This should cover the purchase price, the method of payment and a description of the property involved. In spite of the fact that you will probably make a down payment on the land when this agreement is signed, it does not actually become binding until you have had time to have the title searched and a survey of the land made so that you will be perfectly satisfied that the seller does have title to the land and that the actual description of the land is correct. When you sign this contract, the seller will furnish you with something called an abstract, which is a record of title of ownership to the land.

Title Search and Land Survey

Now you should go to work and have the title searched and the land surveyed. These are two very important steps, since there are often flaws in titles that may come up later on, after you have built your house, and that can cause you a good deal of trouble.

Have an attorney search the title for you. This is money well spent, as the average layman, who is not familiar with law or real estate, will become lost in a maze of legal terms. While the title search is being made, the land should be surveyed by an engineer and the corners of the plot marked with some sort of permanent marker. Boundary lines, especially those in the country or rural areas, can be extremely vague. When original surveys were made, almost anything standing was used as a marker, and the disputes and lawsuits resulting from the use of such ambiguous markers as "the tall oak" are still going on. Many persons buying an inexpensive piece of land do not bother with either a title search or a survey because of the cost. This is a poor idea. Title to a piece of land means title to anything firmly attached to it, such as a building. If you go ahead and build a house on a piece of land that turns out later on to be owned by someone else, the house you built as well as the land may pass into the hands of the legal owner. This can be very discouraging. The same situation exists if the boundary lines of a plot are not correct and you build part of your home on the adjoining plot. Another good reason for a title search and survey is that the average bank will not be inclined to lend you money with which to build unless they are certain that your title to the land is free and clear.

Title Guaranty

Many home owners go one step further than a title search and have the title guaranteed by a guaranty insurance concern. This is a very wise precaution because, as you will see when we take up deeds, even the very best of deeds may leave the buyer holding the proverbial bag unless he is careful about details.

The Deed

After the title search has been made, you are ready to sign the deed for the land. This is the legal document that gives to you and your heirs possession of the land. There are two kinds of deed. One is a warranty deed and the other is a quitclaim deed. Of the two, the warranty deed is much the best. This type of deed, besides including a description of the land and the price to be paid, warrants quiet enjoyment of the property by the buyer. In other words, the seller and his heirs will defend the title against any legal claims. Of course, if you buy the land and some claim comes up against it and the seller or his heirs are not in a financial position to do anything about it, you are still going to be in for some trouble. That is why a title guaranty as well as a thorough title search is so well worth having.

A quitclaim deed promises nothing. In it, the seller passes to the buyer a piece of land for better or for worse. The seller gets out of the whole business and, if any claims come up against the property, the buyer is stuck with them. It is best to stay as far away from quitclaim deeds as you can.

Deed Restrictions and Easements

You will also run into several types of restrictions in some deeds. The first is the deed restriction discussed earlier in this chapter, which can restrict the type of construction on a particular piece of land. Another type of restriction, if it may be called that, is an easement. This is a legal means of giving some party other than the owner access and certain rights to the property for various reasons. For example, if there are electric power lines running across your property, the power company doubtless has an easement on the property to run and maintain those wires. This right or privilege is included in the deed so that you, as the buyer, must continue to grant it. Sometimes an easement is granted to private parties, such as would be the case if a driveway or walk to an adjoining home runs through the property. Be sure that you are familiar with any easement in effect on your plot, because easements can seriously effect any future plans you may have.

After the deed for the land has been signed, it must be recorded by the county recorder before it is complete.

As you can easily see, getting legal possession to a piece of land is rather complex, and you should not try to swing the whole thing yourself. Consult with your local bank, real-estate agent, lawyer, and so on, and get all the advice possible before you finally take legal possession.

CHECKLIST FOR BUYING THE PLOT

Agreement to Buy
Title Search
Survey of Land
Title Guaranty

Deed
    Warranty or quitclaim
    Deed restrictions
    Easements
    Recording of deed

Chapter 3

FINANCING THE NEW HOUSE

IN SPITE of the fact that by building your house yourself, you can save over 60 per cent of the total cost, the chances are that you are going to have to borrow money to buy some or all of the necessary materials. Of course, this is not true in all cases. Some home builders will have enough money saved in the form of saving accounts, war bonds, etc., to pay for all the required materials as well as for any experienced labor that may be necessary. This is the perfect set-up, for when the house is finished, it is all yours, and there are no mortgage payments to worry about in the future.

Pay as You Go

Some builders may prefer the "pay-as-you-go method." Here you pay for the materials as they are used out of your weekly pay check. When the house is finished, it's all yours. But there are several drawbacks to this method. First, the work often goes very slowly because you may not be able to buy certain needed materials until you get your next week's or month's pay check. Another point is that you may be tempted to use less expensive and, often, inferior materials because the few dollars involved can make so much difference in how you eat for the next week. Then there is the question of delivery. Most local lumber yards will not make a special trip just to deliver a few pieces of studding or a bundle of shingles. Unless you can pick up the materials yourself, you may have to wait until there is a delivery coming your way, when your materials can be included and brought out. And, as everyone knows, there is often a reduction in price when large purchases are made.

Loans

For those who do not have the necessary cash on hand to buy their materials outright, and do not care to pay as they go along, the solution is to get some lending institution to finance the venture.

There are relatively few homes built today on which some of the financing is not handled by one type or another of lending agency. The man who builds a $5,000 home and the man who builds a $50,000 home will probably both get some of the money to build from a bank, savings and loan association, building and loan association, mortgage loan company, or other private lender. In return for the money to build his house, the owner gives to the lending agency a note promising to pay the sum back in a certain length of time, together with interest. The house and the land on which it is built are put up as security for this note. This is a mortgage. Many people are afraid of mortgages, possibly because they saw too many old-fashioned movies in their youth, in which the villain foreclosed the mortgage on the old homestead and drove the heroine and her parents out into the snow storm. Despite the hero's last-minute arrival with the necessary money, the idea that a mortgage is bad was firmly implanted in their minds. Unless you have some other method of financing your home, you will end up with a mortgage of one sort or another, and if everything is in order from the beginning, you will have no worries.

HOW TO GET A MORTGAGE

Obtaining a mortgage is something else again. Suppose, for example, you have the plot of ground and want to build a home yourself. You have no money to put into the place, but you are willing to do the work. Let us assume that the cost of the materials will be $3,500 and the value of the finished house will be $8,750.

It would appear on the surface that any lending agency in its right mind would jump at the chance to get an $8,750 house as security on a $3,500 loan. The trouble is that the house isn't built yet and the lending agency isn't interested in the possibility of having to foreclose a mortgage. It is much more interested in having the loan repaid and receiving the interest. This is what it is in business for. The lending agency will probably not show much interest in your proposition until it has checked into the various risks involved. First of all, it will want to find out if you are a responsible person who, once a job has been started, will finish it. A house that is only half finished after a year or so of construction is of little value to anyone. A person may get enthusiastic about building his own home, start work, and then lose interest after he finds that it cannot be finished over night. The only way the agency could get back its investment would be to finish the house so that it could be sold, and this, coupled with poor workmanship on the part of the original builder, may put the price of the finished house far beyond its actual value.

If you have a member of your family who is in the construction business, or even a friend, it will probably help, for this will reassure the agency that if you get into a spot, you will be able to call on free professional advice.

Apart from worrying about whether or not you will complete the house, the lending agency will also check to see if you are able to meet the installments and interest on the mortgage. It will check into your financial background to see if you have a reputation for meeting your financial responsibilities. It will probably also want a summary of your present financial position, which will include the amount of your income, for whom you work and how long you have worked there, the amount of money you owe, the value of your insurance policy, and the amount of money you have in savings such as bonds, saving accounts, stocks, etc. In other words, it will want to know about all your financial transactions.

If You Have No Cash to Invest in the House

If it finds that you are a favorable risk, the next question will be what amount of cash you intend to invest in this venture. Most banks today do not care to finance an entire house without the owner's putting up some cash, but in your case you have no money to put up, only your labor. In this case, the bank or agency will probably say, "Get started on the place so that we know you mean business. When you have the foundation or frame up, come back and we'll see what we can do for you." This leaves things pretty much up in the air. The bank won't lend you money until the house is started, and you can't start the house until you have some money to buy the necessary materials. The thing to do now is to go to the lumber yard or wherever you are going to buy the materials and explain the situation to them. If you have a good responsible record, they will get in touch with the bank and talk things over. If the decision is that you are really in earnest and are going to build a house, and a good one, the lumber yard will advance you the necessary materials to get the job started, by extending you terms of thirty or sixty days on your purchase.

Once you have the foundations in, you go back to the bank with your plans and a list of the materials you are going to need, together with their cost. Now the bank has something concrete to go on. The house is under construction. The bank has looked over your work so far and has found it satisfactory. The officials can assume from that fact that the rest of the job should be satisfactory. They can see from the plans and the work you have done so far what the finished house should be worth, and exactly how much the materials for it are going to cost. And, lastly, they see that you have invested something in the house—your labor. As a result, they will probably be willing to invest the necessary funds so that the job can be finished.

With an arrangement of this sort, it is possible for you to start building without any initial outlay of cash on your part at all. Naturally, if you have some money, you can pay for the necessary materials to get the job started and get the rest of the money from the bank when construction is under way.

Some home builders have been able to go one step further than this. By investing some money of their own in the initial construction, they have been able to get enough money from their local bank to buy the materials they need, and also to pay themselves a small salary while they work. Thus they can devote full time to finishing the house with enough money to live on.

This is a fine arrangement if you are in a profession or trade where you can take a few months off and then go back again at your former salary. But most amateur house-builders will have to hold on to their jobs and work on the house evenings, on the week-ends or during their vacations.

If you have to borrow money to complete your house, it is not always necessary to take out a mortgage. If the sum required is not too large, you can take out a personal note or borrow on your car.

KINDS OF MORTGAGES

For those who will require a mortgage, there are certain terms as well as facts that should be known and understood. First, there is the *principal*, which is the amount of money that is lent. If you borrow $3,500, this is the principal. Next, there is the *interest*. This is the money you pay for the use of the principal. Interest is expressed in a percentage and will vary from place to place and from time to time. The interest may be paid yearly or at some other interval, whichever way you and the lending agency agree upon.

The Straight Mortgage

There are two types of mortgages, a straight mortgage and an amortized mortgage. A straight mortgage is one where you promise to pay at a certain date the full amount of the loan. You may pay the interest yearly, semi-annually, or quarterly, but you make no payment of the principal until the due date. These are short-term mortgages running for five years, and they cannot be for more than 50 per cent of the appraised value of the property.

The obvious drawback to this type of mortgage is the possibility that you will not be able to raise the necessary funds on the date that the mortgage comes due. Very few of us have on hand cash equal to 50 per cent of the value of our homes. Under usual conditions, the lending agency will renew the mortgage for another term, but it may require that you pay something on the principal. But if conditions are unusual, if, for instance, there is a depression, the agency may require you to make the full payment of the principal and if you can't, then the mortgage is foreclosed.

When a mortgage is foreclosed, the ownership of the property passes to the agency holding the mortgage. The property is put up for public sale, and the agency lending the money is paid off from the money received for the house. If there is anything left over, the original owner receives it.

Another drawback to the straight mortgage is that, because it can be only for 50 per cent of the value of the house, it is often necessary to obtain additional funds. This is done through a second mortgage.

If you use a straight mortgage to finance your home, be sure that the date on which it falls due is in writing and is not "on demand." If you have a demand mortgage, you can be called on to pay the full amount of the principal at any time the lending agency asks for it.

The Amortized Mortgage

This is the method used in most of the home financing done today. This type of mortgage runs for as long as it takes to pay off the principal. Payments are made monthly or every three months. Each payment is apportioned among the interest, the taxes, and the principal. In successive payments, the amount allotted to the interest decreases and that allotted to the principal increases because, as the sum is reduced, the interest becomes less and less. However, the amount of the individual payments remains the same. With each payment your equity in the property grows, and this is important in the event that for one reason or another you are unable to meet a payment or so. If you have sufficient equity, there will probably be no trouble.

An amortized mortgage cannot be renewed, nor can the unpaid balance be called in on demand.

Once you have made arrangements with a lending agency to get an amortized mortgage, your next problem is to work out a method of repayment. Everyone likes to get the mortgage paid off as quickly as possible; everyone likes to have the monthly payments as small as possible; and everyone likes to make a minimum down payment on the expenses of their plot and future home. The trick, then is to balance these requirements to your greatest advantage.

A good rule to follow in making the down payment is to pay as much as you can possibly afford at this time, still keeping enough savings in reserve to meet emergencies such as sickness. There is no point to making a large down payment and then not being in a position to pay the first installment. Now there remains the unpaid balance, and the payment of this will be spread out over a period of years in monthly installments. The larger the installments are, the sooner the loan will be paid off. By paying the loan off in ten years rather than twenty-five, you save a good deal of interest charges. On the other hand, it is best not to use over 25 per cent of your monthly income for housing because, in these days of rising living costs, more and more of the family income must go for food and clothing.

There is another factor that must be considered in working out a repayment budget and this is your present and future earning capacity. If you are just getting started in your profession, you may have to start out with a very low monthly installment and a long-term loan. As your income increases, you can re-budget your payments so that they are larger and in keeping with your greater earning power. You can also pay off the balance of the unpaid mortgage, but there is usually a penalty involved in this. If your income is more or less set at this time, you should take into consideration your estimated earning power over the years until the mortgage has been discharged. For example, if you are thirty-five now and you have a twenty-five year mortgage, the last payment will fall due when you are sixty. At this age you may very well not have the earning capacity that you do today. In this event, you should try to figure out a payment plan whereby you will have discharged your mortgage before there is any decline in your earning capacity. Your local bank or lending agency will be able to give you a lot of good sound advice in working out a repayment plan.

As a builder-owner you should not have the same difficulties in working out a repayment plan as someone who is purchasing a finished house or one that is going to be built professionally, because you will not need anywhere near the amount of money that he will. You may be able to get sufficient funds for the materials by borrowing on your insurance or from a private individual. Private loans are perfectly all right if the interest rate is not too high, and the date of payment is in writing. Demand notes are not good. If the lender should get into a tight spot, you might have to pay up in full at a time when it is impossible. Before you knew it, you would have a court action on your hands. Don't get the idea that just because you borrow from a friend you can avoid difficulties of this sort. If you make a private loan, even with your best friend or a close relative, be sure all is in order, and in writing.

FHA LOANS

Many home-builders today borrow money under the FHA plan. The Federal Housing Act passed in 1934 created government insurance on home-financing loans and made it available to home-financing institutions. The act also created the Federal Housing Administration to administer the new law. The FHA does not lend the money to home-buyers or home-builders. A person who wants to borrow money to buy or build a home must get it from a private lending agency approved by the FHA. The FHA simply insures to the approved lenders that they will be repaid fully for loans that they make, in conformity with sound standards, to home-buyers and home-builders. The effect, therefore, is to make more money available to people who wish to borrow it, since the risk is removed for the lender.

Every person who earns a steady income from a job or business and who has a good credit reputation can obtain FHA insurance on a loan to buy or build a home of his own, provided the house is judged to be structurally acceptable, is a sound, long-range value, and is priced within his means.

For the person who wants to buy or build a new home for himself, the FHA will do the following, if the house is built with its inspection and meets its requirements:

If it values a home at up to $6,315, the FHA will insure a loan on it for as much as 95 per cent of its value. If, for instance, the value is $6,000, the buyer can obtain FHA insurance on a loan of $5,700. Loans in this value range must be paid off in thirty years.

If it values the home between $6,315 and $11,000, the FHA will insure a loan on it for as much as 90 per cent of the first $7,000 and 80 per cent of the next $4,000. For instance, if the value is $10,000, the borrower can obtain FHA insurance on a loan of $8,700. This amount is the total of $6,300 for which he can be insured on the first $7,000 of the valuation, and $2,400 for which he can be insured on the remaining $3,000 of the valuation. Loans in this value range must be paid off in twenty-five years.

If it values the home at between $11,000 and $20,000, the FHA will insure a loan on it for as much as 80 per cent of the value. For example, if the

value is $20,000, the home-buyer can obtain FHA insurance on a loan of $16,000. Loans in this value range must also be paid off in twenty-five years.

To secure the maximum percentage loans on a new home, plans must be submitted to the FHA before construction starts and a commitment to insure must be obtained. Otherwise, loans are limited to 80 per cent of the value. The interest rate on an FHA insured mortgage may not exceed 4½ per cent, plus an FHA insurance charge of ½ of 1 per cent on declining balances.

Considerations of the Property

In determining whether the FHA can insure the proposed mortgage loan, FHA gives consideration to the location of the lot and such related matters as suitability of the neighborhood, access to schools, and adequacy of utilities.

FHA has set up certain minimum property standards to determine whether the property is acceptable as security for an FHA insured-mortgage loan. It makes a valuation of the property based on long-term use. If construction is completed, an appraiser inspects the property and places a valuation on it, including the lot. If the property is proposed construction, plans and specifications are analyzed for conformity with FHA minimum property standards, and after an FHA appraiser has visited the site, valuation will be placed upon the land and the proposed improvements when erected on the site. While the house is being constructed, the FHA makes three or more inspections.

Benefits to the Buyer

The precautions taken by FHA as insurer of the mortgage result in the following benefits to the borrower:

FHA's valuation of the property represents an objective estimate of its long-term value. This provides the borrower with a conservative guide in determining how much he should agree to pay under his purchase contract.

The examination of the relationship of monthly payments to the borrower's present and anticipated income and expenses helps protect him from entering a transaction beyond his means. The FHA does not insure a mortgage un-less there appears a reasonable likelihood that the borrower can maintain the payments.

Through the minimum property standards and inspections, the borrower benefits from an objective check and review of the property as to its basic construction and conformity to essential property standards. This is not, however, a guarantee of the house, but it does provide the borrower reasonable insurance that the property has met at least the minimum FHA requirements.

The table on Pg. 32, prepared by an official of the United States Housing and Home Finance Agency in Washington, shows you how much you must pay each month on homes valued from $6,000 to $20,000 that are bought with FHA-insured mortgages.

A GI LOAN

Many veterans are confused as to just what the so-called GI Loan for buying a house is all about. This is actually nothing more than a loan that is made by a private lending institution, such as a bank, and is guaranteed by the Veterans Administration. The government does not lend you any money; it merely insures your loan.

A GI Loan will guarantee up to 50 per cent of the loan, but the guaranteed amount cannot be more than $4,000. This loan may be used to buy, build, or improve a home. The loan must bear interest at a rate of not more than 4 per cent per year, and must be paid off in twenty-five years. In addition, the Veterans Administration pays to the lender, for credit to the veteran's loan account, a sum equal to 4 per cent of the guaranteed portion of the loan. This credit is a gift to the veteran and not a loan. Veterans may apply for GI Loans until July 25, 1957.

At this point, you may begin to wonder just what the advantages of this type of loan over an FHA-insured mortgage may be. In the first place, you get a lower rate of interest. While this may not seem like a great deal, it can add up in twenty-five years or so. Another advantage of the GI Loan is

TABLE I

FHA-INSURED MORTGAGES ON NEW SINGLE FAMILY, OWNER-OCCUPIED HOMES

(National Housing Act, Title II, Section 203)

Appraisal Value	Maximum loan as percentage of value	Maximum amount of loan	Minimum down payment	Maximum maturity (yrs.)	Monthly payment				
					Interest and principal	Mortgage insurance premium (1st yr.) [1]	Hazard insurance (est) [2]	Real estate taxes (est) [3]	Total
$ 6,000	95%	$5,700	$ 300	30	$28.90	$2.32	$1.00	10.00	$42.22
6,500	90	5,850	650	25	32.53	2.36	1.08	10.83	46.80
7,000	90	6,300	700	25	35.03	2.54	1.17	11.67	50.41
7,500	90% on $7,000, 80% over $7,000	6,700	800	25	37.25	2.70	1.25	12.50	53.70
8,000		7,100	900	25	39.48	2.86	1.33	13.33	57.00
8,500		7,500	1,000	25	41.70	3.02	1.42	14.17	60.31
9,000		7,900	1,100	25	43.92	3.18	1.50	15.00	63.60
9,500		8,300	1,200	25	46.15	3.34	1.58	15.83	66.90
10,000		8,700	1,300	25	48.37	3.51	1.67	16.67	70.22
10,500		9,100	1,400	25	50.60	3.67	1.75	17.50	73.52
11,000		9,500	1,500	25	52.82	3.83	1.83	18.33	76.81
11,500	80	9,500	2,000	25	52.82	3.83	1.92	19.17	77.74
12,000	80	9,600	2,400	25	53.38	3.87	2.00	20.00	79.25
12,500	80	10,000	2,500	25	55.60	4.03	2.08	20.83	82.54
13,000	80	10,400	2,600	25	57.82	4.19	2.17	21.67	85.85
13,500	80	10,800	2,700	25	60.05	4.35	2.25	22.50	89.15
14,000	80	11,200	2,800	25	62.27	4.51	2.33	23.33	92.44
14,500	80	11,600	2,900	25	64.50	4.67	2.42	24.17	95.76
15,000	80	12,000	3,000	25	66.72	4.84	2.50	25.00	99.06
15,500	80	12,400	3,100	25	68.94	5.00	2.58	25.83	102.35
16,000	80	12,800	3,200	25	71.17	5.16	2.67	26.67	105.67
16,500	80	13,200	3,300	25	73.39	5.32	2.75	27.50	108.96
17,000	80	13,600	3,400	25	75.62	5.48	2.83	28.33	112.26
17,500	80	14,000	3,500	25	77.84	5.64	2.92	29.17	115.57
18,000	80	14,400	3,600	25	80.06	5.80	3.00	30.00	118.86
18,500	80	14,800	3,700	25	82.29	5.96	3.08	30.83	122.16
19,000	80	15,200	3,800	25	84.51	6.13	3.17	31.67	125.48
19,500	80	15,600	3,900	25	86.74	6.29	3.25	32.50	128.78
20,000	80	16,000	4,000	25	88.96	6.45	3.33	33.33	132.07

[1] Decreases each year since the ½ of 1% premium is based on the declining outstanding balance of the loan.
[2] Assumed annual rate of $2 per $1,000 of appraisal value.
[3] Assumed annual rate of $20 per $1,000 of appraisal value.

TABLE II

LOAN TERMS ON NEW OR EXISTING SINGLE FAMILY, OWNER-OCCUPIED HOMES ASSUMING 100% LOANS AVAILABLE UNDER SERVICEMEN'S READJUSTMENT ACT, TITLE III, SECTION 501

($4,000 or ½ of the loan, whichever is less, would be guaranteed by the Veterans Administration)

Reasonable value	Maximum loan as percentage of value	Maximum amount of loan[1]	Down payment*	Maximum maturity (yrs.)	Monthly payment			
					Interest and principal	Hazard insurance (est)[2]	Real estate taxes (est)[3]	Total
$ 6,000	100%	$ 6,000	0	25	$31.68	$1.00	$10.00	$42.68
6,500	100	6,500	0	25	34.32	1.08	10.83	46.23
7,000	100	7,000	0	25	36.96	1.17	11.67	49.80
7,500	100	7,500	0	25	39.60	1.25	12.50	53.35
8,000	100	8,000	0	25	42.24	1.33	13.33	56.90
8,500	100	8,500	0	25	44.88	1.42	14.17	60.47
9,000	100	9,000	0	25	47.52	1.50	15.00	64.02
9,500	100	9,500	0	25	50.16	1.58	15.83	67.57
10,000	100	10,000	0	25	52.80	1.67	16.67	71.14
10,500	100	10,500	0	25	55.44	1.75	17.50	74.69
11,000	100	11,000	0	25	58.08	1.83	18.33	78.24
11,500	100	11,500	0	25	60.72	1.92	19.17	81.81
12,000	100	12,000	0	25	63.36	2.00	20.00	85.36
12,500	100	12,500	0	25	66.00	2.08	20.83	88.91
13,000	100	13,000	0	25	68.64	2.17	21.67	92.48
13,500	100	13,500	0	25	71.28	2.25	22.50	96.03
14,000	100	14,000	0	25	73.92	2.33	23.33	99.58
14,500	100	14,500	0	25	76.56	2.42	24.17	103.15
15,000	100	15,000	0	25	79.20	2.50	25.00	106.70
15,500	100	15,500	0	25	81.84	2.58	25.83	110.25
16,000	100	16,000	0	25	84.48	2.67	26.67	113.82
16,500	100	16,500	0	25	87.12	2.75	27.50	117.37
17,000	100	17,000	0	25	89.76	2.83	28.33	120.92
17,500	100	17,500	0	25	92.40	2.92	29.17	124.49
18,000	100	18,000	0	25	95.04	3.00	30.00	128.04
18,500	100	18,500	0	25	97.68	3.08	30.83	131.59
19,000	100	19,000	0	25	100.32	3.17	31.67	135.16
19,500	100	19,500	0	25	102.96	3.25	32.50	138.71
20,000	100	20,000	0	25	105.60	3.33	33.33	142.26

[1] Not reflecting VA gratuity payment to veteran's loan account, amounting to 4% of the guaranteed portion of the loan. For example, on $6,000 loan, gratuity payment would be $120 (4% of $3,000).
[2] Assumed annual rate of $2 per $1,000 of reasonable value.
[3] Assumed annual rate of $20 per $1,000 of reasonable value.
* Down payment will be required if valuation of the home is less than price for which it sells.

that you do not have to make as large a down payment as you would on other types of loans, and you can prepay part or even all of your loan whenever you feel like it, without penalty. To get this type of loan, your property must meet with the Veterans Administration minimum property requirements and the property will have to be inspected by an inspector to be sure that these requirements are met. If your home has met the FHA requirements, that will be accepted for a GI Loan.

The table on Pg. 33 shows you how much you must pay each month on homes valued from $6,000 to $20,000 covered by 100 per cent GI Loans.

COMBINATION VA-FHA LOANS

Under the provisions of the Servicemen's Readjustment Act (the GI Bill), a veteran of World War II may obtain a secondary loan up to 20 per cent (but not in excess of $4,000) of the approved purchase price or construction cost under a VA guarantee to cover all or part of the difference between an FHA-insured mortgage and the price of the house. These secondary loans are guaranteed in full by the Veterans Administration. This is the only case in which additional financing may be added to an FHA-insured mortgage.

In effect, the FHA-insured mortgage is a first mortgage, covering from 80 to 95 per cent of the value of the home, depending on the value of the home. The GI Loan covers a second mortgage, which cannot exceed 20 per cent of the purchase price. Under the law, therefore, the veteran is entitled to obtain financing up to, but not exceeding, naturally, 100 per cent of the purchase price. In practice, however, down payments, somewhat lower in amount than would be required in either a straight FHA or straight VA loan, are commonly called for.

The table on Pg. 35 covers the payments under FHA-VA loans to veterans in the most inexpensive interest-charge combination possible.

CONSTRUCTION LOANS

Since you are planning to build your own home rather than purchase it, the plans outlined above must be modified somewhat to fit your special case. To build a home rather than purchase it, it is necessary to obtain a "construction" loan from the bank before you commence building in order to meet costs of labor and material. In your case, it will be mainly material. The Veterans Administration is authorized to guarantee construction loans for veterans. The Federal Housing Administration, however, does not insure construction loans as such on individual homes. However, a conditional FHA commit-

T<small>ABLE</small> III

LOAN TERMS ON NEW SINGLE FAMILY, OWNER-OCCUPIED HOMES, ASSUMING 100% LOANS AVAILABLE UNDER COMBINATION FHA-INSURED FIRST MORTGAGE AND VA-GUARANTEED SECOND MORTGAGE

(National Housing Act, Title II Section 203; Servicemen's Readjustment Act, Title III Section 505a)

Appraisal and and reasonable value [1]	Maximum loan as percentage of value	Maximum amount of loan [2]	Down payment *	Maximum maturity (years)	Monthly payment				
					Interest and principal	Mortgage insurance premium (1st yr.) [3]	Hazard insurance (est) [4]	Real estate taxes (est) [5]	Total
	100% (FHA, 80%;			FHA-30	$30.68	$1.95	$1.00	$10.00	$ 43.63
6,000	VA, 20%)	$6,000	0	VA-25					
6,500	"	6,500	0	25	35.77	2.10	1.08	10.83	49.78
7,000	"	7,000	0	25	38.53	2.26	1.17	11.67	53.63
7,500	"	7,500	0	25	41.28	2.42	1.25	12.50	57.45
8,000	"	8,000	0	25	44.03	2.58	1.33	13.33	61.27
8,500	"	8,500	0	25	46.79	2.74	1.42	14.17	65.12
9,000	"	9,000	0	25	49.53	2.90	1.50	15.00	68.93
9,500	"	9,500	0	25	52.29	3.06	1.58	15.83	72.76
10,000	"	10,000	0	25	55.04	3.22	1.67	16.67	76.60
10,500	"	10,500	0	25	57.79	3.39	1.75	17.50	80.43
11,000	"	11,000	0	25	60.55	3.55	1.83	18.33	84.26
11,500	"	11,500	0	25	63.29	3.71	1.92	19.17	88.09
12,000	"	12,000	0	25	66.05	3.87	2.00	20.00	91.92
12,500	"	12,500	0	25	68.80	4.03	2.08	20.83	95.74
13,000	"	13,000	0	25	71.55	4.19	2.17	21.67	99.58
13,500	"	13,500	0	25	74.31	4.35	2.25	22.50	103.41
14,000	"	14,000	0	25	77.05	4.51	2.33	23.33	107.22
14,500	"	14,500	0	25	79.81	4.67	2.42	24.17	111.07
15,000	"	15,000	0	25	82.56	4.84	2.50	25.00	114.90
15,500	"	15,500	0	25	85.31	5.00	2.58	25.83	118.72
16,000	"	16,000	0	25	88.07	5.16	2.67	26.67	122.57
16,500	"	16,500	0	25	90.81	5.32	2.75	27.50	126.38
17,000	"	17,000	0	25	93.75	5.48	2.83	28.33	130.21
17,500	"	17,500	0	25	96.32	5.64	2.92	29.17	134.05
18,000	"	18,000	0	25	99.07	5.80	3.00	30.00	137.87
18,500	"	18,500	0	25	101.83	5.96	3.08	30.83	141.70
19,000	"	19,000	0	25	104.57	6.13	3.17	31.67	145.54
19,500	"	19,500	0	25	107.33	6.29	3.25	32.50	149.37
20,000	"	20,000	0	25	110.08	6.45	3.33	33.33	153.19

[1] Assuming FHA appraisal and VA reasonable value are the same.

[2] Not reflecting VA gratuity payment to veteran's loan account for first year only, amounting to 4% on VA guaranteed second loan. For example, on $6,000 loan, credit for the year would be $48 (4% of $1,200).

[3] Applies to FHA-insured first loan. Premium decreases each year since the ½ of 1% premium is based on the declining outstanding balance of loan.

[4] Assumed annual rate of $2 per $1,000 of appraisal value.

[5] Assumed annual rate of $20 per $1,000 of appraisal value.

* Down payment will be required if valuation of the home is less than price for which it sells.

ment on a permanent loan can be secured before you start construction, and will make it easier to secure a construction loan from the bank.

All this simply means that the bank will be more willing to make a construction loan if it knows that the loan will be picked up by an FHA permanent financing loan when the house is completed. It is necessary to secure an FHA commitment before beginning construction so that you can be certain that FHA will insure a loan for the required amount when the home is completed. By checking your plans before construction, and inspecting the home during construction, the FHA determines that the house measures up to the standards it requires of all homes on which it makes loans.

The disbursements on a VA-guaranteed construction loan are made during the course of the construction of the home. The final execution of the FHA permanent loan, of course, is made only after the home is finished.

THE LONG-RANGE VIEW

In the long run, the most important question in buying a new home is: Are you going to be able to keep it up once you have built it?

Experts in the mortgage field say that you should figure your monthly payments as the amount of rent you can afford to pay, and that your rent should be no more than 20 or 25 per cent of your monthly take-home pay. This figure should cover all the charges for interest, amortization of the mortgage, taxes, insurance, and maintenance. Some experts suggest that you figure the yearly maintenance costs—which include painting, repairs, and similar expenses—at $1\frac{1}{2}$ per cent of the buying price. In the case of an owner-built home, this figure would be the appraised value. In other words, if the house is worth $10,000, the annual maintenance costs should be figured at $150. You will probably not spend that much every year, but it will average out. A house does not have to be repainted every year, for example, but when it is, the cost will probably be over the year's average.

CHECKLIST ON FINANCING

Price .... _____
Estimated Value ._____
Amount of
     Mortgage ..._____
Interest Rate ...._____
Term of Mortgage._____

Prepayment
     Privilege? ..._____
Down Payment .._____
Closing Charges:
     Title Search and Clearance_____
     Legal Fees ...._____

Other Charges ...._____
TOTAL INITIAL COST_____

Monthly Payment
   on Mortgage ._____
Monthly Payments
   on Taxes and
   Assessments ._____

Monthly Payments
   on Insurance ._____
Total Monthly Payment...._____
Upkeep and Repairs......._____
Probable Cost of Fuel....._____
Probable Cost of Utilities.._____
Taxes ...._____

TOTAL MONTHLY
    COST ...._____

Chapter 4

CUTTING COSTS; THE BASIC MATERIAL; NECESSARY TOOLS

THERE are two ways to cut costs in construction work. One is to use inferior-grade materials and the other is to use the better quality stuff and make every piece and penny count.

As one of the reasons you are building your own home is to save money, cutting costs where possible should be given plenty of thought.

Saving Materials

You will be able to save a great deal just by not wasting materials. For example, take a small item like nails. If you keep the nails where they will not become wet and rust and if you take only enough to do the job and do not toss them around, you will find that you will save $10 or $20. A very substantial way in which you can save is by conserving lumber. Don't ever cut up a long piece of material if there is a short one somewhere about that can be used. Professional builders usually allow 10 per cent or more for waste, but you can cut down on this considerably and at the same time not take up too much extra time. When you use a piece of lumber for a temporary brace, don't,

when you are finished with it, knock it off with your hammer or hatchet. The chances are that if it is light you will split it and it will have no further use except as firewood. Take the time to pull out the nails and put the lumber away. Then, when you need it, it will be there ready for use.

Receiving Deliveries

It will always pay you to be on hand when deliveries of materials are made. Some of the drivers of trucks are just as apt to dump the whole load off as not, and this is almost sure to damage some of the material. If the driver and his helper are not in the mood to take the materials off by hand, do it yourself. Items such as masonry blocks, steel-casement windows, glazed-window sashes and so on, should be handled with care, since, if they are tossed around too much, they will either break, crack or get sprung out of line.

Items that can be damaged by the weather should be brought in under cover as soon as they are delivered. Even if there is no sign of rain, dampness from dew can harm items such as hardwood flooring or interior trim. Cement should be taken inside, and sand should be kept covered because if there is a hard rain, a large amount can be washed away.

Supervising Help

Whenever you have any hired help working around the place, try to be on hand, not only to help out when you can, but to give the necessary directions. This does not mean that help, professional or otherwise, is just going to sit down the minute you leave the site, but it is sometimes difficult to plan an entire day's work for a man, and if he does not have proper instructions, he can do nothing else but loaf around on the job until you show up and tell him what to do next.

Don't make the mistake that one home builder did of hiring a bulldozer to put in a driveway and then going off somewhere and forgetting to tell the driver where the driveway was supposed to be placed.

WHAT MATERIAL TO BUILD WITH

One of the first things that you must decide before you break ground is just what materials you are going to use to build your house. As far as the frame or the shell of the house goes, you have a choice between wood and concrete masonry-blocks. Let us take just a minute here to see the advantages and disadvantages of each type.

Wood

As far as a wood-frame house is concerned, you have a medium—wood —that most of us have had some experience in working with. Almost anyone who plans to build a house by himself probably knows how to saw and nail wood and perhaps has even done a little construction work of a heavy nature, such as building a garage, fences, or something else. Almost everyone knows that wood is an easy medium to work in. If a board is cut too long, it is a simple matter to plane or saw it down

so that it fits just right. Most of us can guess what size nail is about right and which size is too large and will split the board. These are all important points to consider about wood. Wood is something that most of us have the feel of.

Of course, wood has certain disadvantages. First of all, it can be damaged by the weather, insects or decay. It will shrink some unless it is very well seasoned, and this means that cracks may appear in the plaster or wallboard interior walls, windows and doors may stick, and there will be a lot of small maintenance jobs that must be done, even after the house has just been completed. If the exterior siding is of wood, it will have to be repainted at least every five years, perhaps more often. Special care will have to be taken to check and make sure that decay has not set in at various points. A house built entirely of wood is very inflammable, and once it gets on fire it may be totally ruined before the fire is put out. This may be a very important point to keep in mind if you are building far out in the country where the fire department is some distance away.

Masonry-Blocks

Concrete masonry-blocks, on the other hand, are very resistant to fire. They will not be damaged by moisture, insects or decay. If you do not care about appearance, they do not need any sort of paint or finish to protect them from the weather. Many persons don't care for masonry houses just on general principals, but most of them cannot tell the difference between a house made of masonry blocks and one of wood until they are near enough to see the texture of the siding. You can have just as attractive a home made out of masonry as out of wood—if the job is done correctly.

Probably the greatest point against masonry blocks is that most of us are just not used to working with masonry. There are different skills required for this sort of work and few persons care to go into a new element. Of course, there will be a few who have watched a group of skilled masons erect the walls of a concrete house in almost no time at all and, as they work with ease, the ill-informed will assume that building with these blocks is as simple as these skilled craftsmen make it appear. Don't let this fool you. Lifting a block and putting it down in a bed of mortar is not difficult, but making sure that all your measurements are correct, that

the wall is level and true, is something else again. There is no easy way to build a house in a hurry. Any type of construction you choose is going to require time and a little skill. So keep this in mind when you begin to think about materials. As far as the actual cost is concerned, there isn't much choice between wood or masonry.

Exterior Siding

If you decide to build a wood-frame house, you can have a wide selection in the type of materials used for the outside walls. While wood siding requires such maintenance as painting, stucco or asbestos shingles do not have to be painted until they become so soiled from soot that they can no longer be cleaned. The same holds true of brick veneer, but this is both a very difficult and a very expensive type of construction.

Naturally, when we say that stucco, for example, does not require much maintenance, it is assumed that the stucco is properly applied. If it is not, you will be forever patching cracks or spots where the stucco has fallen off the lath, and you will probably begin to long for a house with wood siding that only requires a little paint from time to time.

The Basement

The next point that you have to think about is whether you are going to have a house with a full basement, no basement but crawl space under the first floor, or a concrete slab poured on the ground with or without radiant heating in it.

The main purpose of a basement in many homes is to provide a place for the heating system. This was because old-fashioned heating plants had to be below the lowest radiator or register. This is no longer true. Another reason for basements was storage room. This may still hold true in some cases, but most of the basements you run across are so damp and dirty that they do not make a suitable place to store anything except fuel and a few pieces of gardening equipment, etc., which will not be harmed by a little moisture and dampness. A basement can add 15 per cent to the cost of a house, and if this investment is only going to be used for a heating system and a damp, dirty storage space, it not worth your money. If you want a basement, then let it be used for some useful purpose, such as a game room or den, and build it with care so that it will be dry and properly ventilated and can be used for livable rooms.

Omitting the Basement

If you decide to get along without a basement, you can build your house either on a continuous wall foundation with a wood floor or with a concrete slab floor. Of course, in either case, you will not have quite as much room, as in the house with the basement because the heating system and hot-water heater and other utilities will have to be placed in the utility room. On the other hand, you save a good deal of time and money, which is pretty important too. You will not have any place in which to build a recreation or game room, and this may cramp your style later on, unless you want to build a detached building for this purpose. Personally, if there is going to have to be a rumpus room somewhere, we would just as soon have it as far away from the main house as possible.

A slab floor with radiant heating panels in it has one advantage over a wood floor off the ground, which is that you save space that would be taken up by radiators and registers.

TOOLS REQUIRED FOR THE JOB

In theory, a man can build himself a house with no tools other than a saw, a hammer and a framing square. You probably can build a house with only this minimum amount of equipment, but it probably won't be too good a house when it is finished. To do a good job, you will need quite a sizable collection of tools and they should be good tools. The right tool for the job not only does a better job but makes the work go faster. For example, you can rip a board lengthwise with a crosscut saw, but the cutting will take time and you won't get the same nice, even cut as you will by using a rip saw.

If you are building a house yourself, it is well worth the money to invest in a set of carpentry tools right at the start. If you do this, you will have them right on hand when you need them and not have to put off doing an essential job until you get down to a hardware store or over to a friend to buy or borrow the equipment you need. And anyway, there will always be some work to be done around the house after it has been completed, so investing in tools at this time is really a long-term affair. On the other hand, it is hardly worthwhile to invest in a lot of tools for specialized work. Plumbing tools, for example, will probably be used only during the installation of the plumbing system. After that, with the possible exception of a pipe wrench, they will be of no further use, so don't buy tools of this sort unless you have to. The same holds true of the specialized tools you may need for the electrical and heating systems. If you can possibly get by without buying them, do so.

The tools you will need for the carpentry end of the job are, a crosscut and a rip saw, a hammer, a shingle hatchet, a plane, a screwdriver, a brace and assorted bits, a level, a framing square, a rule, a plumb line and bob, a nail set, a chisel, and two solid sawhorses (these you can make yourself easily enough). Of course, there are many more or less specialized tools that could be added to this list, but this is about the minimum requirement for house building.

For masonry work you will need a small and large trowel, which you will find use for later on in many different jobs.

If you are using BX cable for the electrical system, you must use a hacksaw to cut the cable—and a hacksaw makes a useful addition to any tool kit.

The other tools required for some jobs can be rented or borrowed. Use the money that you would otherwise invest in something like caulking irons to buy the better and more expensive grades of tools, because you will find that good quality equipment is much superior to the cheaper grades, which soon become worthless.

THE FRAMING SQUARE AND ITS USE

It is virtually impossible to do much in the way of house construction without a working knowledge of the framing square. This tool has many important uses besides that of checking to find out if the end of a board is square or if the joint between two boards forms a right angle. The steel framing square contains a quantity of information on both its sides that enables you to figure out, for instance, how rafters should be cut for almost every possible condition or how a flight of stairs can be laid out.

The rafters for the basic house described in this book can be made according to the pattern given in illustration, but some of those for the other homes covered in this book will have to be figured out by the home-builder himself. Therefore, it is important that you know how to use the framing square.

The framing square is made of steel with a tongue that is 1½″ wide and usually 16″ long. The blade is 2″ wide and 24″ long. Stamped on the front and back face of the square are all the necessary figures required for laying out various types of rafters.

Before you can go ahead with marking and cutting rafters, there are a few important terms that you should be familiar with. First of all there is the *span*. The span is the distance between the outside surfaces of opposing wall plates, and therefore, it is the shortest distance between two opposite rafter seats. The *rise* is the vertical distance from the wall plate to the ridge of the roof. The *run* is the shortest horizontal distance that the rafter must cover, and therefore, it is one-half the span, if the building has equal pitch on both sides of the roof.

The *pitch* of the roof is the amount of slope and it is equal to the total rise (the vertical distance of the ridge from the wall plate) divided by the span. For example, if the house has a span of 24 feet and a total rise of 8 feet, the pitch can be found by dividing 24 into 8, which gives ⅓. Therefore, this particular house has a roof with a ⅓ pitch. It is sometimes necessary to find the rise of a roof when only the span and pitch are known. This is simple enough to do. If the span is 24 feet and the roof has a pitch of ⅓, divide the pitch into the span and you get the rise. In this case it would be 8 feet, of course.

The *unit of run* is the unit of measurement used with a framing square for measuring the rafters. It is always taken from a level plane and is always 12 inches. The *unit of span* is always twice the unit of run and, therefore, is always 24 inches.

The *rise in inches* is the number of inches that the roof actually rises for every foot of run. If the rise in inches is not given, you can find it by multiplying the pitch by the unit of span. For example, if the pitch is ⅓ and the unit of span is 24 inches, the total rise in inches per foot of run is 8.

Now, if you look at the tongue of the framing square you will find the number 12. This is the unit of run and is used for roof-framing purposes. Run a diagonal line from this point to "4 inches" on the blade of the square. This shows a 4″ rise per 12″ run, which results in a roof with a ⅙ pitch. If the line were to run from "12 inches" on the tongue to "8 inches" on the blade, the pitch would be ⅓. If the line runs from "12 inches" to "12 inches," you get a ½ pitch, and if it runs from "12 inches" on the tongue to "24 inches" on the blade, the pitch is 1.

The *cut* of the roof is the rise in inches and the unit of run, which is the constant 12 inches.

Now, let us assume that you want to find the length of a main or common rafter, using a steel square with a rafter table. You will find stamped on the blade of the square "Length of Main Rafters Per Foot Run," and the table that follows gives the unit lengths of main rafters from a 2″ to an 18″ rise. As the roof we are discussing has a ⅓ pitch and an 8″ rise, you should look for the figure under 8. This is 14.42, which is the length of the rafter in inches and hundredths of inches per foot of run. To find the actual length of the rafter, multiply 14.42 (the foot-run) by the number of feet in the run. As the span of the roof is 24, the run is 12, and this times 14.42 gives 173.04 inches. Dividing by 12, the total length of the rafter turns out to be 14.42 feet. This is the total length of the rafter from the middle of the ridge board to the outside edge of the wall plate. If there is going to be a ridge board, one-half the thickness of this ridge board should be deducted from the total rafter length; if the rafter is to extend beyond the wall plate, the amount of the extension must be added to its length.

Once you have the right length of rafter, the top and bottom cuts are made. The top cut, where the rafter joins the ridge board, is called *the plumb cut*. It can be made by placing the rafter on its side and then placing the square over it so that the rise per foot—8 inches in this case—is at the top of the rafter while the number 12 on the tongue is on the same edge of the rafter but below the 8″ mark. Now a line can be drawn along the edge of the square to give the angle of the cut. The same general procedure is used

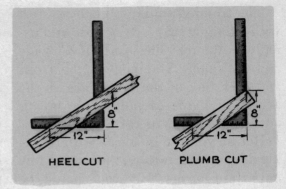

Fig. 1. How the framing square can be used to mark out the rafters for the plumb and heel cut.

to determine the heel cut. See Fig. 1 above.

There are a good many types of rafter that you may run across, and naturally, all are not so simple to work out as the common or main rafter, which extends from the ridge of the roof to the wall plate. However, if you look again at the framing square, you will note that under the information given for the common rafter there is similar information for a hip or valley rafter, a jack rafter at 16 inches on center and at 24 inches on center, and also the necessary data for making side cuts on all these.

A hip rafter is one that runs diagonally from the corner of a building to the roof. A valley rafter is one used where two roofs intersect, as when the garage roof joins the breezeway.

Chapter 5

WORKING WITH CONCRETE, MASONRY BLOCKS AND BRICKS

It is virtually impossible today to do much building without sooner or later having to use concrete in one place or another. Concrete—good concrete—is a vital building material; likewise the knowledge how to mix it properly.

MIXING CONCRETE

Concrete is made of Portland cement to which are added aggregates such as sand and gravel. The cement itself comes in sacks weighing 94 pounds and, unless it has been exposed to moisture, it will not give you any trouble. If the cement in the bag is lumpy and you cannot break these lumps with your fingers, it should not be used. Always store cement in a dry place, even if the bags are sealed tight.

Aggregates

A lot of concrete is ruined by using poor quality aggregates. Sand should be clean and free from dirt or any other organic matter. If you have a sand pit on your lot or one near by, you might save a few dollars by taking the sand from there rather than buying it from a lumber yard, but unless you take the time to wash and screen the sand before use, it will make inferior cement. Con-sidering the cost of sand, it is hardly worthwhile to go to all this trouble. Sand is referred to as the "fine aggregate," gravel or crushed stone is the "coarse aggregate." It is just as important that the gravel or crushed rock is free of dirt and organic matter as that the sand is.

You can test the quality of the aggregates easily enough with a milk bottle or quart fruit-jar. Put in about 2″ of the dry aggregate and then fill the bottle with water about three-quarters full. Shake it for about a minute and then allow it to stand quiet for an hour. Any dirt or silt will form a layer over the top of the aggregate in the bottle.

If this layer is over ⅛″ thick, the sand is too dirty to use and must be washed.

To test the sand for vegetable matter, a 12 oz. prescription bottle is used. This is filled to the 4½-oz. mark with sand. A 3% solution of caustic soda is then added. This can be made by dissolving 1 oz. of household lye in a quart of distilled water. Be careful when you handle this solution because it is very corrosive to clothes and skin. When this solution has been added to the sand, shake the bottle thoroughly and then let it sit for twenty-four hours. If, at the end of that time, the liquid inside the bottle is clear, the sand is clean and good to use. If the liquid is straw colored, there is some vegetable matter but it is not enough to produce an inferior grade of concrete. If the liquid is darker than this, the vegetable content is too high and the sand should be washed before it is used.

Sometimes sand and gravel are used just as they come from the gravel bank with the sand mixed in with the gravel. This is not satisfactory because there is usually too much sand in with the gravel to produce the desired grade of concrete.

Water

The water you use for mixing the concrete should be pure enough to drink. This means that it should be pure enough to drink when it is added to the cement and sand and not just when it comes from the tap. There is no point to worrying about the quality of the water and then carrying it to the mixer in an old bucket that is full of dirt, oil and what not. The water should be free from oil, acid and alkali. Beach sand and salt water are not suitable for concrete under most circumstances.

The strength as well as the water-tightness of concrete depends upon the amount of water used for mixing each bag of cement. In recent years, it has been found that the less water used the better. Of course, you have to use a sufficient amount of water to get a workable mixture, but if more water than is required is used, the finished concrete will be inferior.

It is seldom possible to get sand that is absolutely dry. In most cases, it will be anywhere from slightly damp to very wet. The amount of moisture in the sand must be taken into consideration because there will usually be enough to have a marked effect on the final mix. Sand is usually classed as damp, wet or very wet. You can make a very simple test yourself to see what category the sand you have on hand falls into. Take a handful of sand and press it together. If the sand falls apart when you open your hand, it is damp. If it holds its shape, it is wet, and if it actually wets your hand, it is very wet. It is reasonable, then, to use less water when working with wet sand than when working with sand that is only damp.

Mixing

Table I, on Pg. 47, shows the various types of mixture, along with the amount of water required for each bag of cement, depending on the condition of the sand.

If you are making up a small amount of concrete, that is, when you are using less than one sack of cement, Table II, on Pg. 48, can be used.

The first step in mixing up a large amount of concrete is to make a trial mix using the proportions given in Table I. When this mixture has been completed, it should be workable but not too soupy. If it is too wet or too

TABLE I

RECOMMENDED MIXTURES FOR VARIOUS KINDS OF CONSTRUCTION

Quantities of cement, fine and coarse aggregate, required for 1 cu. yd. of compact mortar or concrete

Kind of Work	U. S. gallons of water to add to each 1-sack batch			Trial mixture for first batch			Maximum aggregate size
	Damp sand and pebbles	Wet sand and pebbles	Very wet sand and pebbles	Cement sacks	Sand cu. ft.	Pebbles cu. ft.	in.
Foundation walls which need not be watertight, mass concrete for footings, retaining walls, garden walls, etc..............	Average sand $6\frac{1}{4}$	$5\frac{1}{2}$	$4\frac{3}{4}$	1	$2\frac{3}{4}$	4	$1\frac{1}{2}$
Watertight basement walls, walls above ground, lawn rollers, hotbeds, cold frames, etc. Well curbs and platforms, cisterns, septic tanks, watertight floors, sidewalks, steppingstone and flagstone walks, driveways, play courts, outdoor fireplace base and walls, refuse burners, ash receptacles, porch floors, basement floors, garden and lawn pools, steps, corner posts, gate posts, piers, columns, etc.........	Average sand $5\frac{1}{2}$	5	$4\frac{1}{4}$	1	$2\frac{1}{4}$	3	$1\frac{1}{2}$
Fence posts, grape-arbor posts, mailbox posts, etc., flower boxes and pots, benches, bird baths, sun dials, pedestals and other garden furniture, work of very thin sections.........	Average sand $4\frac{1}{2}$	4	$3\frac{3}{4}$	1	$1\frac{3}{4}$	2	$\frac{3}{4}$

TABLE II

HOW TO FIGURE QUANTITIES

Mixtures			Quantities of Materials				
Cement	Fine Aggregate (sand)	Coarse Aggregate (gravel or stone)	Cement (in sacks)	Fine Aggregate cu. ft.	Fine Aggregate cu. yd.	Coarse Aggregate cu. ft.	Coarse Aggregate cu. yd.
1	2	...	12	24	0.9	...	...
1	3	...	9	27	1.0	...	...
1	1	1¾	10	10	0.37	17	0.63
1	1¾	2	8	14	0.52	16	0.59
1	2¼	3	6¼	14	0.52	19	0.70
1	2¾	4	5	14	0.52	20	0.74

1 sack cement equals 1 cu. ft.; 4 sacks equal 1 bbl. If concrete aggregates are sold in your locality by weight, you may assume for estimating purposes that a ton contains approximately 22 cu. ft. of sand or crushed stone; or about 20 cu. ft. of gravel. For information on local aggregates consult your building material dealer.

stiff to work with, do not change the proportions of water or cement. Rather, use more or less sand. If you reduce or add to the amount of water your concrete will suffer in quality.

For large jobs such as foundations, footings and slab floors, concrete should be mixed in a machine. Machine mixing does a more thorough job. Small mixes can be made by hand on any watertight platform. Pour out the required amount of sand first and then add the cement. Mix these two materials together until they have a uniform color. Spread out the mixture and add the gravel. Mix thoroughly and then hoe the mixture into a little hill with a hollow in the center. Pour the measured amount of water slowly into this hollow and then mix until every particle has been covered with cement paste.

Concrete in Cold Weather

Concrete should never be poured when the temperature is below 40° or when it is expected to fall below this point in the next twenty-four hours, unless precaution is taken to prevent the fresh concrete from freezing. On small jobs, it may be perfectly practical to cover the fresh concrete so that it will not freeze, but with a large undertaking this may prove very difficult. To be on the safe side, don't try to work with concrete at all in cold weather, because if it does freeze before it has had time to cure, it will not be durable.

Working with Concrete

When concrete is poured into forms, no more than 12″ in depth should be poured at one time. This should be spaded and tamped until it produces a dense mass. Work the concrete against the forms so that when they are removed the surface will be flush. If the concrete is not adequately spaded, there will be voids in the wall that will decrease its strength and watertightness.

Remember that concrete sets in about 30 minutes after the cement has been mixed with water. As the sand is almost sure to contain some moisture, the 30 minutes should begin from the time the sand and cement are mixed together. Do not allow concrete to stand too long before pouring into the forms and then try to thin it back to working consistency by adding more water.

No matter how fast you work, there will be places where the concrete has hardened before the adjoining batch is poured into place. The first thing you should do is to roughen up the hardened surface so that youwill get a good bond with the fresh concrete. Now just before the new batch of concrete is poured, brush the hardened surface clean and paint it with a mixture of cement and water of the consistency of thick paint. Be sure that the new concrete is poured right after this grout is applied, before the grout has had a chance to harden.

Curing Concrete

The longer the concrete has to cure, the stronger it will be, up to a point. For practical purposes, seven days of curing will produce a good grade of concrete. During this period exposed concrete surfaces should be covered with damp burlap, sand or straw and sprinkled with water at least once a day.

BUILDING WITH CONCRETE BLOCKS

If you decide to build the outside walls of the house with blocks, either cinder or concrete, refer to the chapter on how to build foundation walls and study the procedure given there for laying up a foundation wall with masonry blocks. This is exactly the same procedure that is required for building the entire house, with a very few exceptions.

The Foundation

Start at the footing and lay the blocks up just the same as you would if you were building a foundation wall. Leave a recess at each end of the build-ing for the girder or lintel that is to support the first-floor joists. (If your house is to have a concrete-slab floor, this is not necessary.) The girder should be installed in the same manner as explained elsewhere except for one point. If you are going to use a wood girder, it should come up flush with the top of the blocks that it is recessed into. If you are using a steel I-beam, it should be set 1⅝" below the top of the blocks. The reason for all this is that the wood floor-joists are going to rest on edge on the top of the blocks in this same course and, therefore, it is important that the top of the girder or lintel be in the same plane. If it is not, you will have trouble with a floor that is not even. The steel girder has to be set 1⅝" below the top of the blocks because you will need to attach a 2" x 4" to it to serve as a nailing base for the joists. The top of this 2" x 4" should come flush with the top of the blocks.

Floor Joists

Once the girder is in place, you can go ahead and put in the floor joists. These will run from the foundation wall to the girder. You will note from Fig. 1 that they rest on the top of the blocks and that the voids in this course of blocks have been filled with mortar to give them added strength. Jamb blocks are used with the ends open so that the joists have a place to rest. Note also that the ends of the joists are not cut off square but are cut at an angle. The purpose of doing this is to prevent the joist from damaging the wall should it ever fall. If the end was cut square, the joist would hang in the wall recess and perhaps crack the entire wall. By cutting it off at an angle, you make certain that if it should ever fall, it would drop out of the recess without causing any trouble.

Put one set of joists down first and spike them to the girder. Be sure that they are parallel. Now go on the other side of the wall and lay out the other set of joists. You will probably have to do a little arranging here with the spacing of the jamb blocks so that the ends

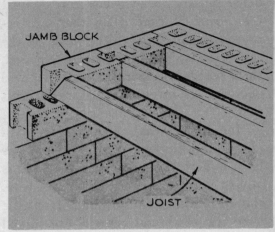

Fig. 1. How wood floor joists can be set into a concrete masonry-block wall. Jamb blocks are used to allow the ends of the joists to extend into the wall for several inches. Note that the end of the joists are cut off at an angle. This is done so that if a joist falls after the wall above has been completed, the joist will fall free of the wall rather than damaging it.

of both sets of joists will meet over the girder, or rather overlap, so that they can be nailed together.

Framing Openings

The next point that comes up is making the openings for doors. In a few more courses you will have to start thinking about the openings for windows but the method of making them is just about the same.

There are several ways to frame these openings. One method is to put the frame in place, plumb and brace it and then build the blocks up right around it. This is an easy way to do the job but it has several drawbacks. First of all, no matter how well the frame has been primed with paint, it is almost sure to absorb some moisture from the damp mortar, which will not do it any good at all. Secondly, there is great danger that in working you will knock the frame out of plumb and have to spend a lot of time checking it and setting it right again. Another point against this method is that the frame is almost sure to become marred or scarred in one way or another. A somewhat better method of making the openings is to build them first to fit the frame and then slip the frame into place. This is fine and dandy but there seems to be considerable risk involved here that the opening may not be quite right for the frame. Probably the best way to handle this business of getting the openings just right is to build a rough frame and then build up around it. After the opening has been finished you can remove this rough frame and slip in the finished frame.

Sills and Lintels

The sill or threshold for the doors can be made out of wood or masonry. It must be set in place so that it will come up at least even with the finished flooring. If you have a slab floor that is to be covered with linoleum, this distance need be only ⅛″ or so. If you are using wood sleepers and hardwood flooring, it must be equal to the combined thickness. The same holds true if you are using wood floor over floor joists.

Windows require a sill as well as the doors and these can be precast con-

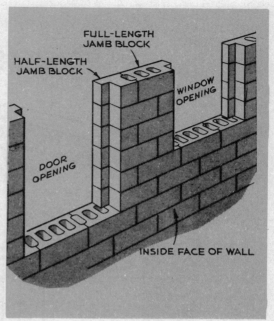

Fig. 2. Openings in concrete masonry walls for windows and doors are made with special jamb blocks, which provide a recess for the door or window frame.

crete. Figs. 2 and 3 show the method of framing an opening either for a window or door with jamb blocks.

The top of the door and window openings are covered with a precast concrete lintel that is reinforced with metal rods and can be had in either one or two pieces. You can get these at the same place where the ordinary blocks are purchased.

Walls

With the exception of the openings for doors and windows, the work of laying up the blocks is just the same as for a foundation wall. Care must be taken to be sure that the wall goes up plumb and that each block is level.

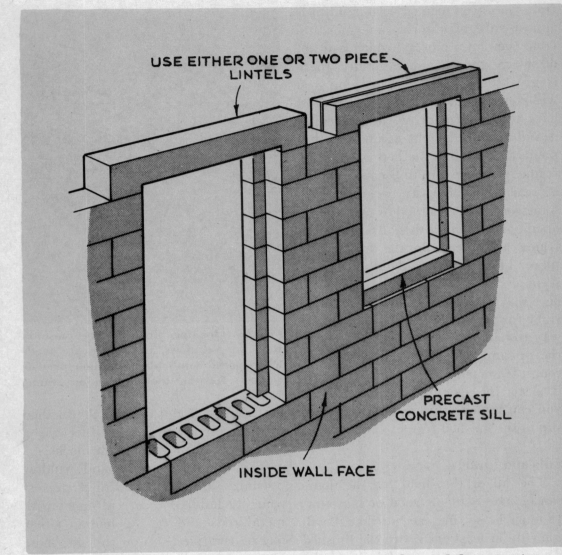

USE EITHER ONE OR TWO PIECE LINTELS

PRECAST CONCRETE SILL

INSIDE WALL FACE

Fig. 3. Precast concrete lintels should be used above window and door openings.

Use a horizontal chalk line to be sure that each course is true and drop plumb lines down to check that it is perfectly upright.

Bring the four walls up to a height of 7' 3". This is as far as we will go with concrete blocks. The gable ends of the building will be framed with wood because, if blocks are used, special equipment will be needed to cut them off at an angle so that they will fit the pitch of the roof.

The voids (hollow cores) in the last two courses of blocks at the top of the wall must be filled with mortar to give them added strength. It is best to lay wire screening along the top of the course of blocks under the last two courses so that the mortar used to fill the upper voids will not fall on down.

You will need to sink ½" x 8" bolts down into the mortar in the last two courses of blocks so that the top plate of 2" x 4" can be anchored to the masonry. These bolts should be spaced every 4' from the corners. The end joints between the top plates can be made up in the same manner as the sills for a frame house on a foundation wall.

After the top plate of two 2" x 4"'s has been anchored in place, you can go on and put in the ceiling joists and then frame the roof. Finally, the studding for the gable ends can go in place. This procedure is the same as that used in building a frame house.

Insulating Concrete Masonry Walls

There are several ways to insulate walls made out of masonry blocks. One of the simplest ways is just to pour granular insulation into the voids in the blocks as you build the wall. This does not require much time and is very effective. Of course, when this is combined with some other type of insulation on the inside, you get a very warm wall.

The inside of a concrete wall can be insulated with any of the materials that are used for frame-house insulation. The insulation is not attached directly to the masonry but to 2" x 2" furring strips, which are used to line the inside wall. These strips should be spaced every 16" on center. It is best to treat them with some sort of wood preservative so that if they should become damp because of a leak in the wall or through condensation, they will not decay. The wood strips can be attached to the masonry by nails driven through the mortar joints.

These furring strips not only serve as a means to attach the insulation but they are also going to serve as a base for either plaster and lath or some sort of wallboard. Many persons make the mistake of applying the interior plaster or wallboard direct to a masonry wall. This is a poor practice because the interior wall material is almost sure to become chilled by being in direct contact with the cold masonry and condensation or sweating will occur. If the wall is insulated and the interior wall is set away from the masonry, you should have no trouble with condensation or cool walls. A vapor barrier is as important for masonry walls as for wood ones.

BUILDING WITH BRICKS

Types of Brick

There are three types of bricks that you should be familiar with: the common brick, face-brick and firebrick.

Common bricks measure 8" long, 3¾" wide and 2¼" thick. They are used for all work where appearance is not of prime importance and where they will not be subject to high temperatures. Face-bricks are the same size as the common but they are more carefully made and come in different colors. These are the bricks that you would use around the fireplace and mantel where appearance is important. Firebricks are somewhat larger than the common or face-bricks and they are used wherever resistance to flame or high temperature is important. Firebrick must be used for lining the fireplace.

Courses

Each layer of bricks is called a course. When the bricks are laid end to end, it is called a stretcher course. When the bricks are set crosswise, they are called headers. When set crosswise on end, they are called a soldier course. See Fig. 4. A combination of courses is called a bond, and there are many different kinds of bonds. One of the most familiar types of bond is the "common bond." This is made up of five courses of stretchers and a sixth course of headers. Another bond is the "English," where you have alternate rows of stretchers and headers. See Fig. 5. You will note that the minimum thickness a wall of bricks can be is 4".

Mortar

Bricks are laid up with a cement mortar made of 1 part Portland cement to 3 parts clean fine sand. Sufficient water is added to this mixture to produce a workable plastic. You can, if you wish, replace 10 per cent of the

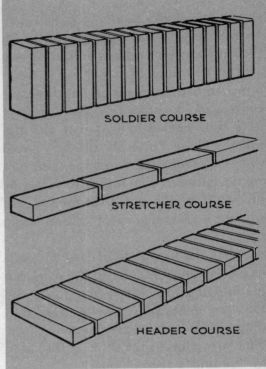

SOLDIER COURSE

STRETCHER COURSE

HEADER COURSE

Fig. 4. Three types of brick courses.

cement with hydrated lime. This will give you a mortar that is somewhat easier to work with than the straight cement and sand mix.

As the strength of the brickwork is going to depend on the strength of the mortar, it is important that this be of the best quality and that only enough mortar should be mixed as can be used in 30 minutes.

Bricks should be wet before they are put into place. This prevents them from absorbing the water out of the fresh mortar. You can hose the bricks down or, if you are only doing a small job, soak them in a bucket of water until they are ready to be laid up.

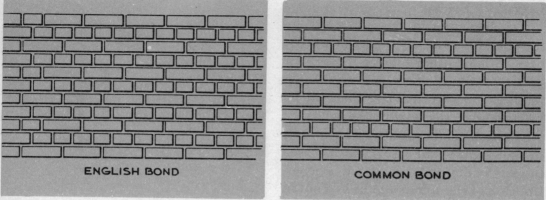

ENGLISH BOND   COMMON BOND

Fig. 5. Two types of bond, the English and the common, that are frequently used in working with bricks. Note that the joints are always staggered.

The mortar joint between each brick should be about ⅜″ thick, but this can be varied slightly so that a row of bricks will come out even. It is very important that all joints be packed thoroughly with mortar. One of the most common causes of leaking fireplace chimneys is that the interior mortar joints are not filled with mortar and moisture works into the brick-work

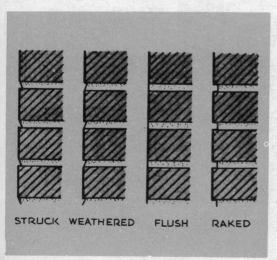

STRUCK   WEATHERED   FLUSH   RAKED

Fig. 6. The common types of brick joints are illustrated above.

from the top and seeps down through these faulty joints.

The exposed mortar joints can be finished in several ways. Fig. 6 shows four of these joints. The struck joint is easily made by running the point of the trowel along the joint after the mortar has begun to set. This joint should not be used for outside work since moisture can easily collect on the brick under the edge of the joint. The best joint to use for outside work is the weathered joint. This is just the opposite of the struck joint and any moisture reaching the joint will drain off quickly. The flush joint is not suitable for outside work because its rough face absorbs moisture. It is, of course, a very simple sort of joint to make. A raked joint is started just as if it were going to be a flush joint but, after the mortar has set for a few minutes, a steel jointer is used to cut back the mortar to the depth required.

This joint, too, should not be used for outside work.

Laying Up Bricks

The first step in this job is to lay the outside course of bricks along the base without using mortar to see how well they fit. If there is a slight difference, it can often be taken up by increasing or decreasing the width of the mortar joints slightly. If this fails to do the job, half-bricks can be used to get the dimensions correct. The entire base of the job should be laid out in this fashion. Fig. 7 shows how corners can be treated.

Bricks can be cut more or less to size with a cold chisel and a hammer. Score the brick where the cut is to be made on

Fig. 7. Detail of construction for the corner of a brick wall.

all sides and then give the chisel a sharp crack with the hammer.

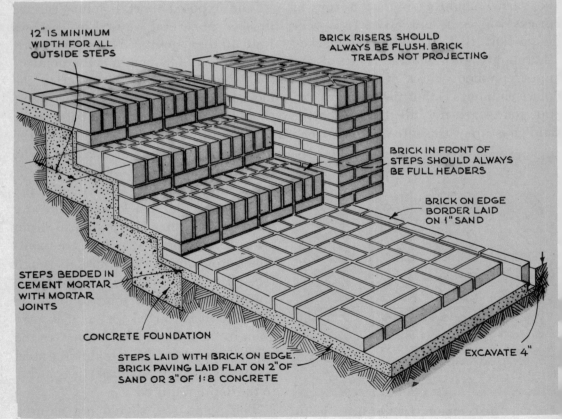

12" IS MINIMUM WIDTH FOR ALL OUTSIDE STEPS

BRICK RISERS SHOULD ALWAYS BE FLUSH. BRICK TREADS NOT PROJECTING

BRICK IN FRONT OF STEPS SHOULD ALWAYS BE FULL HEADERS

BRICK ON EDGE BORDER LAID ON 1" SAND

STEPS BEDDED IN CEMENT MORTAR WITH MORTAR JOINTS

CONCRETE FOUNDATION

STEPS LAID WITH BRICK ON EDGE. BRICK PAVING LAID FLAT ON 2" OF SAND OR 3" OF 1:8 CONCRETE

EXCAVATE 4"

Fig. 8. A flight of attractive brick steps for the front of the house.

Care should be taken not to disturb the bricks once they have been set in place with mortar. As has been mentioned before, cement mortar will set within 30 minutes after the cement and sand have been mixed together. If the bricks should be moved after this interval of time, the mortar joint will never be as strong as was the original.

You will note that the trade mark of the manufacturer appears on only one face of a brick. The bricks should be set in place with the trade mark facing down.

Fig. 8 shows an attractive flight of outdoor steps made out of bricks over a concrete base. The concrete base is poured just as if the steps themselves were to be of concrete. After the concrete is hard and the forms have been stripped away, the bricks are set in place with mortar.

Chapter 6

LOCATING THE HOUSE ON THE SITE

EVEN after you have found and purchased a suitable building site, you may have some additional problems to settle in regard to just how the house should be positioned on the land. Many fine sites and homes have been spoiled to some extent because the house was just set down on the lot without any thought as to what position would be the best.

Facing to the South

As a general rule, a house is always positioned so that the main rooms—including the living room in most cases—will face to the south.

There is a very good reason for so placing the main rooms.

During the summer months the sun is very high in the sky and, therefore, a house facing south will be more or less directly under the sun at all times. This means that the rays of the sun will not shine directly through the windows on the south side of the house. This is an important point for homes in northern climates, including those in the southern sections of this country. During the winter months, the sun is much lower in the sky and its rays will then shine into the rooms that face to the south. A room filled with sunshine during the cold winter months is very pleasant, not only because it will be cheerful, but also because the warmth supplied by the sun can help reduce the fuel bills. Many of us forget how many pleasant days there are during the winter months when the sun is shining brightly and producing a good deal of warmth.

In fact, solar heating, which is just beginning to come into its own, is based on using the sun's heat alone to keep the house warm during the winter.

Of course, a house that is going to depend on solar heat for all, or even a large portion, of its heating must be especially designed for this purpose, with large areas of glass and special overhanging eaves to allow a maximum amount of winter sun to enter and still keep out the hot summer sun. But, with a central heating system, positioning your house so that it faces south is a highly desirable feature.

Fig. 1 shows how it is possible to have the living room of a house face to the south regardless of the direction of the street.

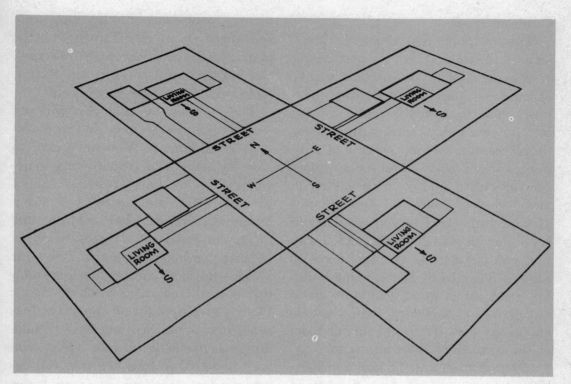

Fig. 1. The general practice is to locate the house on the plot in such a way that the rooms used for living purposes will face to the south.

Other Considerations

There are, however, a lot of other important points to think about besides having the living room face to the south. There is, for example, a question of view. It may be that if you position your house so that the living room faces south you will be looking right out onto a busy street or some unattractive buildings. In the case of a street, you may be able to move your house towards the back of the lot and even put up a screen of trees to hide the street from view. However, if you do this you will need long walks and driveways from the house to the street and you will also reduce the size of your backyard. If there happens to be a particularly pleasant view to the east or west, many probably will prefer to have their living room face in that direction rather than to the south in spite of the sun factor.

Another consideration is the direction of the prevailing winter and summer winds. If there is going to be an outside porch and terrace, it is certainly desirable to place your house so that these will receive the cooling summer breeze. And it is just as desirable not to place your house in such a fashion that the winter winds will blow right across the large glass areas in the living room.

Outdoor Space

Another point that should be given serious consideration is positioning your house so that you will have plenty of outdoor space for recreation purposes. The backyard is really coming into its own today, what with outdoor fireplaces for cooking week-end suppers, various sorts of outdoor games for the entire family to take part in and even sunbathing. If items of this sort are important to you, you should try to locate your house in such a way that you get a large area in back with some privacy to it. Many home builders today care a great deal more about an attractive backyard than they do about the view from the living-room or the warmth of the winter sun.

Other factors are the size and location of your gardens, both flower and vegetable, the location of any attractive trees that may be growing on the site and neighboring houses.

Balancing Advantages and Disadvantages

A very good way to help you to make up your mind as to just how the house should be positioned is to draw a scale plan of your plot showing its relation to the street and the position of trees, other houses, the direction of the prevailing winds and other important features of this sort. Now draw a floor plan of your house at the same scale and place it on the drawing of the plot. Move your floor plan into various positions and consider the advantages and disadvantages of each.

The chances are that you will not be able to find a position that meets all your requirements. You are going to have to make some concessions somewhere along the line, but be careful not to make them for something of only a temporary nature. Do not put too much emphasis on a pleasant view, because you may find that before your house is finished, another house is going up that will completely block it off. Do not give up a lot of important features just so you will not have to take down a particularly nice tree. You may find that in time the tree will become so large that it keeps your house in the shade or that it is attacked by a disease and has to be removed.

A lot of home builders have positioned their homes on a site just for the benefit of their small children and then found that in just a few years the children have outgrown the site.

Naturally, the contours of your particular plot are going to have the last word in how your house is positioned, and they must be carefully studied before you are ready to go ahead with laying out the house and starting the excavation work.

READING PLANS AND BLUEPRINTS

It would take a book of many thousands of pages to describe in minute detail each little step in the procedure involved in building a house from the ground up. As many thousands of houses are built each year and each one is somewhat different from the rest, the building trades depend upon drawings rather than written instructions to show what is wanted. The architect who has designed a house uses these drawings to show the builder exactly how the house should be put together. It is a very good idea to understand how to read such drawings, because once you have mastered them, you can, theoretically at least, build any home that you have the plans for without additional information.

For the basic house described in this book there are framing plans that show the exact location of each piece of studding, each rafter and each joist, together with additional information. These will not be found in the regulation type of building plans, but if you know how to read regulation plans, they will be just as clear to you as the framing plans reproduced here.

The plans for building a house may be called by such names as blueprints, working drawings or simply plans. A set of these drawings will show you everything about the house that you need to know in order to build it. They will show the height of the wall, the location and size of the windows and doors, the position of the fireplace, the location of the interior partitions and other facts needed to construct the house exactly as the architect has planned it.

Blueprints or working drawings are understood by everyone engaged in the building trades and, therefore, they can be used for many purposes. For example, when you go to a finance agency to get the necessary funds for building, the agency will want to see the blueprints of the house you plan to build. One look at these plans will tell anyone with any degree of skill in reading them what the value of the completed house should be. Before you can get a building permit—if one is required—you may have to show a set of blueprints to the local building authorities and they will determine from the plans whether or not a house of that type may be erected on the plot you have in mind for it. If you wish to get bids from contractors for jobs that you do not wish to undertake yourself, such as plumbing and heating, a set of blueprints will be necessary so that each contractor can give you a bid for his particular work.

You may find that before the house is completed, many sets of blueprints will be required. Not only may some be required for other persons, but the set that you are working with will almost surely become dirty and torn before the job has been completed. In almost every community there is a firm that specializes in making blueprints, and it is well worth the expense to have a sufficient number of sets made up in advance so that you will not be caught short or make an error because you were not able to read the blueprint clearly.

Architectural drawings or blueprints can be divided up into four groups.

First there are the *plan views*. These are also called *floor plans* and there will be one for each floor of the house —basement, first floor and attic, for instance. The plan view or floor plan will show the room arrangement on each floor by the arrangement of the partitions. It will also show the location of the fireplace, doors, windows, closets, stairs and similar details.

The *elevation drawings* show the outside of the finished house. As the house has four sides, four elevations are required. These may be called South, East, North and West elevation, or the front elevation, which is the front of the house, the right elevation, which is on your right when looking at the front of the house, the back elevation and the left elevation.

Elevation drawings show everything about a particular side of the house from the ground floor level to the roof. They show the location and size of windows and doors, distance from first-floor level to second-floor level, type of siding and other information.

A *section,* or sections, is a drawing used to show the type and size of construction used on a particular portion of the building. In these views, which are usually vertical, a portion of the construction is cut away to show various details. For example, a wall section will include a cutaway that reveals the necessary construction detail for the studs, joists, rafters, sills, plates, floor construction, etc.

The last type of drawing is the *detail*. This is used when it is required to show some detail work that would not be very clear in a plan view, elevation or section.

For example, it would be difficult to show the cornice detail on an elevation view of a house and, therefore, the architect will make an enlarged drawing that shows the necessary points. Such detail drawings may be placed on the sheet containing the other drawings or, if there are a great many of them, they may be all grouped on a sheet of their own. Details will be required for plans, elevations and sections.

As it would be impossible to draw a house to full size on paper, it is necessary that the drawings be made *to scale*. This means that the house is reduced to a size that it is practical to put on paper. Dimensions must be reduced proportionately so that all members have the same relationship to one another as they did before they were reduced. House plans are usually drawn to a one-fourth-inch scale, which means that each quarter-inch on the plans indicates one foot. For example, if the actual height of an opening is ten feet, it is represented on the drawing by ten quarter-inches, which is two and one-half inches. This enables an architect to draw up the plans of a house on a relatively small piece of paper, which will average about eighteen by twenty-four inches in size.

The scale is always indicated on the drawing so there will be no question as to just what it is. If the scale is one-quarter inch, it will be represented on the drawing by: ¼″ equals 1′0″. If the scale is one-half, it is represented by: ½″ equals 1′0″. Sometimes, very complicated small detail work will be shown at full scale; in this case it will be so indicated on the drawings.

It is seldom that all the various dimensions required for building a house will be found on the drawings. If they were, it would require many pages of plans for one house because of the vast number of dimensions that would have to be given. Therefore, in some instances you will have to figure out the dimensions from the blueprints. This is not difficult if the drawings were accurately made to scale and you have the proper type of rule. The best rule to use for measuring blueprints is a three-sided scale. This contains six scales: 1½ inches to a foot, 1 inch to a foot, ¾ inch to a foot, ½ inch to a foot, ¼ inch to a foot and ⅛ inch to a foot. An ordinary 12-inch rule can also be used if it has fine enough divisions so that you will be able to measure the fractions of quarter-inches.

Care must be taken in measuring any distance on a blueprint because, with the scale used, a small error at this time can mean the difference of several inches when the actual work is made up in feet and inches. Be sure that the blueprint is absolutely flat and then, with a fine pencil, mark the extremes of the point that is to be measured. Place your rule or scale between these points and make your reading. Be sure that all the markings on the rule or square are perfectly legible and do not use this rule for rough work because of the chance of its becoming damaged.

When the actual dimensions are given, they are written in feet and inches. For example, an opening 4 feet wide will be expressed 4′–0″. So that there will be no question as to just where this dimension applies, a dimension line is used to indicate the distances between the points. The ends of such lines have arrowheads and either the dimension figure will be set over the line or the line will be broken in the center and the dimension figure inserted at this point. Sometimes, the dimension line must be brought out beyond the actual dimension that is shown on the blueprint and, in this case, extension lines are used to indicate the extreme limits of the dimension.

Chapter 7

THE FOUNDATION OF THE HOUSE

Clearing the Land

Once the exact location for the house has been decided, the next job is to clear the land of brush and trees. Give some thought to which trees you remove. There is no point in going in with an ax and taking down all forms of vegetation only to have to replace some from a nursery when the house has been finished. Save as many good shade trees as you can, but be sure to allow yourself ample working room. You should also provide enough room for trucks to come in with materials for the house and for temporary storage of these materials.

If you have a wooded lot and there are a great many trees that must be removed, the most painless way to get rid of them is to get hold of a local dealer in fireplace and cord wood. He will probably be only too glad to take down the larger trees for you and may even pay you a few dollars per cord to boot. All in all, you may make enough out of this to pay the cost of a man and bulldozer to rip out a few of the stumps.

Clear the land around the site of the house of all dead wood and stumps.

Any wood left in the ground will attract termites, which may in time get to the house. Get rid of all underbrush surrounding the building site as tools and materials have a bad habit of getting lost in tall grass and much time can be wasted looking for them.

Laying Out the Building

Once you have the site cleared you are ready to lay out the building. If it has been necessary to have the plot surveyed, the four corners of the building can be located and marked by the surveyor. This is probably the best way to take care of the job, but it can be done by the home builder himself without any special equipment.

Before you pick exact location of your house, check to be sure that there are no local codes that govern how far a house must be set back from the road or whether or not the house must line up with the others on adjoining lots.

Fig. 1 shows how a building can be laid out by means of lines, posts and batter boards. First of all, take four wood stakes and drive nails or tacks into their tops at the center. If the

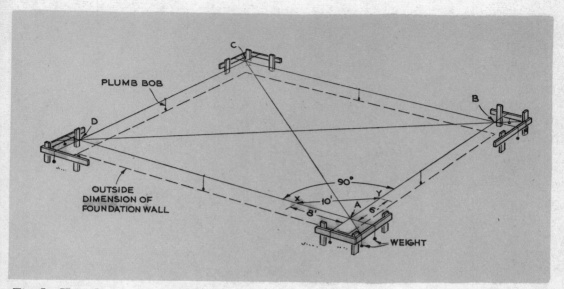

Fig. 1. How lines and batter boards are used to lay out the four corners and dimensions of the building. After the out- side dimensions have been set, additional lines can be strung to show the outside limits of the excavation.

house must be set a certain number of feet from the road or sidewalk, measure off this distance and then drive one of the stakes into the ground, marking off one corner of the building. Measure off from the first stake the length of the side of the building that is to face the road and drive in a second stake. This stake should be the same distance from the road or sidewalk as the first stake. The next job is to measure off the width of the house from these two base stakes and drive in your second set of stakes at their approximate position. See Fig. 2. What you must do now is check to be sure that each of the four corners of the building is exactly 90°. Construct batter boards three or four feet back from the stakes at each of the four corners, as shown in Fig. 3. Now string lines between these

boards so that the lines pass over the tacks driven into the four stakes. As these lines will have to be moved before the job is finished, it is best not to tie them to the batter boards. Notch the boards and tie weights to the ends of the lines so that they hang over the batter boards. Be sure that the batter boards are all at the same elevation. See Fig. 4.

Measure off a distance of 6′ from stake *A* along *AB*. Drive a stake in at this point (*Y*). Now measure off 8′ from stake *A* along line *AD* and drive a stake in at this point (*X*).

Move the lines strung between the batter boards until the distance from stake *X* to stake *Y* is exactly 10′. This will insure that the angle formed at stake *A* is exactly ninety degrees (90°). Reposition stake *A* so that the tack

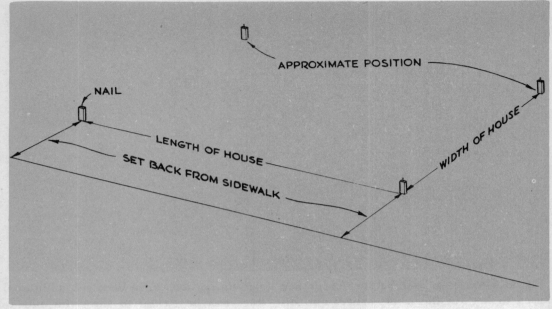

NAIL

APPROXIMATE POSITION

LENGTH OF HOUSE

SET BACK FROM SIDEWALK

WIDTH OF HOUSE

Fig. 2. The first step in laying out the location for the excavation work.

head is directly under the point where lines *AB* and *AD* cross. Drop a plumb line down from this point. Check the other four corners in the same fashion. When you think you have all four corners exactly 90°, run diagonal lines from corner to corner and then meas-ure them. If the lines are equal, your building is square. Lay additional lines across the batter boards to indicate the width of the foundation wall. Keep the batter boards and lines in place. They will serve as guides for building the foundations.

EXCAVATION

Types of Foundation

Before any excavation work gets underway, the type of foundation the house is to rest on must be decided. Too much emphasis cannot be placed on the importance of setting the house on a firm and permanent base that will not settle and that will anchor the house firmly to the ground. Practically every section of this country is subject, at one time or another, to violent storms of some sort, and unless the house foundations are solid and the house bolted to this base, there is a good possibility of the house being torn loose.

The foundation must be able to carry the entire weight of the house without settling. Soil conditions vary greatly and, therefore, before you select any particular type of foundation, it might be wise to check with some local builders and see how they feel about the most suitable foundations for the type of soil you are building on. For instance, you do not want a concrete-slab floor on a badly drained soil, or, if the soil is mostly fill the footings should be larger.

One other remark on the general subject of foundations is that it is the base upon which the rest of the house is to be built and, therefore, it is important that it be square and level. A great mistake made by many amateur builders is to let small inaccuracies go uncorrected on the assumption that they can be covered up later on. Don't make this mistake. A slight error in the foundations or framing can haunt you right through the entire project. The time required to make a double check on all phases of the building operation is well worth while.

There are several different foundations that a house can be built on. The cheapest and simplest one is made of wood or masonry piers sunk into the ground. These posts or piers make a suitable foundation for small summer-homes or homes built in mild climates, but they are not suitable for year-round homes where there are cold winters because the first floor is unprotected and is chilled by the cold air passing under it.

The conventional house, built for all-year-round living in cold climates, with or without basement, should have a continuous foundation wall of masonry. This insures adequate support for the building and also makes pos-

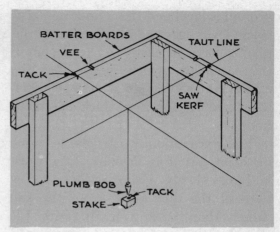

Fig. 3. Dropping a plumb line down from the lines extended between batter boards to check the exact location of a stake.

sible a warm first floor. The masonry used for this type of foundation can be poured concrete or masonry blocks. If masonry blocks are selected, use concrete rather than cinder blocks for below-grade (below ground level) construction.

Excavation for House with Basement

If you decide to build a house with a basement, your first job is a rather extensive one of excavation. If the

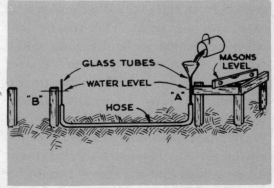

Fig. 4. A simple way to get batter boards at the same elevation.

ground is level and the foundation is at grade level (ground level), you should plan to have at least 7' of headroom in the basement, which means that the excavation should go 6" deeper than this to allow for a 6"-thick basement floor.

The excavation work can be done by hand but it is backbreaking work and goes slowly. Using a wheelbarrow to haul the dirt away from the site rather than tossing it up with the shovel will save time and energy. As you dig, leave a narrow ramp that, when covered with planks, will make a runway. It is hardly practical these days to hire labor to dig out an excavation by hand. The quickest and cheapest way in most cases is to call in a power shovel. While this equipment with an operator costs a great deal more per hour than a day laborer, it does the work so rapidly that there is, in most cases, a considerable saving in cash.

If possible, try to be on hand when the shovel is at work. Unless you are, the operator will probably bury all the topsoil from the excavation under tons of gravel and clay. This means that when you come to landscaping you'll either have to buy topsoil or uncover that which is buried. Have the operator dump all topsoil (usually running to a depth of about one foot) off by itself. After the main excavation job has been done, there are several minor digging jobs that the shovel can do for you that will save time and money later on. Trenches for water pipes and

sewer lines can be dug to within a few feet of the excavation. The excavation for a septic tank or cesspool can also be made and one for an outside fuel-oil storage tank, if this is required. An outside underground coal bin is well worth considering as it gives you more room in the basement as well as removing much of the dirt and dust that accompanies coal when stored indoors. If you plan to build a breezeway and garage in the future, have the shovel dig the foundations for them.

The Area to Be Excavated

If the soil is compact, you may be able to get by without any outside form for poured concrete foundations as the earth will serve the purpose. In this case, you should go to work with a shovel and clean up the corners of the excavation as well as complete any trenching, window wells, etc.

The exact area to be excavated is going to depend on local soil conditions, drainage and the type of material used for the foundation. If the soil is well packed, well drained, and you plan to use poured concrete, it may be possible, as mentioned before, to use the sides of the excavation as the outside forms for the concrete. In this case, the excavation should be laid out and dug to the exact dimensions of the house. If the soil is not well drained and you want to be sure that the basement is going to be dry, drain tile can be laid along the base of the foundation on the outside. This means that the excavation is going to have to be about two feet wider and you'll need outside forms. If you plan to use masonry blocks for the foundation, you will have to make your opening about two feet wider so that you will be able to work on the outside face of the wall.

FOOTINGS

The footings are the base that supports the foundation wall and, of course, the entire weight of the house. They must be used with all types of foundations, even piers. In normal soil conditions, the footings should be as deep as the foundation walls are wide and twice as wide as the walls. In other words, if the foundation walls are to be 10″ thick, the footings should be 10″ deep and 20″ wide. The foundation is then centered on the footing so that the footing extends out 5″ beyond the foundation on each side.

Footings should be made of poured concrete and they must extend below the frost line. If they do not, there is a strong possibility of frost getting in under the footing, heaving it up and thus cracking the foundation wall as well as throwing the entire house out of plumb.

In most cases, you will not require any forms for the footings as the sides of the trench dug for them will serve the purpose. This trench should be dug by hand and you should try to get it as square as possible. Footings poured into a trench with a rounded bottom will not have the carrying capacity of those with a square, even base.

If the walls of the excavation are to serve as the outside forms for the foundation wall, it is going to be necessary to undercut into this wall for a distance of 5″ for the footing. The best way to handle this situation is to place a 2″x4″ on edge 15″ in from the wall of the excavation. Drive stakes along the inside of this board so that it is held securely in place and be sure that it is level because it will serve as a top to the form for the footing. Now go ahead and undercut into the excavation for 5″ and then dig the trench. See Fig. 5. Make the sides and bottom of this trench as clean as possible. If the soil is very dry and tends to crumble, dampen it a little before you pour the footings.

Footings should be poured in one operation. The usual mix is 1 part

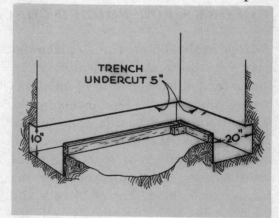

Fig. 5. Excavation cut back to make an earth form for the footing. A 2″x4″ on edge along the inside edge of the cut serves as a form for the top of the footing and also as a means of anchoring the base of the foundation forms in place.

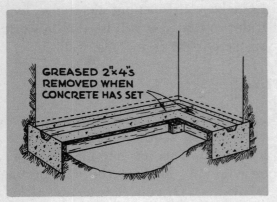

GREASED 2"x4"s
REMOVED WHEN
CONCRETE HAS SET

Fig. 6. A recess can be made in the footing by setting a beveled and greased
2"x4" into the concrete before it is hard.
This is removed before the foundation
forms are installed.

cement, 3.75 parts sand and 5 parts
gravel. The method of surfacing the
top of the footings will depend on
what materials are going to be used
for the foundation wall. If you plan to
use masonry blocks, the top of the foot-

ings should be level and smooth. If you
are going to use poured concrete, you
want to make a key slot in the footings
so that you will get a good bond between footings and foundations. This
key slot can be made by taking a
2"x4" and beveling the edges. Now
before the footings have set, force this
2"x4" down along the middle of the
footings. See Fig. 6. Grease the 2"x4"
before you set it into the concrete so
that it can be removed easily after the
footings are hard. If you are going to
use poured-concrete foundations, be
sure that the footings do not extend
above the 2"x4" that is serving as
the inner form. The reason for this
is that the 2"x4" can be used later on
to attach the foundation forms in place.
Keep the fresh concrete covered and
damp until such time as the concrete
has set hard.

FORMS FOR POURED-CONCRETE FOUNDATION WALLS

As soon as the footings are in place and
have set, the work of assembling the
forms for poured-concrete foundations
can get underway. These forms can be
built of sheathing boards or plywood.
In either case, the materials can be re-
used as wall and roof sheathing or as
sub-flooring. The framework for the
forms can be made out of 2"x4"s and
2"x6"s. Because practically all the
material required for forms can be re-
used, it is important that you do as
little cutting as possible. Use your
lengths of short dimension for the
framework and allow them to extend

up beyond the top of the forms rather
than cutting them to exact size. It is
usually advisable to use special con-
crete-form nails with two heads, as
these can be removed easily and without damage to the wood. You can either
build the forms in sections and then
put them together or build them all in
one piece.

Attaching the Base of the Forms

There are several ways to attach the
base of the forms in place. If you used
a 2"x4" as a form for the top of the
footing, this can serve as a nailing base

for the sole plate of the form. See detail in Fig. 7. Place a 2"x4" or 2"x6" down along the footing, allowing the edge to overlap the 2"x4" staked to the ground. Spike the two together and then use the sole plate to toe-nail the vertical framework of the forms to. When the time comes to put on the sheathing for the forms, be sure that the first course extends far enough down so that its lower edge can be nailed to this base plate as well as to the vertical studding.

If the footings come just level with the ground, a 2"x4" or 2"x6" can be placed on edge on the outside of the footing and held in place by stakes driven into the ground. The studding for the forms is placed inside of this plate and nailed. See Fig. 8.

Bracing the Forms

Poured concrete will exert a tremendous pressure and, therefore, it is important that the forms are not only solidly built but are braced so that the weight of the concrete will not force them out of position. Figs. 7 and 8 show two different methods of bracing the forms. You will note that outside

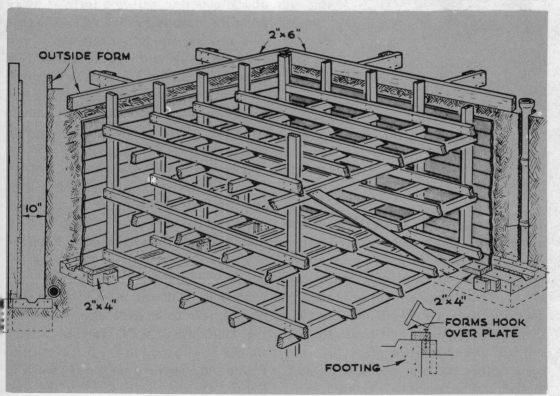

Fig. 7. One method of supporting the forms for the foundations. The detail shows a 2"x4" spiked to the top of the footing form. The siding used for the forms overhangs the form framework enough so it will hook behind this 2"x4".

Fig. 8. Another method of bracing the forms for the foundations. A length of 2"x4" on edge along the base serves to hold the lower portion of the form in place. Diagonal braces support the upper portion.

wall to leak. If no outside form is required, a 2" x 6" or wider board can be set along the edge of the excavation on edge to provide a form for that portion of the foundation extending above the ground and also to serve as a top guide in getting the foundation level. This outside form must be braced adequately and it must be level.

Studding

Studding for the forms should be spaced no more than 18" on center, and the sheathing is applied on the inside of the studding so that the weight of the concrete will not force it away from the studding as would be the case if it were applied on the outside. If you use both inside and outside forms, 1" x 2" spacers should be used to keep the two halves of the form an equal distance apart. The inside and outside studding of the forms should be tied together with No. 10 wire to prevent spreading. Install the spacers first so that, as the wire is tightened, the forms will not be pulled together. See Fig. 8.

as well as inside forms are used in these illustrations. As previously mentioned, whether outside forms are necessary will depend on local soil conditions. Dry soil that tends to crumble easily does not make a very adequate outside form because, in the first place, the dry soil will absorb moisture from the concrete before the concrete is hard, and, second, as the concrete is poured, some of this soil is bound to get mixed in with it. This will cause weak spots in the concrete and may even cause the

Stair Well; Windows; Girder Pockets

Fig. 9 shows details of the forms necessary for the basement outside stair well. The walls around this stair well do not have to be as thick as those for the foundation wall. Beveled cleats should be attached to the forms used to frame the basement door (as shown in the illustration) so that, after the concrete is hard, the cleats, which remain embedded in the concrete, can be used to fasten the door frame in place. For these cleats, use wood treated to resist decay and insects.

You will need windows in the basement, and the openings for these should be cut in the forms and framed. You can build these forms for window frames out of wood or you can purchase metal ones intended for use with metal window sashes. See Fig. 10. As these windows will be below or, at best, near ground level, you will also need wells around them on the outside. These wells can be dug by hand and can be made out of either poured concrete or metal. Concrete window wells should be 18" deep and their walls should be 6" thick. If there is to be a coal chute into the basement, this should be installed in the forms. If you plan on having an underground coal bin with an access door into the basement, frame the opening for the door at the base of the forms.

You must also make a pocket in the foundation wall at each end for the girder, which must be used on all wood-floor houses, to support the floor joists. The pocket for the girder we have chosen should be 8" wide and about 8¼" deep. The girder should extend about ⅛" above the top of the foundation wall. See Fig. 11.

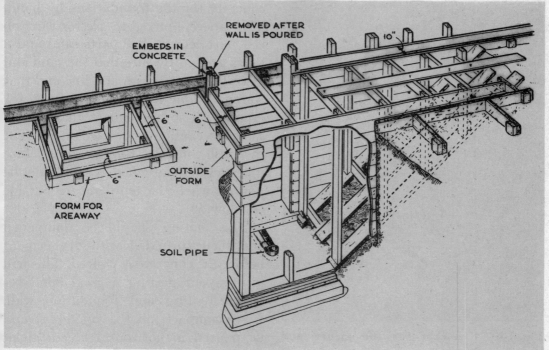

Fig. 9. Forms for the basement stair well should be constructed at the same time as those for the foundation walls. Note the detail of the doorway into the basement. Beveled cleats are embedded into the concrete and will serve as a nailing base for the basement doorway frame. The areaway around the basement window should extend for at least 18" below the bottom of the window opening.

The inside of the wood forms are often greased to make it easier to remove them after the concrete has set. However, do not grease them if you plan to finish off the inside foundation wall with paint later.

POURING THE FOUNDATION WALLS

If you want the foundation walls to be watertight, the entire wall must be poured in one operation. There are several ways in which this can be done. One is to order ready-mixed concrete delivered to the site. This comes in trucks and is ready to pour on arrival. The other method is to rent a concrete-mixer and have enough extra help on hand to mix, pour and tamp the concrete in the forms. In fact, even if ready-mixed concrete is used, you should have additional help to aid you in tamping and spading the concrete as it is poured.

It is not practical to try to mix the concrete for the foundations by hand. The concrete mixed to use for this job is 1 part cement, 2¼ parts sand and 3 parts gravel. Be sure that the sand and gravel used are clean and fine and that water suitable for drinking is used for mixing. Also remember that unless some precaution is devised to prevent the fresh concrete from freezing before it has set and hardened, it should not be poured when the temperature outside is below 40°.

The footing should be dampened and then sprinkled with dry cement before the concrete is poured. This will insure your getting a good bond between footing and foundation wall. For a compact job, the concrete should be poured in horizontal layers about 6″ deep. These should be spaded so that the concrete is compact and free from air pockets. Do not, however, spade and hoe too much, for this will bring the large-size aggregate to the

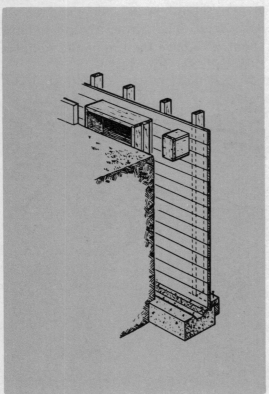

Fig. 10. A pocket for the girder and openings for basement windows must be built into the form. The frame for the window opening has beveled cleats on the sides which remain in the concrete after the forms are removed and serve as a nailing base for the window frames.

top. Keep in mind that concrete must be poured 30 minutes after mixing the dry cement with the sand. If the concrete is not used during this period, it will begin to set and will not have the same strength as freshly mixed concrete. Do not try to make concrete that has once set workable again by adding water to it; this will produce inferior concrete. As the concrete is poured, remove the 1" x 2" spacer boards from between the forms. Be particularly careful that the concrete is worked in around window and other openings.

Installing Anchor Bolts

After all the concrete has been poured, give it time to set a little and then install the anchor bolts. If you prefer, these can be installed in the forms before the concrete is poured by hanging them on spacer strips in the forms. These anchor bolts are used to tie the wood sills and framework to the foundation. Anchor bolts should be ⅝" or ¾" in diameter and should be spaced between 6' and 8' apart, with bolts a foot or so from each corner. They should extend about 18" into the concrete and should extend above the finished wall about 3" to allow them to be slipped through holes in the sill and then fitted with washers and nuts. Keep the bolts about 3" from the outside of the foundation wall so that they will come at about the center of the sill. After these anchor bolts are in place,

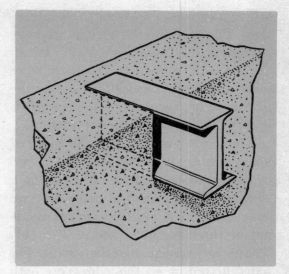

Fig. 11. The steel I-beam, if one is used, should extend ⅛" above the top of the foundation wall.

smooth off the top of the concrete and then cover it with damp burlap, tar paper or boards to save the surface from damage and to keep it from drying out too quickly. Allow the concrete about a week to set and cure before you strip off the forms. Be careful when you take the forms apart so that you do not damage the wood beyond further use. Knock off any odd bits of dry concrete that may cling to the boards and then store them where they will be ready for the next job. While waiting for the poured-concrete foundations to harden, you can go to work and install the additional footings and piers that will be needed for the girder, and footings for the chimney and fireplace.

THE GIRDER

This heavy wood or steel beam is used to support the ends of the floor joists.

It is not required for homes with concrete floor slabs because no wood joists are required in this type of construction. The ends of the girder are supported by the foundation walls. When the walls were poured, recesses were made at the proper locations so that the girder could be set into them and be level with the top of the foundation.

The girder can be one solid piece of heavy timber, it can be built up of two or more pieces of stock or it can be a steel I-beam. For our purposes, we have selected a built-up girder made out of three pieces of sound 2″ x 10″. These are nailed together with 20d nails placed near the edges on both sides. The nails are spaced every 2′ and, by alternating the spacing on the sides of the girder, you will have a nail at top and bottom passing right through the girder every foot or so. A 6″ steel I-beam can be used in place of this built-up girder.

Bearing Posts

Of course, you will never be able to get one solid piece of timber that will run from wall to wall. There will be some joints and these must be spaced in such a way that they come over the bearing posts. For our purposes, posts of 4″x6″ will do.

The amount of weight a girder can effectively carry will depend on its size and the number and the distance apart of the bearing posts. The more bearing posts used, the lighter the girder can be, but, of course, a great many bearing posts will make the basement unfit for other purposes. The trick is to hit a happy medium between the thickness of the girder and the number of posts used to support it.

Many persons make the mistake of assuming that the load on the girder is the same as that on the foundation wall and, therefore, does not require a solid footing and support. This is a very grave error and is the cause of many weak and sagging floors. A girder that is located in the exact center of a floor will carry about half the total floor weight. The other half will be divided equally between the two foundation walls. Even when the girder does not run through the exact center of the floor, it will carry about one-half the total weight of the floor and the load imposed on the floor. You can see, therefore, that it is important that the girder be as strong and solid as possible without wasting money or materials.

Installing the Girder

If the house is not to have a fireplace, setting the girder in place is more or less a simple matter. The first step is to pour the footings for the bearing posts that support the girder. These can be of the type shown in Fig. 12. They are approximately 1 foot square and about 6″ in depth. Their location should be such as to divide the total distance between the foundation walls into thirds, but, of course, a slight difference one way or the other is permissible. After these footings are hard and the forms have been removed from the poured-concrete foundations, you can put the girder in place and then install the bearing posts. The posts should be cut to the exact size and then placed on the footings and braced so that they will stand upright. The sections of the girder can then be put into position, one end resting in the recess made for it in the foundation wall and the other end resting on the bearing posts. The additional sections of the girder can be installed in the same manner. Naturally, it is very important that the girder be absolutely level. If it isn't, your floor will have either a crown in the middle or a slight depression.

Steel girders can be put into place before the footings are in and, in fact, you may find that this is a great deal easier to do than trying to get the girder level after the footings have been poured.

The sections of the girder should be hooked or bolted together and the girder set in place. Support it by "figure A" or other temporary braces placed near the joints and get it absolutely level. Then bolt the posts or beams in place. Now the concrete can be poured around the ends of the posts to form the footings. As soon as the footings are hard, the temporary braces can be removed and the girder

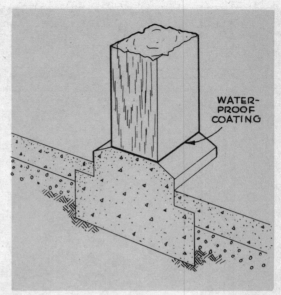

WATER-PROOF COATING

Fig. 12. An excellent type of concrete footing and foundation to use for wood bearing posts. The thin coat of waterproofing prevents the end of the post from rotting and if the footing should settle it will not crack the basement concrete floor.

will be supported by the posts resting on the footings.

If you pour the footings first, you may have some trouble in getting the steel beams cut to just the right size. They should fit exactly because of the importance of having the girder level.

THE CHIMNEY FOOTING

Footings for the chimney should be 12" in depth and at least 6" wider on all sides than the chimney itself. Before deciding the final dimensions of the footing, be sure to consult the installation specifications for the type of heating equipment you intend to use, in

case they require some minor readjustments.

If the house is to have a fireplace in basement, first floor or both, the footing must be 12" in depth and 3' by 6' in area. Rather than use a wood or steel girder under the first floor, a wall of

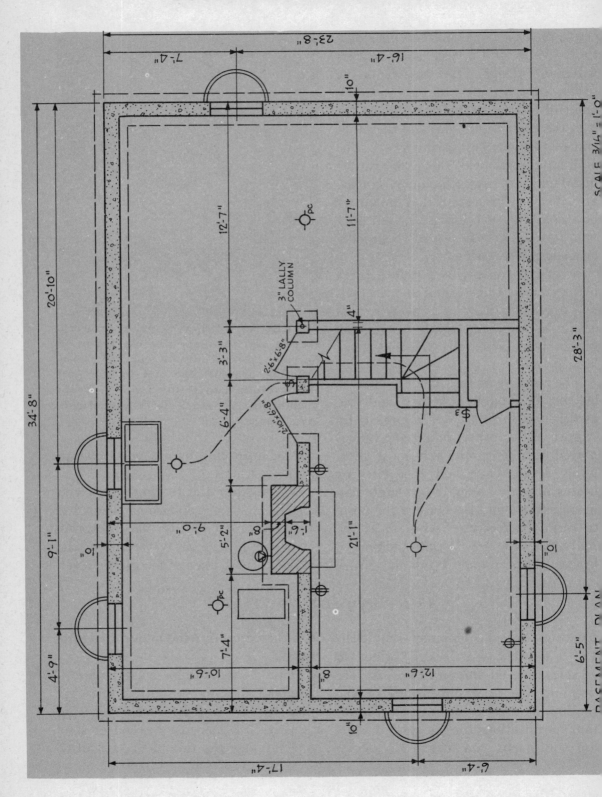

masonry blocks can be built out from each side of the fireplace to support the floor joists. One of these walls can run right over to the nearest foundation wall. The other wall must be broken a few feet from the fireplace to allow an opening for a door. A reinforced concrete lintel should be used over the top of this opening. This wall can continue to a point directly under the stairs, where a steel or wood bearing post is installed, and a girder is run from this point to the pocket in the foundation wall. See Fig. 13 on pg. 78.

MASONRY-BLOCK FOUNDATION WALLS

Foundation walls made out of concrete masonry-blocks offer several advantages over poured concrete to the home builder. First of all, one man can do the entire job of building the foundation himself. Second, the work does not all have to be completed in one day or in one operation. You can take as long as you wish to lay up the wall when you use blocks. The disadvantage in using these blocks is, first, a somewhat higher cost than poured concrete and, second, the necessity of waterproofing the outside of the wall if the site is not well drained.

The Excavation

If you plan to use masonry blocks for the foundation, have the excavation made several feet wider than the dimensions of the foundation in order to provide space for you to work on both sides of the wall. Due to the dimensions of masonry blocks, footings for a block-foundation wall do not have to be as large as for poured-concrete walls. A footing 8″ deep and 16″ wide is sufficient.

Standard Blocks and Joints

The standard size of masonry building-block is 7⅝″ wide, 7⅝″ high and 15⅝″ long. This obviously produces a wall approximately 8″ thick. Aside from the standard block, there are corner blocks, with one end square, and half-blocks, which allow a wall to be built up with staggered vertical joints between courses and lintels for framing the top of window, door, and other openings. The mortar used with masonry blocks is made with 1 part cement and 2 parts clean fine sand. Add enough water to this mixture to produce a workable plastic and do not make more mortar than you can use in 30 minutes. The normal mortar joint, horizontal and vertical, is about ½″.

Building the Wall

Your first job in building a foundation wall with masonry blocks is to determine the exact points for the corners. This can be done by dropping a plumb line from the building lines that are strung between the batter boards. The four corners should be

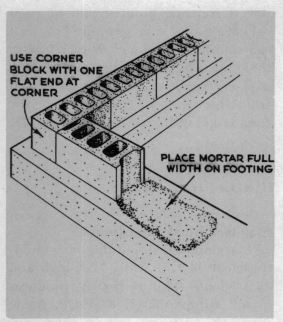

USE CORNER
BLOCK WITH ONE
FLAT END AT
CORNER

PLACE MORTAR FULL
WIDTH ON FOOTING

Fig. 14. The first course of masonry blocks should be laid over a bed of mortar the width of the footing. Note the special corner block with a flat end.

built up first, to a height of three or even four courses. Place a guide post at each corner to enable you to check

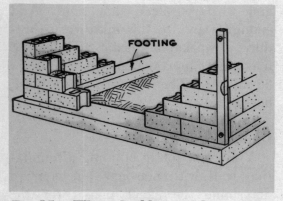

FOOTING

Fig. 15. When building with masonry blocks, the corners are set up for several courses first, and then the blocks are put in between them. Note the level used to check a corner to be sure that it is plumb.

and be sure that the corners are straight. A line strung between these posts will act as a guide in positioning the blocks between corners. After the corners have been built up, lay the first course of blocks between the corners without any mortar. The purpose of laying the blocks dry is to get a general idea of how they will fit between the corners. See Fig. 14. Needless to say, they will seldom come out just right. It may be necessary to use a half-block at some point or even to decrease the width of the mortar joint. Blocks can be cut in half with a cold chisel and a hammer.

Once you have worked out the manner in which the first course of blocks should be laid out, set them in with mortar. Be sure that the footing is clean and level. See Fig. 15.

Unlike bricks, which are completely buttered with mortar; the mortar for masonry blocks is applied in two strips along the edges. This provides an air space between the mortar strips that will help to keep the wall dry. Apply the mortar along the edges of the block in the course below the one you are working on. See Fig. 16. Now, apply mortar to the vertical strips of the block that is to be laid up. Lift the block and place it gently in position. Be sure that it comes out flush with the guide line strung between the posts at the corners. Tap the block into position and, with the aid of a level, check to be sure that it is sitting right. See Fig. 17. Remove the mortar that is squeezed out along the joint. When the mortar has become a little stiff, it should be tooled so that it will be compressed and make a waterproof joint. A v-shaped steel joiner is used for this job.

Openings; Anchor Bolts

Openings for windows, doors, etc., can be made with the use of half-blocks. A recess for the girder or I-beam is made by breaking off a section of the block as shown in Fig. 18. The voids (hollow cores) in the blocks for two courses below the girder should be filled with concrete to prevent the masonry's cracking at this point because of the heavy load.

Anchor bolts for the sill are fastened to the blocks by filling the cores or voids with mortar and sinking the bolts into this before the mortar has set. The mortar should extend through two courses of blocks. A piece of screening can be placed below these two courses to prevent the mortar falling down through the wall or old newspapers can be packed down into the cores. Anchor bolts should be placed in the same way as for a poured-concrete foundation.

Waterproofing

After the foundation wall has been laid up, it should be waterproofed on the outside. This is done by applying a ½″ coat of cement plaster to the masonry. Use the same mixture as was used for the mortar and apply the plaster in two coats, each ¼″ thick. The wall should be painted over with a cement grout (a mixture of cement

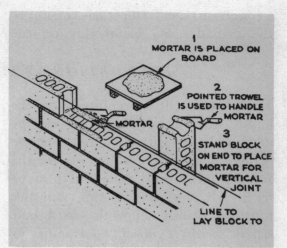

Fig. 16. Three steps in mortaring concrete masonry blocks. Note that mortar is only applied to the edges of the lower course of blocks.

and water mixed to the consistency of a thick paste) before the first coat goes on. The first coat should be given

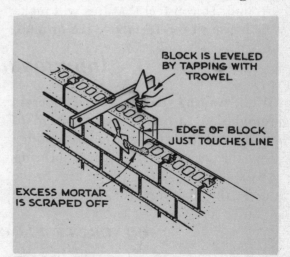

Fig. 17. Method of setting a concrete block into place. A line is run along the wall to serve as a guide so that all blocks will be even. A level is used to make sure that the blocks sit perfectly level on the course below.

a rough surface. After it has set, apply the second coat. Keep this cement plaster damp and covered until hardened; then coat with hot asphalt.

FOUNDATIONS WITHOUT BASEMENTS

If no basement is required for the house, the job of excavating can be done by hand. Either poured concrete or masonry blocks can be used for the foundation. Local stone can also be used. All require a footing and this must be placed below the frost line. Check with a local contractor or builder to find out the depth of the frost line in your locality. The foundation should be high enough so that there is a space of at least 18″ between the ground and the floor of the house. If you want adequate crawl space under the house—and it has many advantages—build the house 24″ off the ground. If you feel that this will make the house sit too far above the ground, some excavation can be done so that, while the house is only 18″ or so off the ground on the outside, there is a 24″ clearance under the floor.

Openings for ventilation (as well as for access to the space under the floor) should be made in the foundation wall. If the space under the house is not ventilated, it will become damp and musty. This may lead to decay of the wood members. If the soil appears to be extremely damp, cover it with strips of roll roofing. These strips should overlap about 3″ at the seams. Be sure that no roots of trees or bits of wood left over from building remain under the floor on the ground, because they will attract wood-destroying insects.

ADDITIONAL FOOTINGS

While waiting for the poured-concrete foundation to harden, you can go to work and install additional footings for the chimney, fireplace, bearing posts, etc. If steel posts are to be used, the footings for these can be poured after the post is in place. Fig. 12 (Pg. 77) shows the type of footing and base to use for wooden bearing posts. Fig. 13 (Pg. 78) shows the location and size of both the fireplace and the chimney footings.

CONCRETE FLOORS ON GROUND

This type of floor can be used for homes with or without radiant floor heating. See Fig. 19. It should not be used, however, if you are building on a site that is low lying or damp or where there is a danger of surface water reaching the concrete slab. The ground should slope away from the house with adequate drainage. The floor must be at least 6″ above ground level.

Excavation; Foundation and Footings

The excavation for this type of floor includes the removal of all roots and other organic matter from the floor area. After this, the site should be rough graded so that it stands a little higher than the finished grade. Now it should be tamped down until it is compact. Once all this work has been completed, you can go ahead and build the foundations. They are the same as those required for a continuous foundation. Do not try to build the house up from the concrete slab floor; it requires a foundation and footing. You will also need footings for the chimney and under the bearing partition.

Fill

The next step is to cover the subgrade with a layer of granular fill. This gravel fill serves two purposes. First, it prevents ground moisture from getting to the finished concrete slab and, second, it acts as insulation. The fill used should range in size from ½″ to 1″. Do not use small-size gravel, as it will reduce the insulating value of the fill and also increase the chances of the concrete slab's becoming damp through capillary attraction. Before the fill is poured, utility lines, such as water pipes and sewer lines, should be laid under the floor and brought up so that they will open above the level of the fill and slab. See Fig. 20.

All water pipes must be laid in trenches sufficiently deep so that they will not be subject to either frost or freezing.

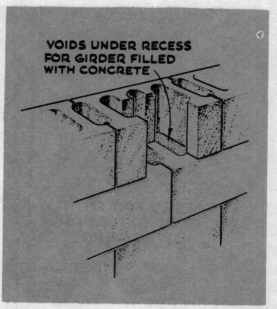

Fig. 18. Recess for girder made in wall of masonry blocks. The voids in the two courses of blocks directly under this opening are filled with mortar so that the blocks will not crack under the weight of the girder.

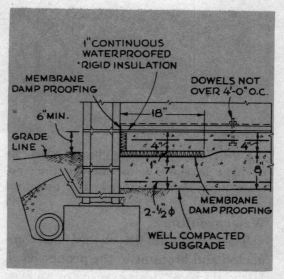

Fig. 19. Construction detail of concrete floor slab on ground. Note the insulation between the slab and the foundation wall.

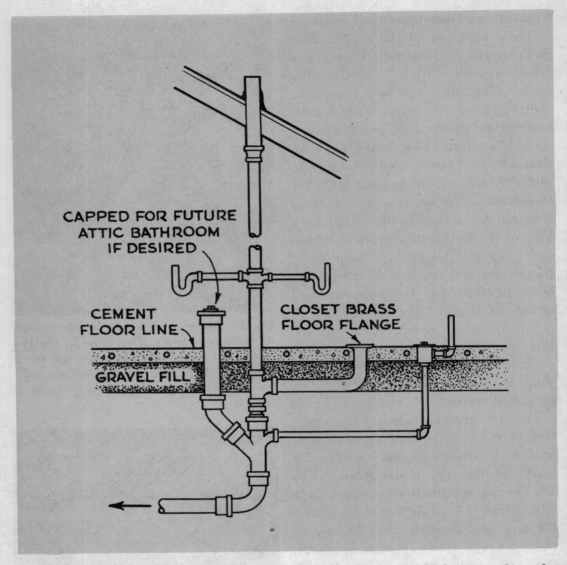

CAPPED FOR FUTURE
ATTIC BATHROOM
IF DESIRED

CEMENT
FLOOR LINE

CLOSET BRASS
FLOOR FLANGE

GRAVEL FILL

Fig. 20. All plumbing lines must be brought into the house before the concrete floor slab is poured. The openings of these lines should be capped so that nothing will fall into them during the building operation.

Waterproofing

The granular fill should be compacted and brought to the proper level. It should be 6″ deep except for an area extending in 18″ from the foundation walls, where it is 5″ deep to allow for the insulation required here. The fill should now be covered with a ½″ coating of cement grout made with 1 part cement to 3 parts sand. The purpose of this grout is to provide a smooth surface for the membrane waterproofing that is to follow. Once the grout is hard, mop it over with hot asphalt. You should also coat the top of fireplace and bearing-partition footings with asphalt. Before the hot asphalt has time to harden, a layer of 15-pound asphalt-saturated roofing felt should be placed over the surface. Be sure to allow plenty of overlap along the edges between each strip. After the entire surface has been covered with the roofing felt, mop this down with hot asphalt and apply a second layer of felt. Bring this felt paper up along the foundation wall to at least 1″ higher than the finished floor level.

The next job is to lay a 1″ thick strip of continuous, waterproof, rigid insulation between the foundation walls and the edges of the floor slab. See Fig 21. This should run up the foundation wall as high as the finished floor slab and should extend under the slab for at least 18″. This insulation is most important, for while the granular fill below will prevent heat loss there, if the slab comes into direct contact with the masonry of the foundation wall there will be considerable heat loss at this point.

The Concrete Slab

Before the concrete slab is poured, it is wise to make lines or to tack strips of wood to the inside of the foundation wall to indicate the exact point that the surface of the floor will be brought to. These check points will help you to get the floor level with the foundation. The concrete mix for the

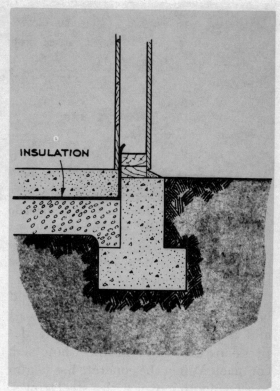

INSULATION

Fig. 21. Detail of concrete floor slab on ground. Note that insulation is used between the slab and the fill and foundation to prevent the slab's becoming chilled during cold weather.

slab is 1 part cement, 2¼ parts sand and 3 parts gravel up to 1″ in diameter. After the concrete has been poured, it should be tamped or spaded.

It is necessary to put metal reinforcement in the concrete, and it should not weigh less than 40 pounds per 100 square feet. Standard metal mesh is available for this purpose. Pour a layer of concrete to about 1½″ from the top of the finished slab. After this layer has been properly spaded, put the metal reinforcement in place and pour on the

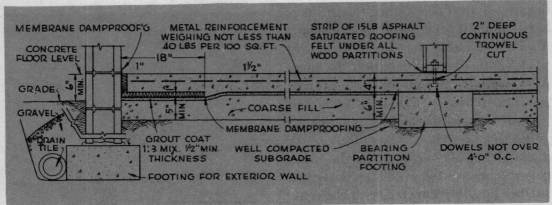

Fig. 22. Concrete floor slab on subgrade showing the details of the membrane dampproofing, insulation and bearing partition footing.

rest of the concrete before the first layer has hardened.

The surface of the concrete should be worked over with a leveling board and a wood float to remove any depressions and to make the whole slab compact. When the concrete has begun to set, smooth it over with a steel trowel. See Fig. 22.

Clips and Bolts

If a wood floor is to be installed over the concrete slab, wire clips should be installed before the concrete hardens so that the wood sleepers can be tied to the concrete. At the point on the slab where the bearing partition is to rest, a narrow, 2"-deep, vertical trowel-cut should be made and bolts installed in it, so that the plate of the partition can be attached to the slab. Bolts should also be installed at other points on the slab where partitions are to be erected, although the wood plates can be attached to hardened concrete with masonry anchors.

If radiant-heating floor panels are to be installed in the concrete floor slab, consult Chapter 16 for modifications to these instructions.

STONE WALL FOUNDATIONS

If you are building on a site where there is an ample supply of native stone, the foundation wall can be made out of it. You will need a footing for this type of wall, too. It can be made of poured concrete. Sometimes you will find large rocks set far enough below the ground to be used as a footing; of course, they must be below the frost line.

A stone or rubble wall must be at least 16" thick. A thinner wall can carry the load of the house but, because of the manner in which these walls are erected, it is almost impossible to build one less than 16" thick and have it hold together. Random-size stones can be used, and there should be a bond stone—one long enough to extend through the wall or almost through the wall—every 10 square feet of vertical wall area. See Fig. 23.

Rather than use large quantities of cement mortar to fill out irregularities in a stone so that the next one can be set in place, small rocks should be mixed in the mortar joints. All joints should be completely filled with mortar if the wall is to be solid and waterproof.

Building a foundation wall out of rocks is hard work. It takes a tremendous number of rocks and the work does not go very quickly. On the other hand, if you have the rocks on hand and do the work yourself, it is about the least expensive type of continuous wall foundation you can build.

You will find that in the long run it does not pay to use very large rocks, even though they fill a great deal of space once they are in position. Working with them is very exhausting after a short time and trying to position them properly may knock a portion of the wall loose. If you insist on the large stones, use a block and tackle so that

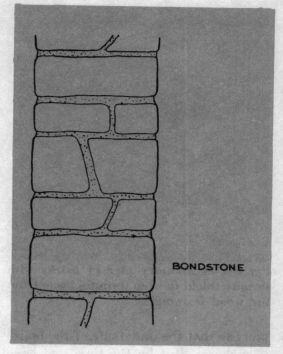

BONDSTONE

Fig. 23. Section of a foundation wall made of stone. Note the bondstones running through the width of the wall.

they can be lifted up and put in the right place.

To get a good bond between the stones and the mortar, the stones should be clean, that is, free of dirt and moss.

The mortar used is made of 1 part cement to 3 parts sand.

POST AND PIER FOUNDATIONS

Another inexpensive type of foundation is made with wood posts or masonry piers. This type of foundation is often used for summer homes or homes located in mild climates. The drawback to using it for all-year-round living in the cold climates is that the underside of the first floor will be chilled during the cold weather. This drawback can be offset by installing a curtain wall (a vertical non-load bearing wall) made of masonry between the

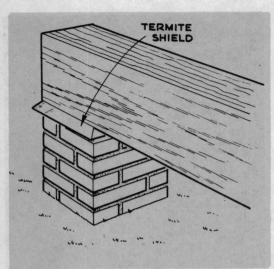

Fig. 24. A masonry pier of bricks with termite shield to keep termites away from the wood framing.

piers so that the underside of the house is enclosed. But by the time you have

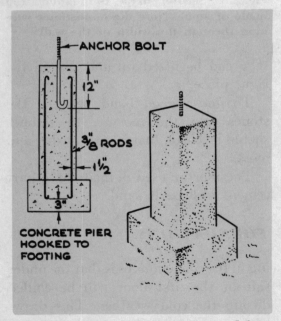

Fig. 25. A poured concrete pier and footing. ⅜" rods are used to anchor the pier to the footing.

installed this curtain wall, you might just as well have made a continuous wall foundation, because it is going to have to be set below the frost line and the work and money involved in putting it in will almost nullify the saving of the pier foundation.

Masonry Piers

Piers of concrete, stone, masonry blocks or bricks should be spaced from 8' to 12' apart. See Figs. 24 and 25. The piers should be about 16" square. All should be set on solid concrete footings that are poured below the frost line. Holes for the piers will have to be dug by hand. The piers need extend only about 12" or so above ground, because you are going to need a very heavy sill for this type of foundation and the thickness of the sill will bring the floor to the required 18" above the ground. Masonry piers should be fitted with anchor bolts so that the sill can be anchored to the pier. If you are building in a section of the country where there are high winds, the piers themselves should be anchored to the footing. See Fig. 25.

Wood Posts

These posts are usually spaced 6' apart in rows 6' to 8' apart. Their usual diameter is 8". Wood posts are usually made of rot-resisting woods such as cypress, black locust or cedar. The best types are those treated with a preservative under pressure. Like the masonry piers, the posts should be set on a solid concrete footing poured

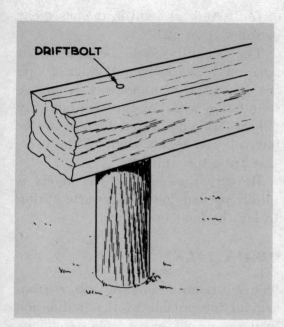

DRIFTBOLT

Fig. 26. Pier foundation made out of a wood post. The heavy house-sill is anchored to the post by means of a driftbolt.

be strung along the posts and checked with a level. Mark the posts and then cut each one to size. Two strips of wood nailed on either side of the posts will help you to make the cut accurate. See Fig. 27.

Fig. 27. Two boards tacked across the post will serve as a guide in sawing off the top of the post so that the cut is perfectly flat.

below the frost line. Sometimes a heavy solid rock far enough down will serve as a footing for the posts. If you are building in soil that is free from rocks, a posthole digger can be used for making the holes. See Fig. 26.

Posts can be cut to the right length after they are in place. A line should

BACKFILLING

After the foundation wall has been completed, the dirt removed during the excavation is put back around the outside of the foundation wall and later on is covered with topsoil and seeded.

The usual practice is to toss anything you can lay your hands on into this space around the foundation walls—

odd bits of lumber, empty cement sacks, empty nail kegs, in fact everything that sooner or later will have to be disposed of. This practice is one reason for so many damp basements. It is also the reason for a lot of homes being troubled with termites. The only materials that should be used for backfill are gravel, cinders and earth. If refuse is used, it not only makes it easy for surface water to drain down along the foundation wall, but in the course of time the refuse is going to rot away and this will cause depressions or even holes to appear in the finished grading. Odd bits of lumber underground are almost sure to attract the attention of termites sooner or later, and once they get this close to your home they may easily find an entrance through a crack or faulty mortar joint in the basement or foundation wall.

The backfill should be applied in horizontal layers about 1' thick. Slope the layers down and away from the foundation wall, for this will not only aid in draining away surface water but will also relieve some of the pressure from the wall.

Be sure that each of the layers is solidly packed down before attempting to lay the next one down.

INSTALLING DRAIN TILE

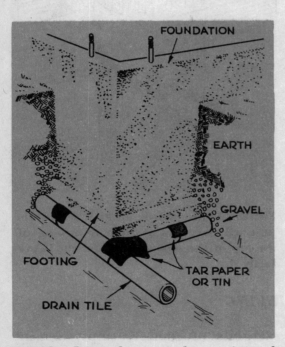

Fig. 28. Joints between the section of drain tile around the foundation wall should be covered with strips of tar paper or tin to prevent dirt from getting into the system. Be sure that the system has sufficient pitch to carry the water away from the building before putting back the fill.

Tile to remove surface water from around the outside of the foundation wall is required for concrete slab floors. It should be used for poured-concrete or masonry foundation walls where there is a basement, for it is one of the best ways to insure the basement's being dry at all times. If you are building in soil that does not drain very well and you plan a basement, drain tile is a "must."

The excavation should be made wide enough so that after the foundation has been completed, 4" drain tile can be laid around the outside of the footing at its base. This tile should not be joined together, rather, a slight crack of about ⅛" should be left between sections. Put a piece of tar paper or tin over the top of this crack so that dirt will not get into the tile. See Fig. 28. The drain tile should be given a little downward slope so that water entering it will flow through the system and eventually end up in a connected sewer or dry well. You can check each section of tile with a level to be sure it has the required pitch. After the tiles are all in place, fill the trench up to within about a foot of the surface of the finishing grading, if you are protecting a concrete slab floor. Gravel or stone up to about 1″ in size and not smaller than ¼″ can be used for this fill. Now cover the gravel over with burlap, sod or even old brush. This is done to prevent the loose dirt from washing down through the gravel. Over this covering can go the topsoil. Be sure, when you pour the gravel in, not to disturb the position of the drain tile.

THE BASEMENT FLOOR

The concrete basement floor may be poured when the other concrete work, such as the foundations, is done or, if you do not wish to spend the time on this sort of work at the moment, it can be done later on when it may be more convenient.

If the soil is well drained, the concrete can be poured directly over the ground in one operation. If the soil is poorly drained, you will need two layers of concrete with a membrane waterproofing between them.

Fig. 29 shows how the floor should be poured over well drained soil. First, the ground should be leveled off so that it is flush with the top of the footing. Be sure that all roots and other debris have been removed from the soil and that it is well compacted. If it is not, there will be danger of the concrete floor's cracking.

Expansion Joints

The concrete floor should not come directly up against the foundation wall. You need a waterproof expansion joint at this point. Before the concrete for the floor is poured, line the bottom of the foundation wall with three pieces of beveled siding. These should be soaped or oiled so that they can be removed after the concrete is hard. See Fig. 29.

If you are pouring the concrete at the same time that the foundations are put in, be sure that you make allowance in the floor for any openings required for utilities.

The correct concrete mix for the floors is 1 part cement, 2¼ parts sand

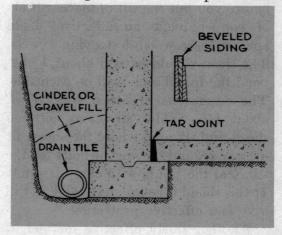

Fig. 29. **The basement concrete floor should not come directly in contact with the foundation wall. An expansion joint is required at this point and is made with beveled siding and tar.**

and 3 parts gravel. The floor should be at least 4″ thick.

After the concrete has been poured and is hard, remove the pieces of beveled siding along the edges and fill the seam between the floor and the foundation wall with hot tar or some similar mastic.

The same procedure should be followed for the joints between the basement floor and the footings for the chimney and bearing posts.

Waterproofing

If the soil under the house shows signs of being damp, pour a 2″ layer of concrete that comes up level with the top of the footing. When this slab is hard, mop it over with hot asphalt. Before the hot asphalt has time to harden, put down 15-pound asphalt-saturated roofing felt. You want two layers of the felt and you will need an application of hot asphalt between them. The strips of asphalt felt should be given ample overlap and the ends should be brought up along the foundation wall so that they will extend at least as high as the top of the finished floor. See Fig. 19. A final application of hot asphalt should be applied over the felt and then the remaining portion of the floor, that is, the second layer, can be poured.

TERMITE SHEATHING

If you decide to use a termite shield, it should be put on top of the foundation wall all the way around the house before you put the sill in place. Sheets of copper make an effective shield against these wood-destroying insects. The sheet should extend about 1″ beyond the foundation wall on each side. The extensions are then bent down about 45°. Solder all seams between sheets tightly and, where the sheets fit over or around the anchor bolts for the sill, seal the joints with coal tar pitch. If this shield is completely solid, it will give you effective protection.

Another fairly effective method of guarding against termites is to lay a course of slate just under the sill. The slate, however, must be embedded in a strong cement mortar. Termites are able to burrow through concrete that is lean or porous as well as through poor mortar.

Such methods of termite-prevention as those just described will usually keep the insects out of the house. Occasionally, termites will build tunnels outside and around obstructions. This is particularly likely to happen where honeysuckle, or some such plant growth, has been growing against the house for some years and not only contains some old dead wood but also provides contact between the ground and the wood of the house above the foundation. Inspection once or twice a year will reveal any such tunnels, which are easily identified and destroyed. Termites must return to the ground to obtain moisture, otherwise they die; also, they intensely dislike light. Therefore, breaking their tunnels will keep them out of the house.

If you do not wish to use a shield or other impervious course but do want to have some measure of protection, treat the sill with a chemical, such as creosote or zinc chloride, that will poison the fibers of the wood. Bear in mind, however, that many of the chemicals will remain effective for only a few years.

MATERIALS LIST FOR FOUNDATIONS AND FLOOR SLAB FOR THE BASIC HOUSE

Footings	6 cu. yds.	1-5-3 cement
Floor slab	10.2 cu. yds.	1-5-3 cement
Foundation walls (20″ deep)	6 cu. yds.	1-5-3 cement

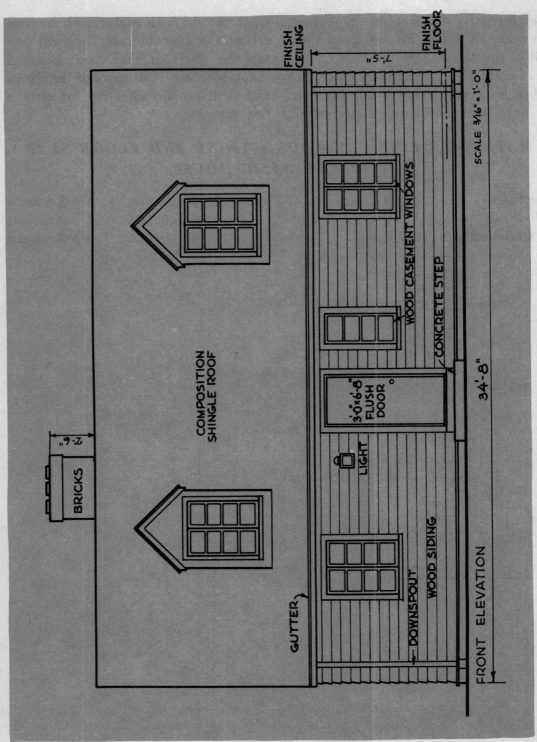

Front Elevation of House

The following labels appear within the drawing:

FINISH CEILING

FINISH FLOOR

7'-5"

SCALE 3/16" = 1'-0"

WOOD CASEMENT WINDOWS

CONCRETE STEP

COMPOSITION SHINGLE ROOF

2'-6"

BRICKS

3'-0"x6'-8" FLUSH DOOR

LIGHT

GUTTER

DOWNSPOUT

WOOD SIDING

34'-8"

FRONT ELEVATION

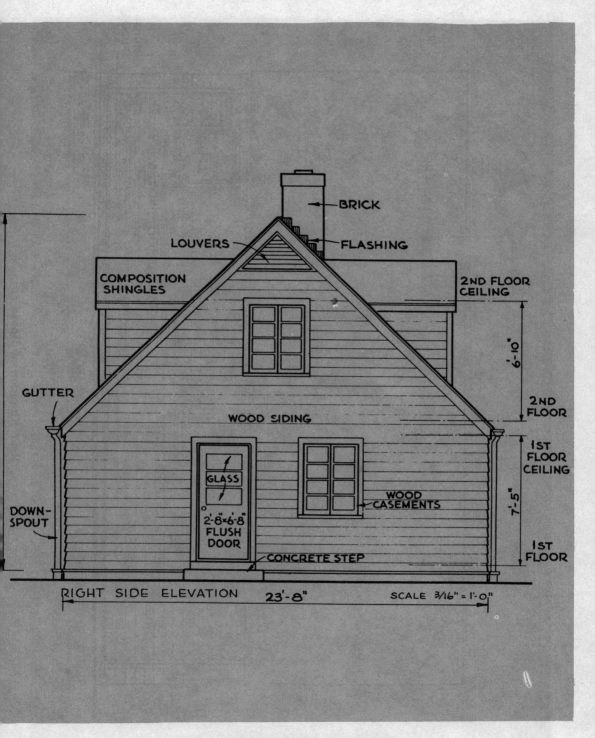

BRICK

LOUVERS

FLASHING

COMPOSITION
SHINGLES

2ND FLOOR
CEILING

6'-10"

GUTTER

2ND
FLOOR

WOOD SIDING

1ST
FLOOR
CEILING

GLASS

7'-5"

WOOD
CASEMENTS

DOWN-
SPOUT

2'-8"x6-8"
FLUSH
DOOR

1ST
FLOOR

CONCRETE STEP

RIGHT SIDE ELEVATION   23'-8"   SCALE 3/16" = 1'-0"

Right Side Elevation of House

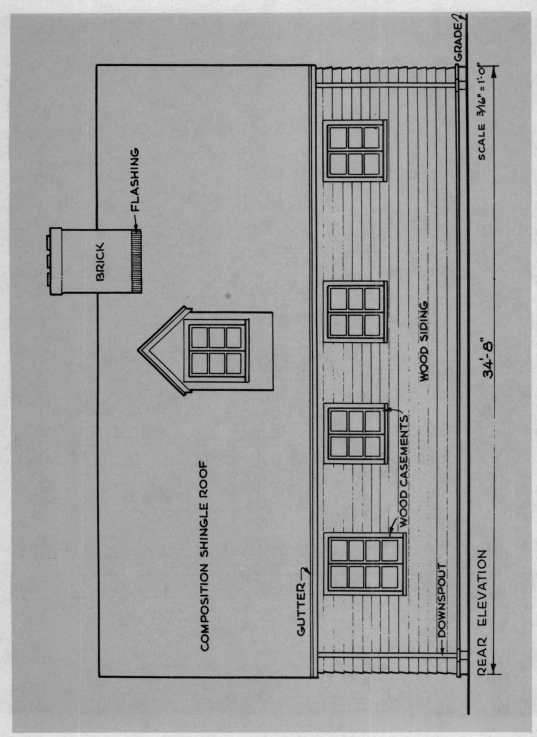

Rear Elevation of House

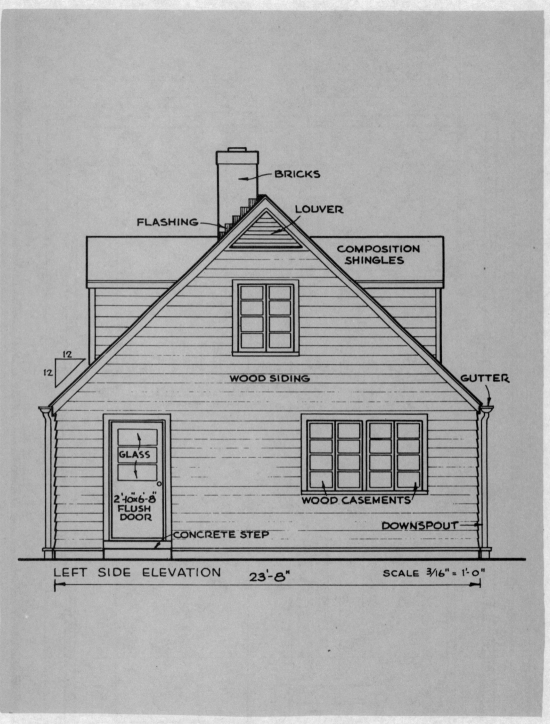

BRICKS

LOUVER

FLASHING

COMPOSITION SHINGLES

WOOD SIDING

GUTTER

12

12

GLASS

2'-10"x6'-8" FLUSH DOOR

WOOD CASEMENTS

DOWNSPOUT

CONCRETE STEP

LEFT SIDE ELEVATION   23'-8"   SCALE 3/16" = 1'-0"

Left Side Elevation of House

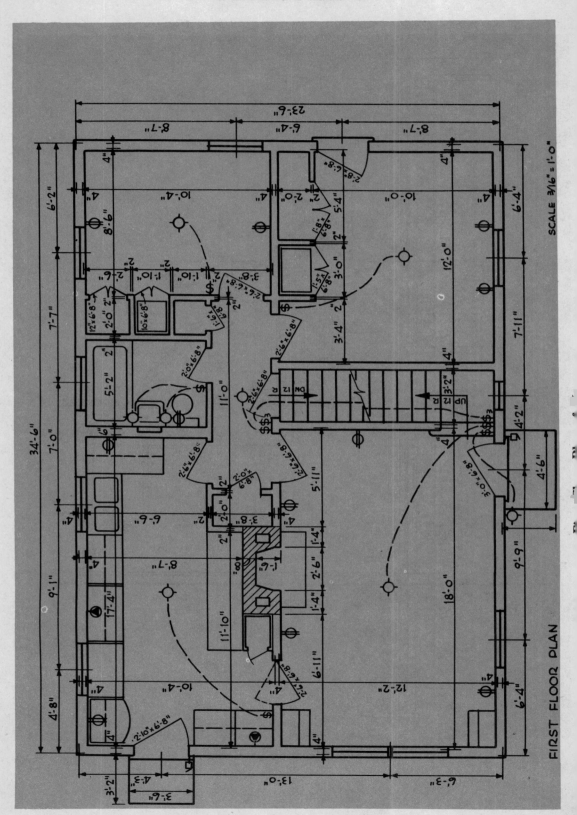

FIRST FLOOR PLAN

SCALE 3/16" = 1'-0"

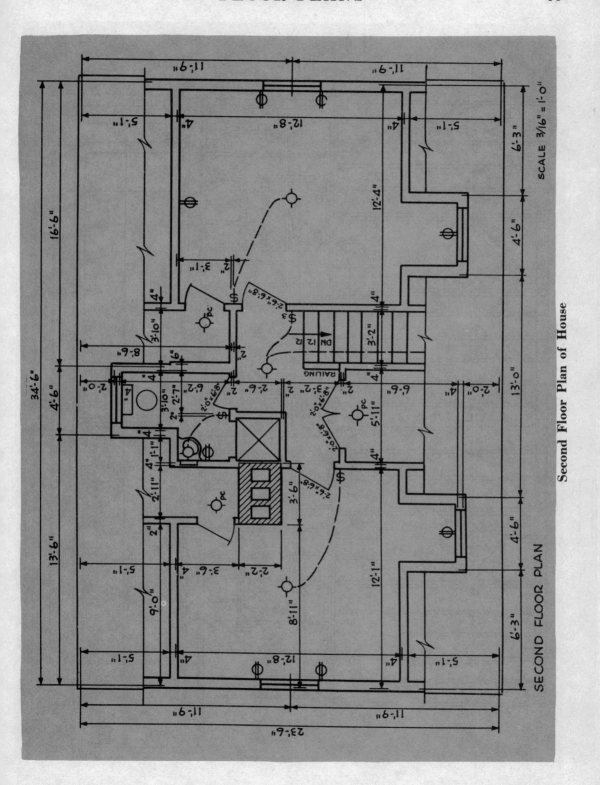

SCALE 3/16" = 1'-0"

Second Floor Plan of House

SECOND FLOOR PLAN

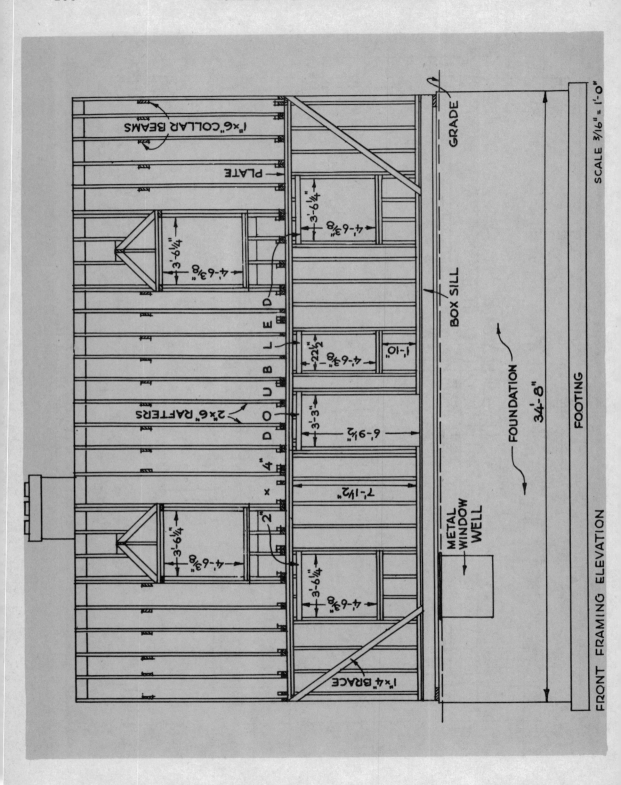

FRONT FRAMING ELEVATION

SCALE 3/16" = 1'-0"

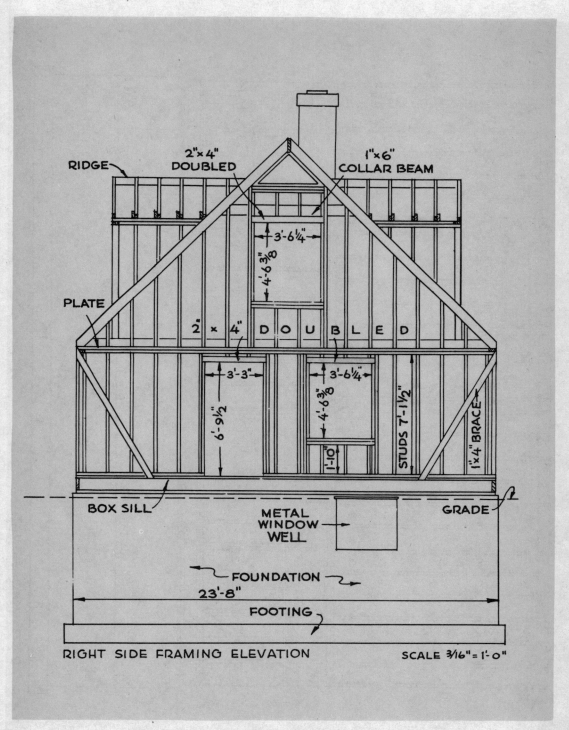

RIGHT SIDE FRAMING ELEVATION   SCALE 3/16"= 1'-0"

Right Side Framing Elevation of House

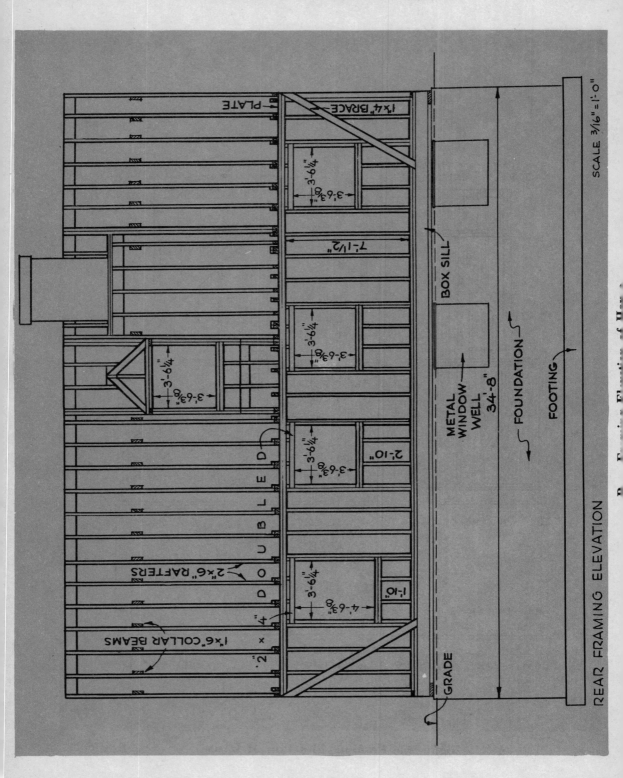

REAR FRAMING ELEVATION

SCALE 3/16" = 1'-0"

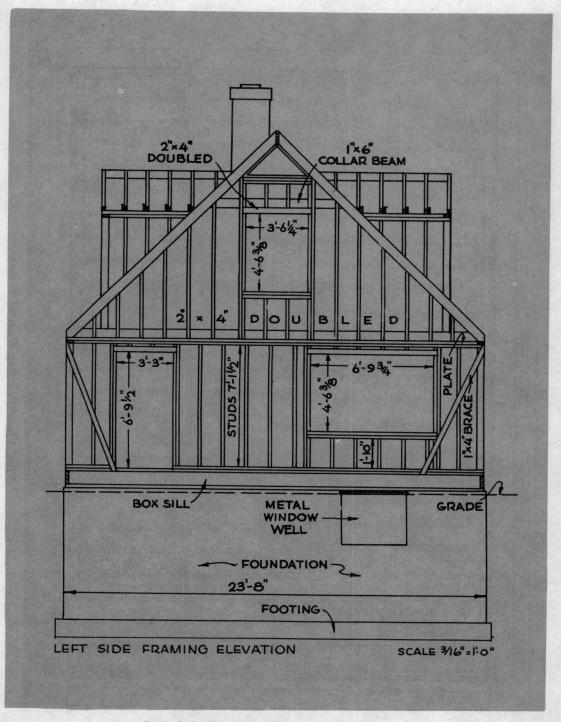

Left Side Framing Elevation of House

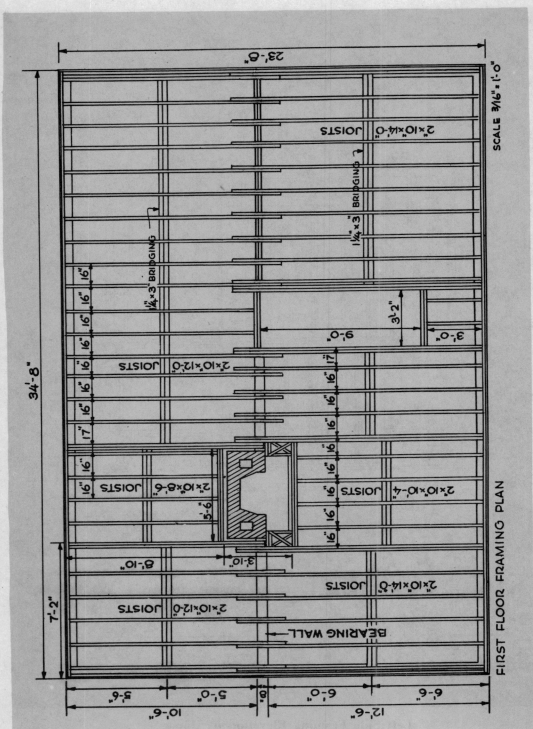

First Floor Framing Plan of House

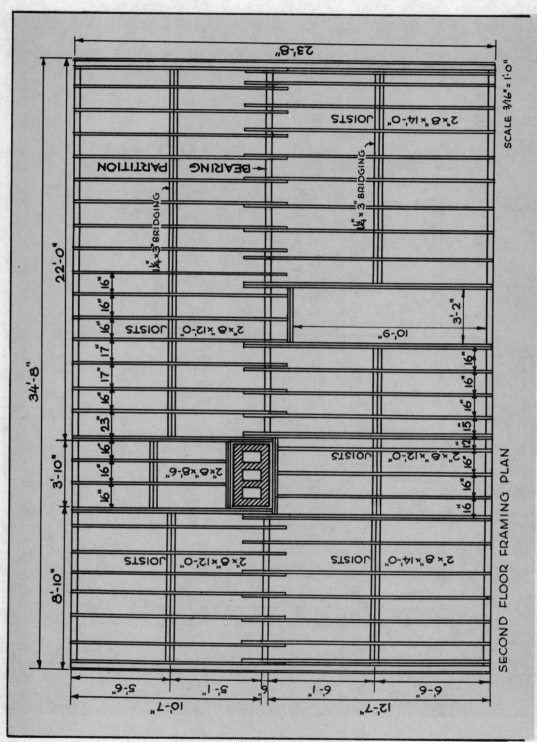

Second Floor Framing Plan of House

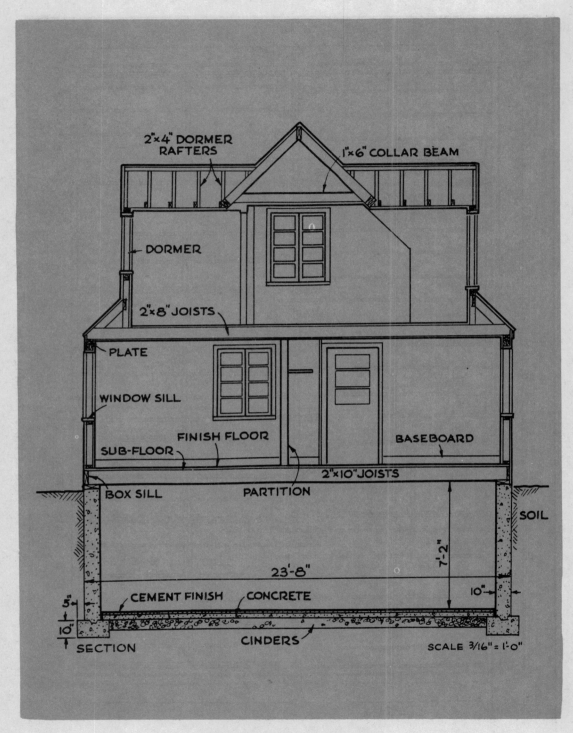

Cross Section Through Dormers

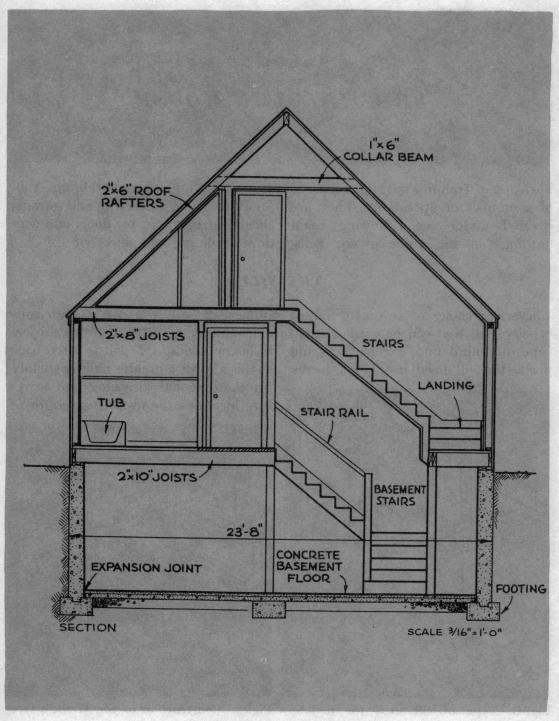

Cross Section Through Stairs

Chapter 8

FRAMING THE HOUSE

THE JOB of framing the house consists of a number of operations. They are covered under the following main headings in the order given: Sills, joists, floor openings, bridging, subflooring, walls, breezeway and garage, sheathing, openings for doors and windows, ceiling joists, and roof.

THE SILL

There is a choice of several different types of sill that can be used. For all types of foundation, except piers and posts, the sill need not be of heavy timber—2″ x 6″ or 2″ x 8″ is quite suitable. In sections of the country subject to heavy winds, a 4″ sill is often used as this affords a greater nailing surface for the diagonal sheathing and therefore increases the over-all strength of

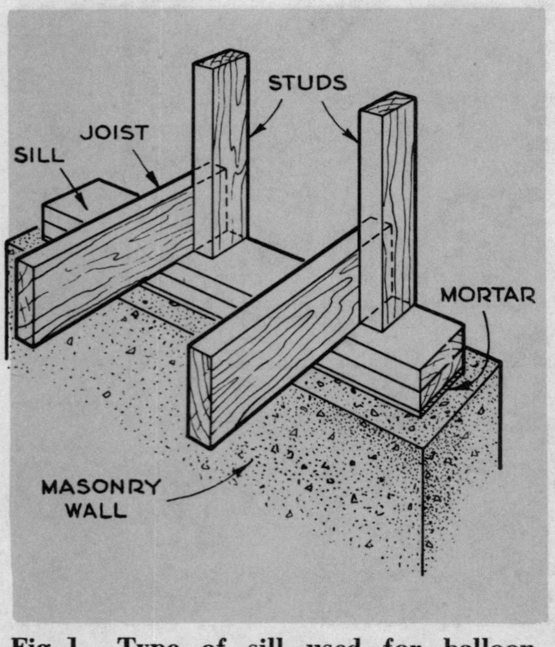

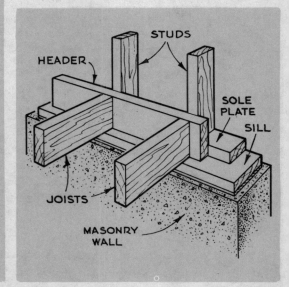

Fig. 1. Type of sill used for balloon framing.

Fig. 2. Construction of the T sill, a type frequently used.

the building to withstand the heavier strains to be expected.

Figs. 1, 2 and 3 show three types of sill that are in common use today. Each one has advantages and disadvantages, but in the long run, one is probably just as good as the other. When it comes to framing a house, probably no two builders will frame in quite the same manner, and for each method there will be critics as well as champions. For our purpose the box sill shown in Fig. 3 is perfectly adequate and so we shall follow through with this type.

The sill itself is a 2″ x 6″ No. 1 Common grade lumber. It is set in a thin bed of mortar and anchored to the foundation wall by means of the anchor bolts that were set in the masonry during its construction. The sill is joined at the corners with a simple half-lap joint, and this should be cut and fitted with care to provide maximum strength for the sill and the house frame.

The distance that the edge of the sill is set in from the outside edge of the foundation wall will depend on the thickness of the sheathing that you are going to use. The sheathing should come out perfectly flush with the outside of the foundation wall, so if you are going to use ¾″ sheathing, the sill should be set in ¾″ from the outside of the wall. If you are using composition sheathing, find out how thick it is and then place the sill this same distance in from the outside of the foundation wall.

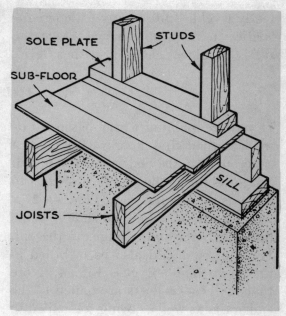

Fig. 3. Detail of box sill construction. The 2″x6″ sill is anchored to the top of the foundation wall by means of anchor bolts. Note the thin bed of mortar between the sill and the foundation wall. This not only makes a tight seam between wall and sill but also helps you to get the sill level. The header joist which is on edge comes out flush with the outside edge of the sill. The floor joists are toenailed to the sill and nails are driven through the face of the header into the ends of the floor joists. The sub-flooring is then laid, and over this goes the sole to which the wall studding is attached.

Holes should be drilled in the sill for the anchor bolts and the sill should be given a coat of white-lead paint to prevent decay. The mortar used for bedding the sill to the foundation wall is 1 part cement to 3 parts sand. It will not only make a good tight joint between the top of the wall and the sill, but will also enable you to get the sill to sit perfectly level in spite of any little irregularities in the wall surface. Once the sill is in place, check it with a level.

Allow time for the mortar to harden, slip washers over the ends of the anchor bolts and then run down the nuts.

JOISTS

If you are building with a basement or with a wood first floor rather than a concrete slab, the next step is to install the joists for the floor. The first joist to go on is the header joist. This is a 2″ x 10″ placed on edge. It should come flush with the outer edge of the sill. End joists should also be installed in the same manner. See Fig. 4. Note that the header joists are nailed to the end joists as well as being toe-nailed to the sill. Twenty-penny nails are used to secure the header to the end joists. Ten-penny nails are sufficient to tie the header and end joists to the sill. If diagonal sheathing is to be used, the joists need be secured to the sill only with a sufficient number of nails to hold

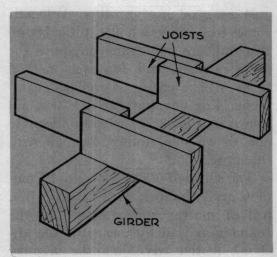

Fig. 5. How the floor joists rest on the girder. The joist should overlap the width of the girder and can be nailed together and then toe-nailed to the girder.

them erect, because the sheathing will tie both sill, header and end joists together.

The floor joists required are also 2″ x 10″. These are placed on edge and are spaced 16″ on center. If the joists are not perfectly level, that is, if they have a slight crown or high point, the high point should face up. The joists will run between the sill and the girder that runs down the approximate center of the house. If a steel girder is used, it is necessary to fasten a 2″ x 4″ to it by means of clinched nails or lag screws so that there will be something to which the joists can be spiked. This 2″ x 4″

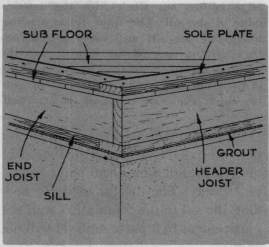

Fig. 4. Detail showing the relationship between the sill, the header joist, the joists and the sole plate.

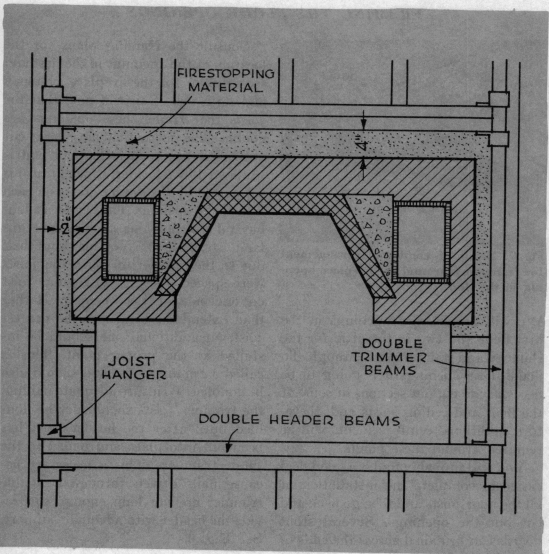

FIRESTOPPING MATERIAL

4"

2"

JOIST HANGER

DOUBLE TRIMMER BEAMS

DOUBLE HEADER BEAMS

Fig. 6. Correct method of framing around the fireplace opening. Note that trimmers and headers are doubled. A cantilever is installed at one side of the opening to support the flooring over that portion of opening not covered by fireplace hearth.

should be flush with the sill so that the joists will be level.

If you decide to use a steel girder, be careful to allow for the 2″ x 4″ when you are figuring the dimensions of the pocket in the foundation wall in which

the girder is eventually going to rest.

Fig. 5 shows how the joists bear on the girder. The joists are nailed together with two 10*d* nails and then toe-nailed to the girder with one 10*d* nail on each side of the two joists.

FRAMING THE FLOOR OPENINGS

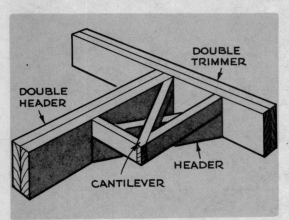

Fig. 7. Detail of cantilever arrangement for framework around the fireplace opening in the floor.

We will require two openings in the first floor and two in the attic for the chimney and stairs to pass through. To make these openings it is going to be necessary to cut out sections of some of the floor and ceiling joists and, therefore, additional reinforcements will be required around these points.

You will probably find it a good deal easier to complete the installation of all the floor joists and then go back and cut out the openings. Several stout boards can be nailed across the ends of the joists that are to be cut out so that they will stay in place while they are being cut and until the necessary arrangements can be made to hold them solid.

Consult the framing plans for the location of the openings in the first and second floor for the fireplace, chimney and stair well. You will note that the joists that frame these openings are double. The joists that have been cut are called tail beams. The cut end is supported by a header, which in turn is supported by the double joists on each side of the opening. The header is double and is of the same stock as the regular joists, 2″ x 10″. You may find that, due to the manner in which the joists were spaced, there is no regular joist on one side of the opening. Rather than extend the header to the nearest joist, an additional one should be installed at the proper point. This is called a trimmer joist and should also be doubled. To insure adequate nailing, the trimmer joists should not be doubled until after the header joist has been put into place and nailed to the single trimmers. This is necessary because nails driven through a double trimmer are not long enough to provide the header with adequate support. See Fig. 6.

A special type of framing, called a cantilever, is sometimes required on one side of the fireplace opening, since this area will not always be covered by the hearth. See Fig. 7.

BRIDGING

Cross bridging is made up of strips of wood nailed between the floor joists to form an X. See Fig. 8. Bridging serves two very important purposes. First, it tends to stiffen the joists and, therefore, the floor as well. Second, it helps to distribute the load on the floor among several joists. In cheap construction, the bridging is often left out because it requires a good deal of time and work to install. This is false economy since a floor without bridging is almost sure to be weak.

Bridging is required for every eight feet of joists. This means, in our particular case, that a set of bridging is required on each side of the girder. It should be located in the approximate center of the joists on each side.

Bridging can be made out of rough 1″ x 3″ No. 2 Common grade. If you have some wider or heavier stock that is going to waste, it can be used, too. If you want to save some time and spend some extra money, metal bridging is available and, in addition, is very easily installed.

The best and quickest way to cut the bridging is to cut the first piece by hand according to the necessary measurements and then make a miter box so that the rest can be cut on this pattern. Be sure that the first piece of bridging that is to serve as a pattern is correctly cut.

Most of the benefit of bridging will be lost if the pieces do not fit correctly between the joists.

Run a chalk line across the joists at the point where the bridging is to be placed. If 1″ x 3″ stock is used, the bridging should be nailed at each end with two 8d nails. Sight down the joist before nailing to be sure that it is sit-

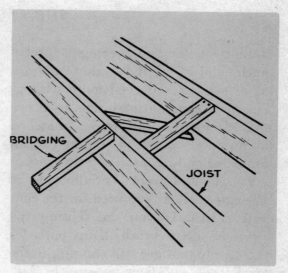

Fig. 8. Bridging between the floor and ceiling joists can be of wood or metal. The bottom ends of the bridging are nailed in place after the sub-floor has been laid.

ting correctly. If it is not, push it upright. At the present time, only the top of the bridging is nailed to the joists. The lower end will be left free until the sub-floor is in place. The reason for this is that when the sub-floor is installed, it will tend to pull the joists into correct alignment. If the bridging is nailed before the sub-floor is installed, the sub-floor will not be able to correct the position of the joists. It is wise, however, to *start* the two nails in the bottom of each piece of bridging before the sub-floor goes down. This will save a lot of time later on and is of special value when there is no basement and you have to tack the lower ends of the bridging to the joists from the cramped position that crawl space affords.

SUB-FLOORING

Nailing on the sub-flooring is pretty much child's play if you don't mind a lot of sawing and even more nailing. The most common materials used are 1" x 6" tongue-and-groove matched flooring, ⅝" plywood, random-width lumber or end-matched sub-flooring.

Tongue-and-groove sub-flooring is the same stock as was used for the concrete forms. If you are reusing the forms, be sure to brush off any particles of concrete that are still clinging to the wood. The sub-flooring can be laid either diagonally or at right angles to the floor joists. The best method is to run the flooring diagonally, because this will allow you to lay the finished floor in any direction you choose. The boards should be nailed at each point where they cross a joist with two 8d nails. If you use boards that are wider than 6" use three 8d nails. See Fig. 9.

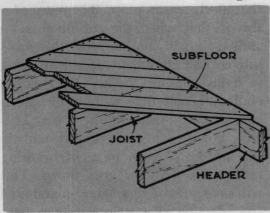

Fig. 9. How to apply diagonal sub-flooring. Note that the end joint between two of the boards is centered over a joist so that there will be no chance of these boards cracking.

Some authorities feel that if tongue-and-groove lumber is used, the end joints between pieces do not have to come over joists. There is, however, some difference of opinion on this matter, so perhaps it is best to play safe and have the end joints come over joists.

Sheets of plywood should be nailed with 8d nails spaced every 6" along all edges and 12" along the inside joists. The grain of the face ply should run at right angles to the joists.

Random-width lumber is about the least expensive material you can use for sub-floors. It has square edges and is nailed in the same manner as tongue-and-groove. All end joints must come over joists. Random-width lumber will run all the way from 4" to 12". Of all the materials, it requires the most time to install.

End-matched sub-flooring is rather expensive, but it is a great time saver because the end joints do not have to come over joists. The only sawing required is to cut off the end of the board that extends beyond the floor. It should be nailed in the same manner as tongue-and-groove, and it is important to nail it wherever it crosses a joist near the end of each board.

The sub-flooring should be tight all over and come flush with the outside edge of the headers and end-joists. If you use tongue-and-groove or random-width stock and lay it diagonally, be sure to cut the ends on an angle so that the entire joint between two abutting ends will come over a joist for nailing.

As soon as the sub-floor is in place, go underneath and nail on the lower ends of the bridging, which were left loose until the sub-floor was in place.

FRAMING THE WALLS

Study Fig. 10 and you will see that the wall framework is based on a 2″ x 4″ sole plate that is nailed through the sub-floor into the joists. This serves as a nailing base for the bottoms of the 2″ x 4″ vertical studding. The top of the studding is tied together with a top plate made of two 2″ x 4″'s.

There are several methods you can use to erect the frame of the house, but the best method is to make up complete units of the wall on the ground and then hoist them into position. This method is not only quicker than the others but you get a stronger wall section, because the ends of the studs are fastened to the sole plate with nails driven right through the plate rather than being toe-nailed into it from the sides of the studs.

The Studs

But regardless of which method of framing is used, the first job is to cut all the studding to the right length. You can save a good deal of time right here by marking out a master stud-pattern on the sub-floor and then using this to cut groups of studs to the correct size rather than measuring and cutting one stud at a time. See Fig. 11. It is important that all the studs be of equal length.

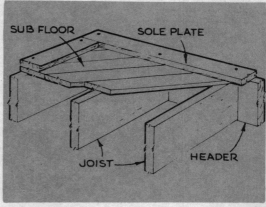

Fig. 10. The sole plate should be nailed through the sub-flooring into the joists and the header joist.

You will need approximately 110 studs for the wall framework and main bearing-partition of the house. They should be 7′3″ in length.

Corner Posts

When the studs have been cut to length, go to work and build four corner posts. As far as the load that they must carry goes, the corner posts are no different from the rest of the studding and one 2″ x 4″ would be adequate, but this would not provide any nailing surface for the interior wall lath or wallboard.

Fig. 12 shows a very efficient type of corner post that is easily constructed out of ordinary 2″ x 4″'s and provides

Fig. 11. A simple jig of this sort laid out on the sub-floor will save a good deal of time when it comes to cutting the wall stud-ding to size. You'll also find that it is easier to get all studs the same length than if you measure and cut each individually.

the necessary nailing surfaces for the inside wall materials. Note that the middle stud is pulled out for about one-half its width to provide one of the nailing surfaces. The only drawback to this type of post is that one edge measures 3⅝", which is the width of the wide side of a dressed 2" x 4", while the other nailing edge of the post is only 3¼". This means that the difference between the two thicknesses will have to be taken care of by nailing furring strips to the 3¼" edge to bring it out to 3⅝". If you have some 4" x 4" stock around, this can be used for the posts, but you will have to tack strips of 1" x 2" to the edges to provide the necessary nailing surfaces. Fig. 13 shows another method of constructing a corner post out of 2" x 4"'s.

Sole Plate and Top Plate

The next step in making up a section of wall on the ground is to lay a 2" x 4" sole plate along the edge of the sub-floor. Make this extend flush with one corner and then nail it lightly in place so that it will not move out of position. Next, lay a 2" x 4" top plate alongside it. Now what we want to do is measure off on both sole and top plate the location of each piece of studding. Studding should be spaced 16″ on center.

Be sure that these measurements are accurate. This is important, not because it would make any difference in the strength of your house if the studs were not spaced quite 16″ on center, but because the materials that are to follow—the insulation, wall lath, wallboard, etc.—are all cut to fit studding spaced either 16″ or 24″ on center. If you don't get the studding positioned properly, you are going to waste a lot of time later on tacking strips of wood to studs so that you can fasten on in-

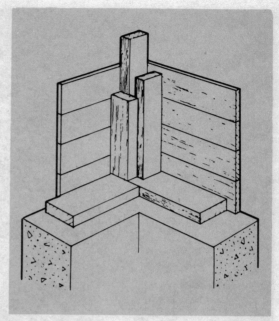

Fig. 13. This type of corner post is also suitable but is somewhat more difficult to construct than the one shown in Fig. 12.

sulation or wallboard. Studding is often spaced 24″ on center, but this will not provide as rigid a frame as when it is spaced 16″.

Start measuring off the 16″ intervals from the corner. Remember, however, that the corner post is wider than the other wall studs, so make your first measurement not from the middle of the corner post but from the *middle of the nailing surface*.

As neither the sole nor top plate will extend the entire length of a wall in one solid piece, their joints must come over a piece of studding. Therefore, cut sections of both sole and top plates off so that they are of equal length and the cut ends come in the middle of a piece of studding. As you mark off the

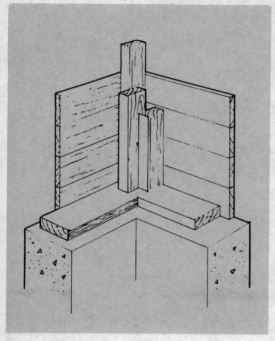

Fig. 12. A very satisfactory type of corner post built out of 2″x4″'s. Note that the center stud is pulled out for about one-half its width so that there will be a nailing surface for the lath or wallboard at the inside corners.

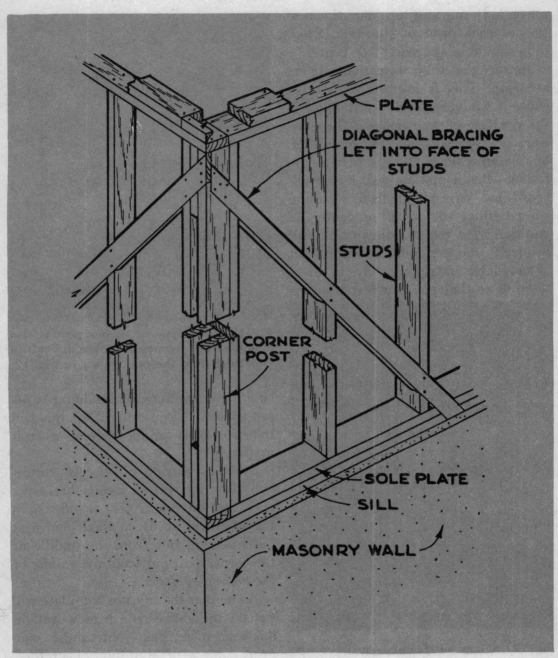

Fig. 14. The method used to install let-in bracing and the top plate. Note that the framework has been notched out from the corner post to the sill so that the brace will provide maximum support. The brace is nailed to each piece of the framework. The joint between the lower top plate and the upper top plate is staggered in order that the corner post will be tied into the studding.

location of the studding on both the top and sole plate, be sure that you indicate with an X on which side of the marked line the studding is to go. At this time do not bother to make any openings in either the studding or the sole plate for windows or doors. What we shall do is make up the entire wall framework and then go back and cut out the necessary openings. This may sound like a waste of both time and lumber. Actually it is not. You will find it much easier and quicker to frame the walls without making allowance for these openings, and cutting them out later on will not take much time. The lumber that is removed can be reused to double the framework around the openings.

Installation

Once you have a section of sole and top plates measured off and cut, nail the studding between them. The corner post should be installed as well as the regular studding. The studding is fastened to both sole and top plates with two 16d nails driven up through the sole and down through the top plate into the studding. As soon as the section has been completed, tack some braces across it so that it will be more or less rigid and hoist it into position. The sole plate should be flush with the outside edge of the sill. See Fig. 14.

Use temporary braces to hold the section of wall in position while you plumb it to be sure that it is straight up and down. Once you get it right, provide additional braces to hold it there

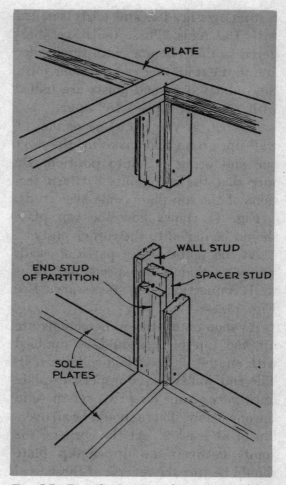

Fig. 15. Detail showing how a partition is joined to a wall. The upper part of the partition plate is nailed through into the lower part of the wall plate. A spacer stud is inserted between the wall studs to provide a nailing base for the partition stud at the end.

until the entire house has been framed. Much time can be wasted by getting a section of wall plumb and then having it knocked out of plumb because it was not sufficiently braced.

Once you have the section plumb, nail the sole plate down. The sole plate resting over headers and joists is nailed with 16*d* nails. These nails are staggered so that one goes into the header and the next into the regular floor joist. Sole plates over end joists are nailed with 16*d* nails spaced 16″ apart.

As soon as you have one section of wall up, go on and make up the next one and bring this into position. Be sure that the end joints between sections of the top plate come over studs.

Fig. 14 shows how the top plate should be nailed to the corner posts.

At the point where partition walls join the outside walls, special partition-wall connections are necessary. See Fig. 15.

As soon as all the wall sections are up, the top plate should be doubled with another 2″ x 4″ laid right over it. The end joints in the upper top plate must *never* come directly over those in the one below. There should be an overlap of at least 2′. At the corners, the joints between the upper top plate should be just the reverse of those used for the lower top plate. The top plate is nailed to the lower plate with 10*d* nails spaced 16″ apart. See Fig. 14.

Other Methods

Another method of framing the walls is to nail down the sole plate and then place the top plate alongside it so that the two can be measured for studding. Then nail the tops of the studding to the top plate, brace this framework and lift it into position. When the section has been plumbed and braced, the ends of the studding can be nailed to the sole plate with two 8*d* nails in each of the wide faces of the studs. You will find that a block of wood nailed to the sole plate with one edge up against the stud will hold the stud in position so that it will not move when the nails are driven down. After the wall sections are up, the upper top plate is fastened on in just the same way as previously described.

Another method—and by far the slowest—is to frame the walls one piece at a time. The sole plate is nailed down and then the corner posts are placed on it, plumbed and toe-nailed down. The posts should be braced on both sides. Next, several pieces of studding are put up and braced into the correct alignment. When this has been done, the top plate is put on. Now the rest of the studding is put into position.

Bracing the Walls

Once the outside walls have been framed and checked to be sure that they are plumb, they should be permanently braced. Many experts feel that if either plywood or diagonal sheathing is used over the framework, no additional bracing is required. However, if horizontal sheathing or composition sheathing is going to be used, bracing is absolutely necessary for a strong solid building.

The material used for the braces does not have to be heavy stock, 1″ x 4″ is perfectly adequate. It is the manner in which this type of brace is installed that provides the strength. The most effective type of brace is a 1″ x 4″ run from the top of a corner post down across several pieces of studding and into the sole plate. Each member of the framework that the brace crosses is cut out with a chisel so that the brace can be recessed into the member. This not only provides a flush surface for the sheathing to be nailed over but it also increases the strength of the brace many times over. A board just nailed across the studding does not provide any great amount of strength. The let-in brace is nailed to the sole plate and the corner post with three 10d nails. Where it crosses studding, it is nailed

with two 10d nails. It is important that you cut the recesses for the brace as accurately as possible, because if they are too large, you will not get the same value from the brace as when it fits snugly into the recesses. See Fig. 14.

As soon as the four outside walls have been framed, frame the main bearing partition. See Fig. 15. This consists of the same materials as used for the outside walls. A sole plate is nailed through the sub-floor into the girder. Studding is spaced 16" on center and the openings for doors and so on can be cut out later on.

FRAMING FOR HOUSE WITH CONCRETE SLAB FLOOR

The same framing methods will apply to this type of house as to the one with a wood floor on wood joists.

The only difference is, of course, that

the framework is built up from a 2" x 4" sill anchored to the foundation wall.

See Fig. 21 in Chapter 7.

THE BREEZEWAY AND GARAGE

The floor of the breezeway should be one step below the finish-floor level of the house, and the floor of the garage one step below the breezeway floor.

Foundations and Floors

Footings for the breezeway and garage should extend below the local frost line and should be 6" deep and 12" wide. The foundations for both should be 6" thick.

The floor of the breezeway should be a slab of concrete 6" thick. It is poured over a solid base of cinders or gravel.

The floor of the garage should be set

6" below the top of the garage foundation and can be either poured concrete or earth. There should be expansion joints between the breezeway floor and the house and garage foundations, and also an expansion joint between the concrete garage floor, if one is used, and the surrounding foundations.

Anchor bolts must be installed in the top of the garage foundation so that the sills can be attached in place.

Framing the Garage

The best method of building the breezeway and garage unit is to con-

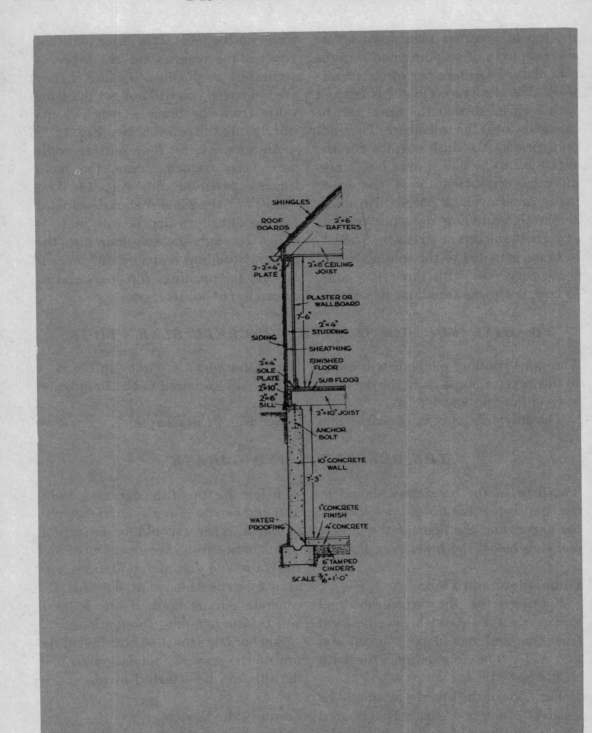

Section View of House Wall and Foundation

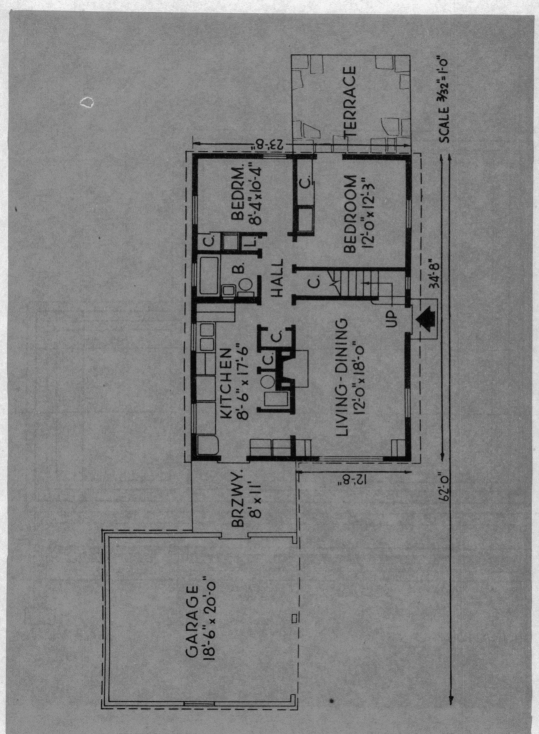

General Floor Plan of House, Garage and Breezeway

SCALE 3⁄32"=1'-0"

TERRACE

BEDRM.
8'-4"x16'-4"

C.

BEDROOM
12'-0"x12'-3"

23'-8"

HALL

C.

B.

L.

C.

KITCHEN
8'-6" x 17'-6"

C. C.

LIVING-DINING
12'-0"x18'-0"

UP

34'-8"

12'-8"

62'-0"

BRZWY.
8' x 11'

GARAGE
18'-6" x 20'-0"

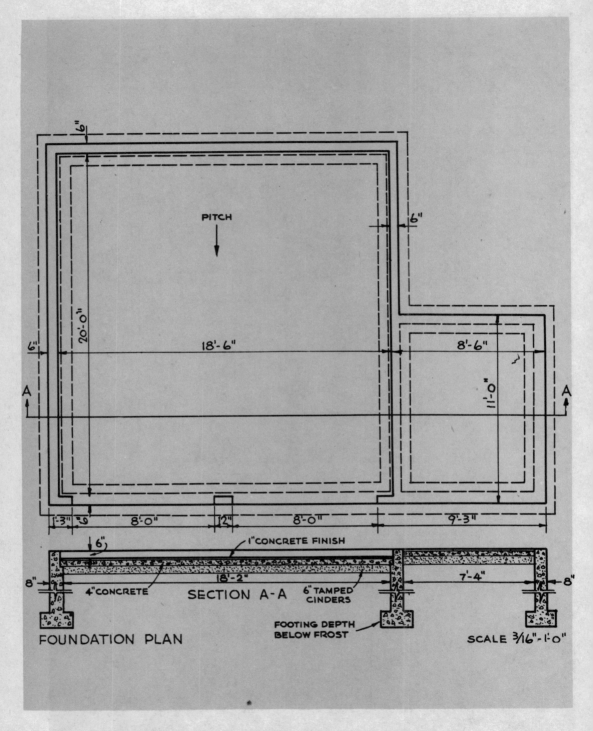

Foundation Plan and Section of Garage and Breezeway

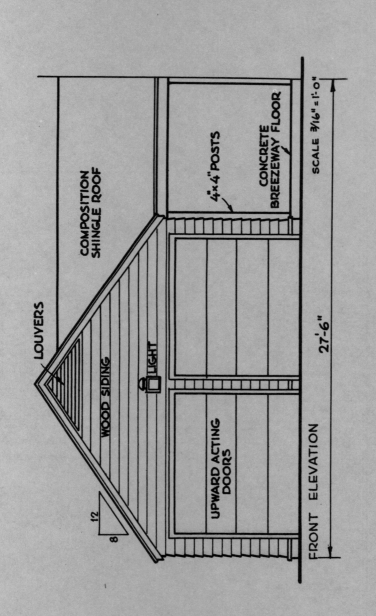

COMPOSITION SHINGLE ROOF

LOUVERS

WOOD SIDING

LIGHT

UPWARD ACTING DOORS

FRONT ELEVATION

4"x4" POSTS

CONCRETE BREEZEWAY FLOOR

SCALE 3/16" = 1'-0"

27'-6"

12
8

Front Elevation of Garage and Breezeway

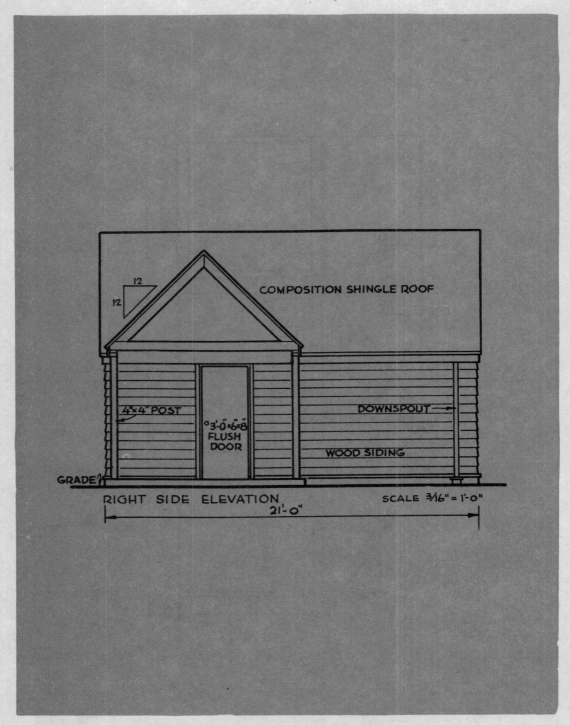

Right Side Elevation of Garage and Breezeway

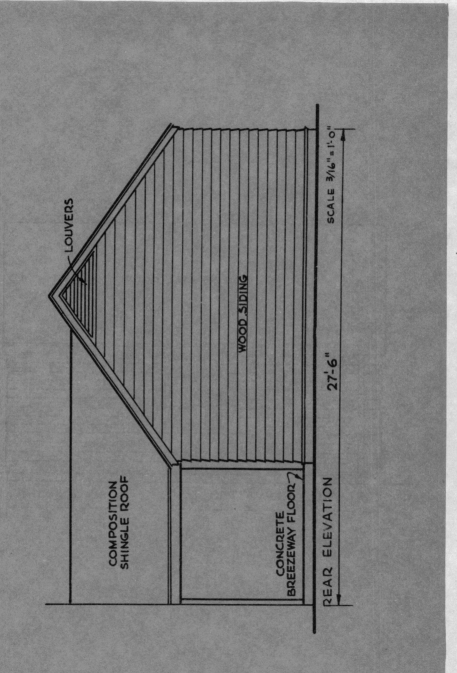

LOUVERS

COMPOSITION SHINGLE ROOF

WOOD SIDING

CONCRETE BREEZEWAY FLOOR

REAR ELEVATION

27'-6"

SCALE 3/16" = 1'-0"

Rear Elevation of Garage and Breezeway

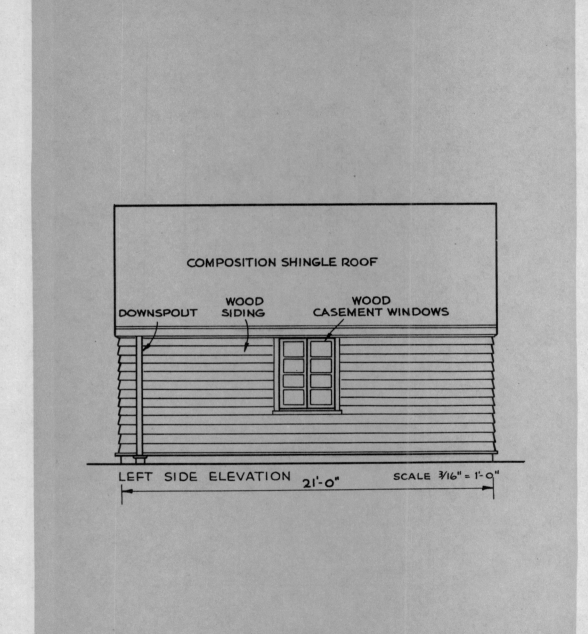

COMPOSITION SHINGLE ROOF

DOWNSPOUT   WOOD SIDING   WOOD CASEMENT WINDOWS

LEFT SIDE ELEVATION   21'-0"   SCALE 3/16" = 1'-0"

Left Side Elevation of Garage

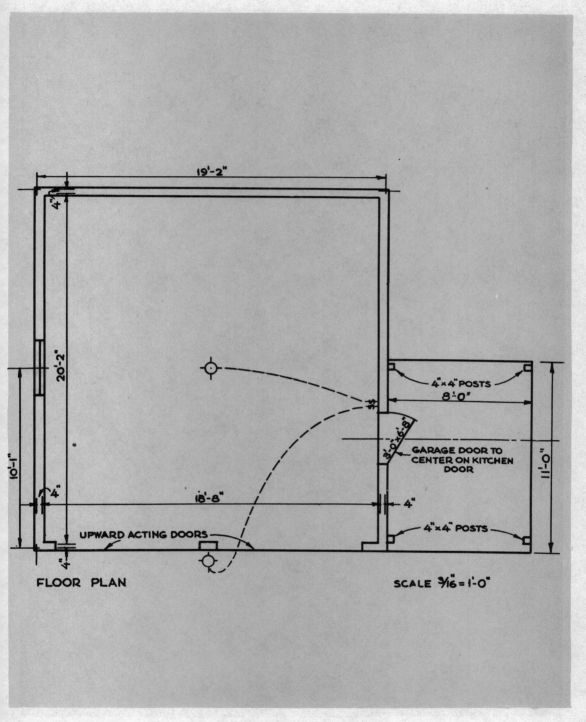

Plan of Garage and Breezeway

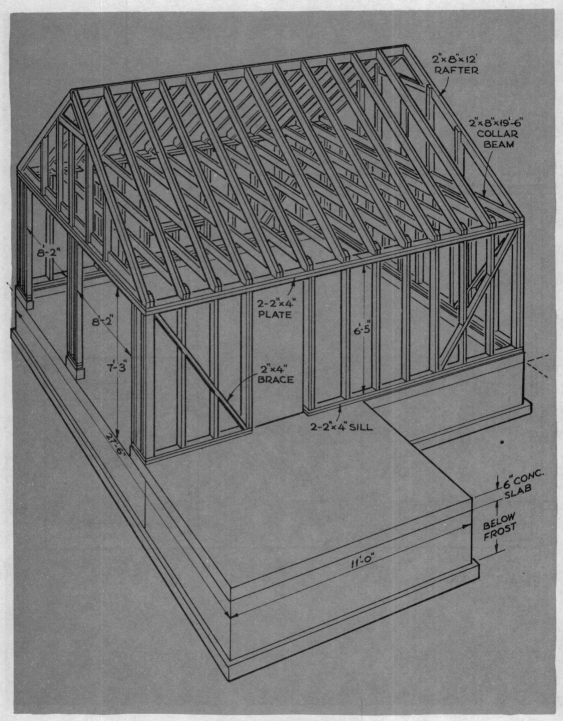

Framing the Garage

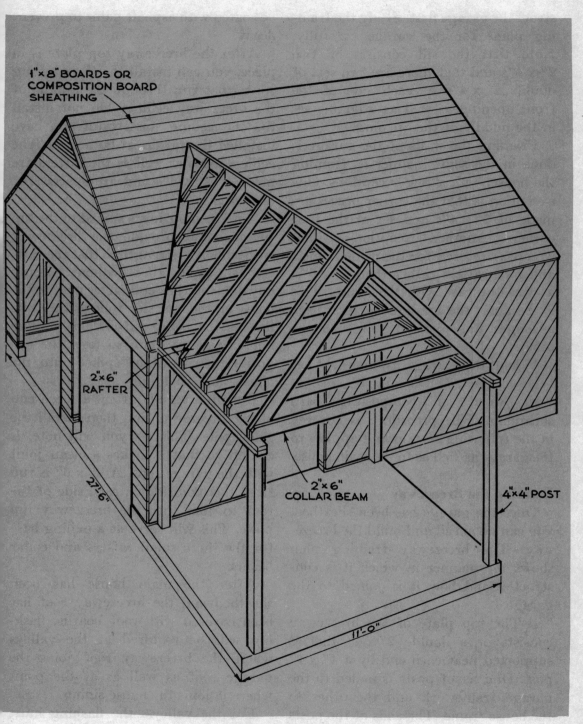

Framing the Breezeway

struct the garage first. Study the framing plans for the garage carefully. Note that the sill consists of two 2″ x 4″s and that there are two sets of double 2″ x 4″s at each side of the front opening as well as a double set in the middle of the opening.

Framing the walls of the garage is done in the same manner as framing the house, with a few exceptions. One exception is that the corner braces are made of 2″ x 4″s and set at the four corners. Another exception is that 2″ x 8″s are used for the ceiling joists and roof rafters rather than 2″ x 6″s, as was the case with the house. This is because the garage rafters have a longer unsupported run than the others.

When the garage framework has been completed, it should be covered with wood or composition-board sheathing. This procedure is covered in the following section and applies to the garage as well as to the main house.

Framing the Breezeway

Once the garage has been sheathed, you can go ahead and build the breezeway. The breezeway framing plan shows the manner in which it is constructed and how it is joined to the garage.

The top plate of the breezeway consists of a double 2″ x 4″ that is supported near each end by a 4″ x 4″ post. One set of posts is nailed to the garage framework and the other to the house frame. The ends of the posts that rest on the concrete slab should be coated with asphalt paint to prevent decay.

After the breezeway top plate is in place, you can install the three ceiling joists that run through the middle of the breezeway ceiling. Do not install the end ceiling joists until you have installed the rafters at both ends. The ceiling joists as well as the rafters are made of 2″ x 6″s and are spaced 16″ on center.

Three ceiling joists spiked to the top plate should provide the breezeway with sufficient strength so that the rafters can be installed without causing any damage. The end rafter next to the house on the rear side follows the same line as the house rafters but it does not extend up quite so far. The opposite rafter can be spiked into the house wall studding.

Put up a set of rafters at each end of the breezeway and then install the ridge pole. This, as you will note, is cut off so that it makes a clean joint with the garage roof. A 2″ x 6″ is run from this point down each side of the roof to join with the breezeway top plate. This will serve as a nailing base for the three small rafters and collar beams.

After the main house has been sheathed and the breezeway roof has been covered with roof boards, flashing will be required at the valleys where the breezeway roof joins the garage roof as well as at the point where it joins the house siding.

For the valleys, the flashing must extend from a point a little above the ridge pole down to the eaves of the garage roof. All flashing, both for the valleys and between the breezeway roof and the house siding, should extend 6" on each side. The flashing will eventually be covered by the roofing on the garage and breezeway or by the breezeway roofing and the house siding.

SHEATHING

After the four walls have been framed, plumbed and braced, the next job is to apply the sheathing over the outer surface of the wall framework. Sheathing serves several purposes. It helps to brace the entire wall structure. It also has some value as insulation in addition to making the wall airtight. Wood sheathing will further serve as a nailing base for the wall siding. And last but not least, sheathing gives considerable hope to the amateur builder because it goes on fast and, when it is in place, the structure begins to look like a house and not just a miscellaneous collection of 2" x 4"'s.

Materials for Sheathing

There are several common materials that you can use for sheathing. One is regular sheathing boards, 1" x 6", 1" x 8", or 1" x 10". This is the same lumber as used for the forms for the concrete foundation. Another kind of wood sheathing is plywood, which comes in sheets 4' x 8'. Composition sheathing board, also called insulating sheathing, is another type. Each type of sheathing has certain advantages and disadvantages.

As far as cost goes, wood sheathing is the least expensive of the three, especially if the forms used for the concrete foundations are knocked down and the lumber is used for the sheathing; on the other hand, it requires a good deal more work to apply it to the wall, as each piece must be separately measured, sawed and nailed. The other two materials are applied to the wall a section at a time and only a minimum

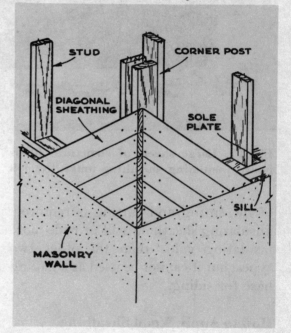

Fig. 16. Correct method of applying diagonal wall sheathing. Note that the sheathing runs right down over the edge of the sill. The sheathing should be nailed with two nails where it crosses framing members except for the corner post where three nails are used to help tie the corner post together.

Fig. 17. Large sheets of structural fiber-board insulating sheathing make the job of sheathing the house a very simple matter for the owner-builder.

of measuring and cutting is required. Insulating sheathing will provide more insulating value than the other two types, but it cannot be used as a nailing base for siding.

How to Apply Wood Sheathing

There are two ways in which wood sheathing can be applied to the framework. One method is to nail the boards on horizontally and the other is to have them run diagonally to the studding. There is no doubt that sheathing can be applied much faster if the horizontal method is used. But by nailing it on diagonally, you get the maximum stability and strength in your wall.

The sheathing boards should be nailed to the studding with two 8d nails. If you use the wider-size boards, such as 1″ x 8″ or 1″ x 10″, use three nails. Sheathing should be nailed at each point where it crosses studding. When sheathing is applied diagonally, it should run right down to the sill and should be nailed to the sill as well as the studding. This ties the sill and studding together. See Fig. 16.

At the cost of a little time to do some extra measuring and fitting, you can save considerable lumber by utilizing short lengths to fill in one some of the longer runs.

Be sure that the sheathing is laid tight and that all the joints come over studs.

Installing Structural Fiberboard Insulating Sheathing

This type of sheathing comes in many sizes and in different thicknesses. The size of nail used will depend on the thickness of the material; the manufacturer usually recommends the right size of nail. If this information is not given, select a nail that will penetrate into the studding for at least 1¼″. See Fig. 17.

Some brands of insulating sheathing board have a tongue-and-groove edge, while others have a plain edge. Still others have a shiplap joint or a v-groove. These boards should never be butted close together because of the possibility of expansion and buckling. Leave a space of about ⅛″ between boards. Be sure that all joints come over studs. When you apply these boards it is important to center the ends accurately over studs and other frame members so that you leave enough nailing surface for the next board. If this is not done you will find yourself spending a good deal of time and using a lot of extra lumber tacking strips to studding in order to provide the necessary nailing surface.

If you use structural fiberboard insulating sheathing and you plan to use shingles for the exterior siding, you will need 1″ x 2″ furring strips applied over the sheathing to act as a nailing base for the shingles. Horizontal siding, on the other hand, can be applied directly over the sheathing without the need of any furring, because it can be nailed to the studs in back of the sheathing.

Installing Plywood Sheathing

Plywood used for wall sheathing is ⁵⁄₁₆″ thick and is an exterior plywood that will not be damaged by moisture. It can serve as a base for shingles or horizontal siding. Special barbed nails are used to apply shingles, wood or asbestos, to the plywood. Plywood is nailed, and often glued as well, to the studding. This combination of nails and glue will give you great structural strength. However, it takes time to achieve it.

MAKING THE OPENINGS FOR DOORS AND WINDOWS

If you went ahead and framed all the outside walls without leaving any openings for doors and windows, these should be made now. The elevation plans give the dimensions for these openings. These dimensions are for the particular stock window and door frames used in the plans. If you use frames of somewhat different size, check with your local dealer and get

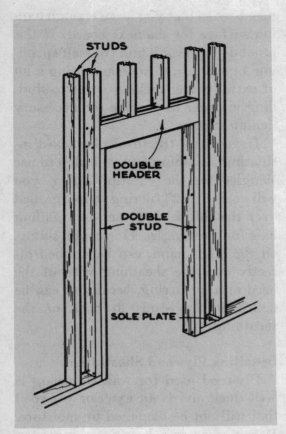

Fig. 18. Shows correct method of framing a door opening. The studs at the sides are double as well as the header. The inside stud runs from the floor to the bottom of the header while the outside stud runs from the sole plate up past the header. The header can be 2"x4" or 2"x6". These should be set on edge to provide maximum support and prevent the header from sagging.

some temporary braces across the studding that is to be cut. This will hold it in place while you make the cuts and keep the ends of the studding from moving out of plumb before you have been able to complete the frame.

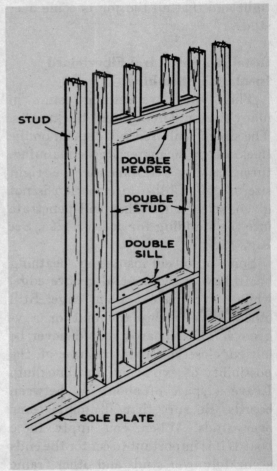

Fig. 19. Method used to frame opening for window. All framing is double. Note that the inside stud is cut out so that the double sill is supported at the ends. Short lengths of studs are placed under the sill to provide added support. The header is of 2"x4" or 2"x6" and this should be placed on edge and supported at the ends by the inside studs of the opening.

the rough framing dimensions for those particular window and door frames. This is important, for the measurements of various frames will often differ.

You should not have much trouble making the openings. First of all, tack

Note that the studding around all the openings is double. The 2″ x 4‴'s at top and bottom are set on edge to give maximum support to the opening. As the thickness of these two pieces of studding will not be quite sufficient to bring them out flush with the edges of the vertical studding, shim them out a little with strips of wood lath so that all surfaces, inside and out, are flush.

You can save a lot of time and trouble later on by making the openings for doors and windows as accurate as possible. If the rough opening is correct, you will have no trouble installing the frame later on. See Figs. 18 and 19.

Be sure that the rough frames for doors and windows are adequately nailed. If they are not, you will be troubled with windows and doors that stick and cracks in the plaster or wallboard around these openings.

The first step is to cut off the ends of the joists that will form the tail beams. These cuts must be plumb, as a tight fit between the ends of the tail beams and the header joist will increase the strength of the opening. Now, cut a single header joist that will just fit between the two single trimmer joists. Nail a strip of 2″ x 4″ along one side of the header, allowing its edge to come flush with the bottom edge of the header. Use 20d nails for this job.

There are two methods of supporting the header between the trimmer joists. One method is to use metal joist-hangers. If a joist-hanger is used, the trimmers can be doubled before the header is installed. The other method of supporting the headers is to nail a ledger strip of 2″ x 4″ along the bottom edge of the trimmer joists and notch out the bottom edge of the headers so that they fit over it. After the bottom edge of the tail beams has been notched and the ledger strip has been nailed to the bottom edge of the trimmer, the first header is put in place and nailed to the tail beams. Then the second header is installed and nailed to the first. The notches in the tail beams should be made with accuracy, as a good fit over the ledger strip is essential. The header is nailed to the single trimmer by driving 20d nails through the trimmer into the header. Be sure not to double the trimmer at this time. The single header is nailed to the tail beams by driving nails in through the face of the header into the ends of the tail beams. When this has been done, the second part of the header is put into position, notched to fit over the ledger strip on the trimmers and then nailed to the first header and to the trimmer. After this, the second trimmers are installed and spiked to the first.

SCAFFOLDING

From here on out there is going to be a good deal of work done beyond reach from the ground, so some thought must be given to adequate scaffolding. Good scaffolding is not only important to avoid injury, but you will be amazed

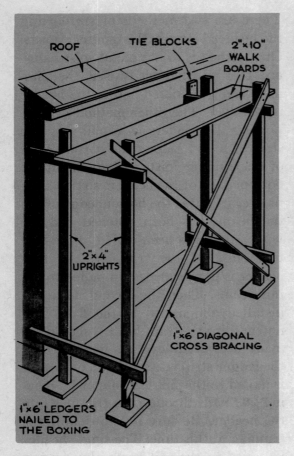

Fig. 20. Scaffolding of this type can be built on the job with the materials at hand.

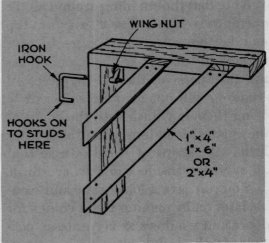

Fig. 21. A scaffold hook such as shown above makes it possible to erect scaffolding quickly on any side of the building. A hole must be cut through the sheathing to allow the hook to extend in back of the studding, thus it can get a tight hold.

at how much faster the work goes if you have a good solid base to work from. Do not neglect spending a little extra time rigging good scaffolding, because in the long run it will actually save you time.

A ladder is a very poor substitute for scaffolding. To be safe on a ladder you should have one hand free to hold on with. As most of the jobs in building a house require the use of two hands, working from a ladder is a definite hazard. Also, there is no place on

a ladder to store either tools or materials, which means that you will forever be running up and down, wasting both time and energy.

Fig. 20 shows a type of scaffolding that is easily constructed from the materials you have on hand. Just like the forms used for concrete, the materials used for scaffolding can be used again on the house, so do as little cutting as possible. Scaffolding should be solid but should not be so heavy that it must be taken apart before it can be moved from one location to another. Fig. 21 shows another type of scaffold that is put up on a scaffold jack. You can build a jack yourself or buy one ready-made. Its great advantage is that the scaffolding can be moved from one location to another very quickly.

CEILING JOISTS

The ceiling joists for the Basic House are 2" x 8"s. These will be sufficient here, even if you plan to finish off the attic at a later date.

For the most part, these joists are installed in the same manner as the joists used on the first floor. They will run between the top plates of the walls and of the main bearing-partition. They are spaced every 16" on center except around the openings for the stair well and the chimney, where they are doubled. The two end ceiling-joists should be spaced 1⅝" from the outer edge of the top plate of the walls. This is to allow room for the roof rafters, which should be set flush with the edge of the top plate. The joists are nailed to the top plate with two 10d nails on one side. Later on, when the roof rafters are in place, the joists will be nailed to them and the rafters in turn nailed to the top plate. The joists meeting over the main bearing-partition can be fastened with five 10d nails. The upper corner of each joist-end resting on the top plates of the walls will have to be cut off so that it will be flush with the edge of the roof rafter, but this can be done after the rafters are in place.

As was the case with the first-floor joists, you will need bridging for the ceiling joists. Do not nail the lower ends of the bridging in place until the sub-floor has been nailed down.

Rather than take the time at this point to cover the joists with sub-flooring, it is best to move right on and get the roof framed so that it can be covered. There is a great advantage in getting the house weathertight just as soon as possible—it will provide a safe as well as a dry place for storing various building materials, and this will save you time by allowing you to order enough materials for several different jobs.

It is a good idea, however, to bring up the lumber for the sub-floor and lay some of it across the joists so that you will have a surface to walk on and work from. Also, after the roof has been finished, hauling up all this lumber is going to be rather difficult, so it is best to get it up now.

FRAMING THE ROOF

Fig. 22 shows a master rafter that gives you the exact length that the rafter must be and also the angles for the two cuts. You will need 61 rafters and they should be 2" x 6" stock. Be sure that you cut each rafter accurately. The first job is to install the four end rafters. These should come flush with the outer edge of the top plate. Use braces to hold each rafter in position. The heel cut of the rafter must sit for its entire surface on the top plate. As soon as you have one rafter up, put up the other one to complete a pair. You

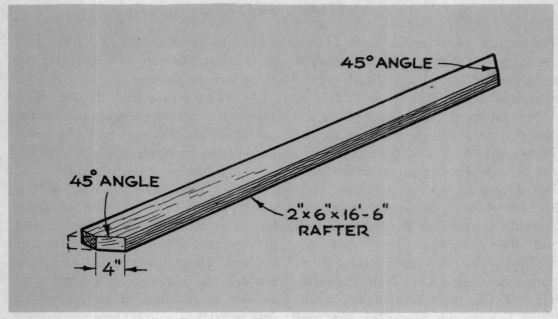

Fig. 22. Dimension, plumb and heel cut for the roof rafter of the basic house.

All rafters should be cut to this exact size to insure a perfect fit.

will notice that there is a slight gap between the tops of the rafters. This is for the ridge board. You can make a ridge board out of several pieces of 1″ x 6″. They will have to be spliced together and the splices must come between rafters. Rafters are spaced 16″ on center. As soon as the two pairs of end rafters are in place, go ahead and install the intermediate rafters. Put them up in pairs. Nail the first rafter to the ridge board with two 16d nails driven in through the ridge board into the face of the rafter. Nail the end of the rafter to the ceiling joists with five 10d nails. Secure the rafter to the top plate with two 10d nails toe-nailed in. The second rafter in the pair is nailed through its top with one 10d

nail to the ridge board and then another 10d nail is toe-nailed in. See Fig. 23.

Tack temporary braces across the rafters to hold them in place until the roofing has been applied. If a rafter has a slight crown, the crown should face up.

To tie the rafters together and to provide a ceiling for the attic space, collar beams are installed. The bottom of these should be spaced 7′ 2½″ from the top of the ceiling joists and spiked right to the sides of the rafters. Cut off their upper corners flush with the rafter. 1″ x 6″s are used for the collar beams.

The next step is to frame the gable ends. This studding should be spaced

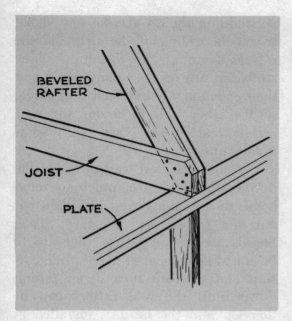

Fig. 23. Detail showing joint between rafter, ceiling joist and top plate. Joist and rafter are nailed together and toe-nailed to the plate with two nails driven in through the rafter and two through the joist.

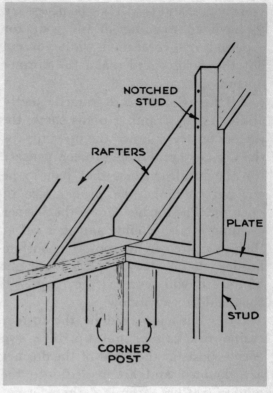

Fig. 24. Studding at the gable ends must be notched out at the top so that it will fit around the roof rafters. The bottom of the notch is cut to the same angle as the roof pitch. After the stud is in place, its top can be cut off flush with the top of the rafter.

16″ on center and should come directly over the studding below. All studs should be notched as shown in Fig. 24, so that they will fit up alongside the rafters. Two 10*d* nails are used to nail the studs to the rafters. The studs are nailed to the top plate with two 8*d* nails on each wide side. You will need an opening for a louver at each gable end. This should be framed to take a standard stock-size louver. If you wish to install windows instead of louvers at the gable ends, the frames for them should be doubled.

FRAMING THE DORMER WINDOWS

You do not have to spend time or money at this point to complete the dormer windows in the attic, but if you plan to put them in later on, you will be wise to make the necessary frames in the roof at this time. If you do this, you will not find it very difficult to put the windows in whenever you choose, and it will not be necessary to have an opening in the roof for a period of several days while you cut out the rafters and make the dormer openings.

All three dormers are framed exactly alike. As the framing plans show, the rafters on the sides of the opening for the dormer are doubled to compensate for the inside rafters that had to be cut out to make the proper size of opening. The top header for the dormer opening is also double and it is set at the same pitch as the roof. The bottom header, double too, is placed upright because it will serve as the rough sill for the dormer window.

After this has been done, the dormer framework can be put up. The two corner posts at the front of the dormer are doubled and are nailed into the double rafters framing the dormer opening. Additional studding is spaced 16" on center and is also nailed to the tops of the roof rafters.

Studding should also be placed between the ceiling of the attic and the rafters framing the opening. These studs can rest on the ceiling joists and their ends should be cut off at an angle so that they will fit under the roof rafters and provide them with additional support.

Probably the best way to frame the dormer opening is to complete the main house-roof framing first and then cut out the rafters as necessary. Tack boards across the rafters that are to be cut to hold them in place while cutting and to keep them from falling down until the side rafters can be doubled and the headers installed at both top and bottom. When this has been done, a rafter can be put back into the center of the opening and spiked to the top and bottom headers. When the time comes to install the dormer, the only additional framing work to do will be the removing of that one temporary rafter.

ROOF BOARDS

In all cold climates and wherever asbestos or composition shingles are to be used, the roof should be completely sheathed with roof boards. These can be either shiplap or matched tongue-and-groove. The joints between the boards should be staggered so that no more than two of them fall on the same rafter. The board should be nailed with two 8d nails to each rafter. A good tight deck-roof of this type will do much toward keeping the house warm,

so be sure that the boards are tightly laid together.

The chimney should be built before the roof boards and roofing material are put on. The chimney can be installed after the roof boards are in place, but it is obviously easier to do it before.

You should have no difficulty getting the roof boards in place quickly. To save time, do not bother to trim the ends of the boards one at a time. Let

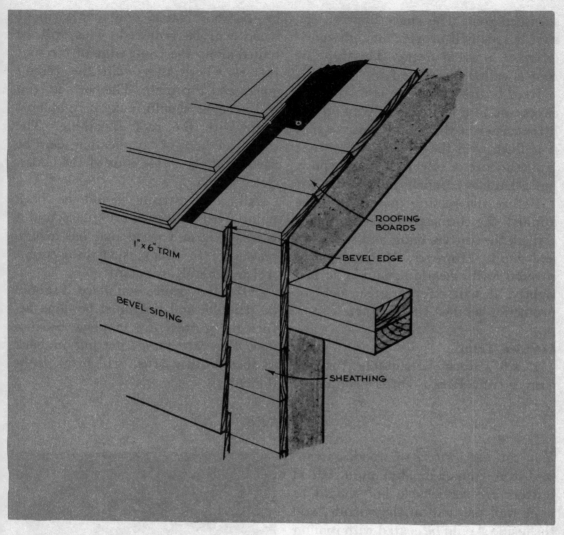

Fig. 25. Detail of cornice trim construction. It is worth the added effort to back-

prime the cornice material before it is installed.

them hang over a little and, when the roof has been covered, just trim them off with a saw.

Lay the roof boards horizontal and level from the eaves up. As you move up the roof, you can nail temporary walking strips to them so that you can get about more easily and safely.

In warm, moist climates where wood shingles are used, it is customary to place the roofing boards with a space between them equal to the length of the shingle that is laid to the weather. The reason for this practice is that in these climates the shingles may rot if they are fastened to a tightly sheathed roof. The space between the roof boards will provide enough ventilation to prevent decay. This type of roof is called a slat roof.

Roof boards should be laid from the eaves up. You will have to trim off the little corner of the ceiling joist so that it is flush with the edge of the rafter. You can use a saw for this purpose, but a hatchet is much quicker.

Before the roofing material can be applied, the cornice trim should be installed, the gutters hung and the chimney built. However, if the roof is covered with sheathing and it is laid tightly, it will offer a great deal of protection against the weather.

Cornice Trim

1" x 6" stock is suitable for the cornice trim. Because of the simplicity of the roof frame, only one strip of wood will be required. This will be nailed along the front edge of the roof rafters where they join the ceiling joists and top plate. The cornice trim at the eaves should make a tight butt joint with the roof sheathing. The same method of application can be used as at the gable ends of the house. See Fig. 25.

All cornice trim should be back painted before it goes into place, and it is wise to use a wood that has a high resistance to decay, such as cypress, which is highly resistant.

After the cornice is in place, it should be painted, and this must be done before the gutters are in place because once they are hung, getting in back of them with a brush will prove to be difficult.

GUTTERS

You can use gutters of wood, galvanized iron, copper or aluminum. Wood gutters are serviceable but should be kept well painted on the outside, and the inside should be coated with roofing compound or metal to prevent decay. Galvanized iron gutters will give many years of good service if they are kept painted—inside and out. Copper gutters will last indefinitely, but they tend to cause stains on white siding unless they are coated with paint or varnish, neither of which will stick to the copper unless it has had time to weather. Aluminum is weather resistant and will not cause stains. But if aluminum

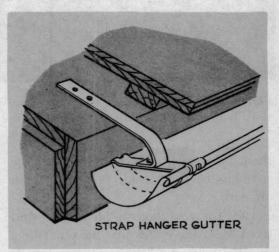

STRAP HANGER GUTTER

Fig. 26. Gutter hangers should be installed before the roofing is applied and should be nailed to roof sheathing.

gutters are used and the flashing is copper, the two metals should not come into contact with one another; insulate them with roofing compound, or they will set up a corrosive action. Properly hung gutters should slope about ⅟₁₆″ per foot towards their outlet. The outside edge of the gutter should be below the pitch of the roof. Be sure that enough hangers are used and that they are securely fastened to the roof. See Fig. 26.

ROOFING MATERIALS

As far as cost is concerned, the least expensive roofing you can use is roll roofing. This is a heavy felt-and-asphalt material that comes in rolls 36″ wide. Each roll will cover about 100 square feet. While roll roofing offers good protection against the weather, it is seldom used on homes because it presents a rather drab and uninteresting appearance.

Asphalt Shingles

A more popular type of covering is asphalt shingles. These come as individual shingles or in strips of from two to four shingles each. They give protection and many years of service and come in many designs and colors. Fig. 27 shows several types of asphalt shingle. Consult the manufacturer's directions as to the size and number of nails required for each strip of shingles.

The first step in applying this type of roofing is to cover the roof with roofing felt. This should be applied in horizontal strips from the eaves to the ridge board. Each strip should overlap the strip below it about 6″ and the topmost strip should also go over the ridge board. Roofing felt needs to be nailed

only in a few places to hold it down. Before these strips go down, check over the wood sheathing to be sure that there are no nail heads sticking up, as these may easily puncture the material and cause the roof to leak.

Now tack a course of wood shingles along the eaves. These should extend beyond the eaves and the gable ends of the roof from ½″ to ¾″. Their purpose

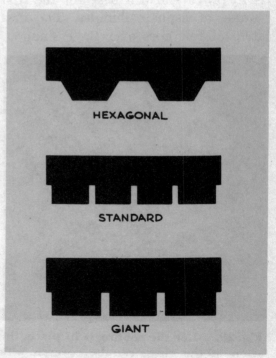

HEXAGONAL

STANDARD

GIANT

Fig. 27. Asphalt Shingles.

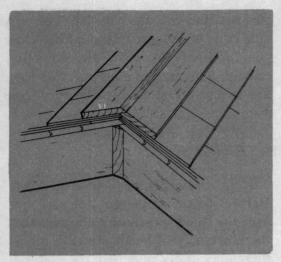

Fig. 28. If you prefer, the ridge of the roof can be covered with a wood ridge-cap. For this purpose, 1″x6″ stock is suitable. The underside of the cap should be painted before it is nailed in place.

is to provide a firm base for the first course of asphalt shingles. The first strip of felt goes over these shingles.

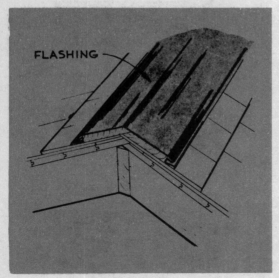

Fig. 29. After the roofing is in place, the seam at the ridge can be covered with stock metal ridge-flashing.

Now apply the first course of asphalt shingles. Apply successive courses from the eaves upward. Lay the shingles tightly and stagger the joints from course to course. You don't have to worry about how much of the shingle should be exposed because this is clearly indicated on each one.

A common practice in applying felt and shingles is to put down a section or two of felt and then the shingles before moving on to the next section of felt.

It is not advisable to work with asphalt shingles in very hot weather because they become rather soft and can be damaged by being walked on. Bring up enough bundles of shingles to do the job before you start work so that you will not have to be walking back and forth over the completed portion of the roof with various materials.

The ridge of the roof can be capped with shingles, a strip of roll roofing, or wood or metal ridge caps. See Figs. 28 and 29.

Wood Shingles

Wood shingles are considerably more expensive than asphalt shingles, especially if edge-grain, all-heartwood shingles are used. Flat-grain shingles are less expensive but they have more tendency to curl and split and do not have as good weathering characteristics as the others. Unless you can afford the best quality of shingles, you will do better to roof with asphalt shingles rather than wasting time and money on shingles that sooner or later will have to be replaced.

Wood shingles come in lengths of 16″, 18″ and 24″. The amount of exposure (the length laid to the weather) will depend on the length of the shingle: 16″ shingles can be given 5″ of weather exposure; 18″ shingles, 5½″; and 24″ shingles, 7½″. Shingles come in random widths. If the shingles are laid over a tight deck-roof, the roof should first be covered with a rosin-treated paper. If a slat roof has been built, the paper is not necessary.

Shingles are often stained with a preservative that not only helps them resist decay but gives them a touch of color. The best time to stain the shingles is before they go on the roof. Have a large container of the stain on hand and dip each shingle to within about 3″ of the covered end. Now stand the shingle in a wood trough until the stain is dry. Shingles can be stained after they are in place but in that case only a small portion of the shingle can be coated. Do not paint wood shingles on a roof. The paint may seal moisture inside the shingles and cause them to decay.

The first course of shingles, at the eaves, should be double. The joints between shingles in each course must be staggered so that each joint is covered by at least 1½″ of the width of the shingle above. Dry shingles should be spaced ¼″ apart. If the shingles are wet or green, this distance can be reduced to ⅛″. If the shingles are butted tight against one another, there may be buckling when the shingles become wet and swell. Nails used for shingles

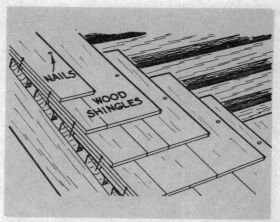

Fig. 30. Detail showing the proper nailing for wood roof shingles.

should be rust-resistant. The nails should not be placed more than ¾″ from the edges of the shingles and about 2″ above the butt line of the course of shingles above. See Fig. 30. This will allow all nails to be covered by the next course. For 16″ and 18″ shingles, use 3d nails, for 24″ use 4d nails. You will need two nails for each shingle.

Do not try to use the wide shingles as they are easily split by the nails. It is better to split them in half before they are used. The best tool to use for working with wood shingles is a carpenter's hatchet. This allows you to split the shingles and nail them without having to use two different tools.

The ridge can be capped either with wood or metal. If you use wood, 1″ x 6″ stock is perfectly suitable.

Use a line running parallel with the eaves of the roof or tack down a strip of wood so that you will be sure to get each course of shingles on evenly.

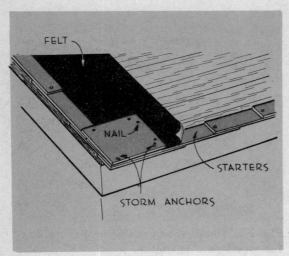

Fig. 31. How the first course of asbestos roof shingles should be applied.

Asbestos Shingles

Asbestos shingles, made of Portland cement and asbestos fibers, are an excellent roofing material. They are highly resistant to fire and will not rot or decay. If properly installed they should last the lifetime of the house. They come in several colors and it is perfectly practical to paint them. Ordinary oil paints can be used, but special paints designed for this purpose are more satisfactory.

Asbestos shingles are very brittle, so you must be careful when handling and working with them not to crack or damage them. You have to be especially careful when nailing, because, if you should strike the shingle with your hammer, you may easily crack and ruin it. Once the shingles are in place, do not walk over them. This will mean that you are going to need some sort of roof scaffolding for the job. This can

be easily built by nailing two strips of wood to the end of a ladder and using them to hook the ladder over the ridge.

Asbestos shingles should be installed over a solid deck-roof. Be sure that all roof boards are secure, that they fit close together, and that they are perfectly dry before you start applying the shingles. Once you are satisfied with the condition of the roof, cover it with 15-pound asphalt roofing-felt. All the seams between the strips of felt should be lapped at least 4″. After all this has been done, nail a ¼″ by 1½″ strip of wood along the edge. Before you tack this strip of wood in place, roll back the edges of the roofing felt along the eaves; the first row of shingles is going to be double and this felt should be placed between the two layers. The strip of wood should be flush with the eaves of the roof.

The first row of shingles put down is of special starter-course shingles. This first course should extend about 1″ beyond the eaves to form a drip edge. After this first layer of the first course is in place, roll the roofing felt down over it and apply the second layer. See Fig. 31.

The shingles are nailed with 1¼″ galvanized nails driven through the holes provided for them in the shingles.

The amount of weather exposure will depend on the length of the shingle. This information can be obtained by reading the manufacturer's specification sheet.

Asbestos shingles can be cut by scoring them with a sharp instrument and then breaking along this line, or they can be cut with an asbestos-cement cutting machine, which you may be able to rent or borrow from your local dealer.

At the time that the roofing material is put on, the base flashing and cricket for the chimney should be installed. See Figs. 12, 13, 14 and 15 in Chapter 9.

MATERIALS LIST FOR FRAMING THE BASIC HOUSE
(On Concrete Slab Floor)

Material	Quantity	Dimensions
2″ x 8″	27	14′
	31	12′
2″ x 6″	65	16′ 6″
	30	8′
2″ x 4″	136	16′
1″ x 6″		170′
1″ x 4″	8	8′
1″ x 3″ No. 2 Common grade	192 feet	
Sheathing	5,050 board feet	1″ x 8″
Asphalt shingles	12 squares	
8d common nails	2 kegs	
16d common nails	50 lbs.	
30-lb. asphalt felt	5 rolls	
Metal adjustable louvers	2	

Chapter 9

THE CHIMNEY AND FIREPLACE

It is obvious that the method of constructing a fireplace and a chimney for both the fireplace and the furnace is going to differ considerably depending upon whether or not you have a basement in your house, whether there is to be a second fireplace in the basement gameroom and where the furnace is to be located. Let us start out with an explanation of how the work is done when there is a basement with the furnace in it and a fireplace in the living room only. After directions for this situation have been given, we shall take up how to build two fireplaces, one in the basement and one in the living room, and how to handle the job in homes with basements and a furnace in the utility room and in basementless homes with wooden first floors or poured-concrete-slab first floors.

There are several important points that you must keep in mind about fireplace and chimney construction. In the first place, these structures must be built up from a solid and free-standing footing of their own. They should not be built up from the basement floor, as this slab is not thick enough to carry the load of fireplace or chimney. To eliminate any possibility of the chimney's or fireplace's sinking, the footings must be rather massive. Directions for pouring the footings and their dimensions are given in the chapter on the foundation walls. The second point to remember is that the fireplace and the chimney must stay clear of all the house framework. The minimum clearance should be 2″, and the space between the masonry and the woodwork must be filled with a fire-resistant insulation. There are other reasons than the possibility of fire for keeping the masonry and woodwork separate. If any of the house framework is built into the masonry, the slight difference in expansion and contraction of the two materials plus the normal amount of settling that takes place is enough to damage the masonry work. The third point to remember is to keep the work level and plumb and to be sure that all mortar joints are thoroughly packed with good-grade mortar. Faulty mortar joints in the masonry are a fire hazard and a cause of leaks.

THE CHIMNEY BASE

Since the fireplace is located on the first floor, you will need a masonry base built up from the footing in the basement on which the fireplace and the chimney will rest. The back and two side walls of this masonry base should be at least 8″ thick. The front wall can be 4″ thick, as it does not have to support the same load as the other three walls. The mortar formula and the thickness of the mortar joints are the same as those given under the section on working with bricks, if you are using bricks, or the section on working with masonry blocks, if you are using concrete chimney-blocks.

The opening left in the base will serve as an ash pit for the fireplace. A dump-door for ashes will be installed in the fireplace hearth, so that ashes in the fireplace can be easily removed, without fuss or mess. At the bottom of the ash pit you will need an ash-pit door, so that the ashes that have dropped down can be removed from time to time.

The first step in building the base is to drop four plumb lines from the opening that was framed for the fireplace in the first floor. These lines should extend 2″ in from the framework on all four corners. The points where these four lines touch the concrete footing will indicate the outside measurements of the chimney base. Before you can accurately lay out the dimensions of the base, you will have to decide what size of flue you are going to use for the furnace. This is necessary because the flue runs up through the base and you will need 3¾″ of masonry on all sides of it.

The best way to find out what size of flue to use and exactly how high up in the base the opening for the stove pipe from the furnace should be is to consult the installation specification-sheet of the type of heating equipment you plan to have. This will give the recommended flue size and the height for the opening. For our present purpose, we have selected a 8½″ x 13″ flue for the furnace, and this will mean that the thickness of one of the walls of the chimney and fireplace base must be 21″.

The Ash-Pit Door

Once you have laid out the base, you can begin to build it up. Either common bricks or concrete chimney-blocks can be used for this work. A few inches above the basement finished-floor level, a cast-iron ash-pit clean-out door should be installed. It goes into the front wall of the base, so that you can remove the ashes in the pit. A door 10″ x 12″ is quite adequate. These doors come as complete assemblies and can be purchased along with the other necessary equipment for the fireplace and chimney from lumber yards and masonry-supply houses. Put the door frame in place first and then build up around it. The frame should be securely mortared into the masonry so that you have a good tight fit between the walls and the metal door frame.

Flues

Now you can go ahead and build the base up until you reach the height where the flue for the furnace should begin. The furnace flue as well as the fireplace chimney flue should be lined with fire-clay flue-lining. It is possible, of course, not to use this special lining if it is not required by the building code, but this economy is not recommended. In the first place, if it is not used, the wall thickness must be at least 8″ on all sides. Also, since the inside of the flue will be rough, it will collect soot easily. Fire-clay flue-linings must always be used with gas heating equipment, because when gas burns, it produces a considerable amount of water vapor plus some acids that would cause the mortar in the flue-joints to disintegrate. The wall thickness of the flue-lining should be ⅝″ thick. Flue-lining can be either round or rectangular. The round lining is the more efficient and is more easily cleaned, but more care is required in putting it up to be sure that it is properly mortared into the masonry.

The Clean-Out Door

The flue-tile lining should begin at least 8″ below the point where the stove pipe from the furnace enters the flue. You will also need a clean-out door so that the soot from the furnace flue can be removed when necessary.

The top of this door should come almost flush with the bottom of the first section of flue-tile. Therefore, the clean-out door should be set in place first and the bricks or blocks built up around it on all sides. Now the first section of flue-tile can go into place.

The Stove-Pipe Opening

Before it goes in, however, you will have to cut an opening in it so that the stove pipe may enter. The bottom of this opening should be 8″ from the bottom of the flue-tile. Fill a bag with damp sand and stuff it down into the flue-tile at the point where the opening is to be cut; then tap a cold chisel very lightly with a hammer along the line where the cut is to be made. You can get special thimble sections of flue-tile that already contain the opening for the stove pipe. Before you cut the opening or get the special thimble section, check the size of the stove pipe you plan to use. An 8″ diameter is a standard size and the one we have chosen for our present purposes.

All flue-tile that must be cut should be cut before it is put into position.

After the first section of flue-tile for the chimney flue has been put in place, build up around it with brick until you are just below the bottom of the opening. At this point, a thimble of fireclay should be installed so that the smoke pipe from the furnace can enter the flue.

The joint between the thimble and the flue-tile and the surrounding masonry must be tight at all points.

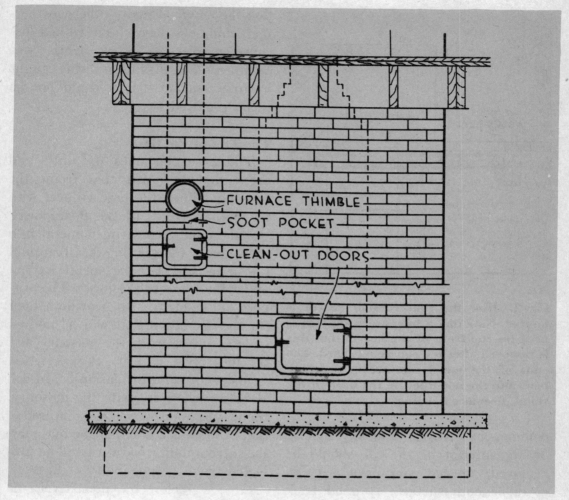

Fig. 1. Elevation of fireplace base.

The opening for the smoke pipe in the flue must be at least 18″ below the ceiling and it should be at least 6″ away from any woodwork or combustible materials. It may be necessary to alter the location of the flue opening so that these requirements can be met. See Fig. 1.

The thimble should be set absolutely level, so that the metal stove pipe can enter it straight.

Do not try to lay a few courses of masonry and then slip the flue-tile into position. In the first place, your opening may be just a little too small and the work will have to be undone. What is more important is that you will not be able to fill all the spaces between the tile and the masonry with mortar. The joints between sections of flue-tile should be mortared (using the same mortar formula as for the

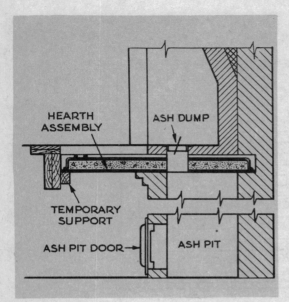

Fig. 2. How the concrete-slab hearth is poured. Note that a temporary support is used for the front of the hearth, but this is removed after the concrete is hard. The ends of the metal reinforcing rods are bent into the notch left in the back of the rough fireplace opening.

chimney base itself) and any mortar on the interior of the tile should be removed, so that you have a good, clean, smooth surface. A good trick to use in laying up the flue-tile is to fill a bag with sawdust or shavings so that it just fits snugly into the tile. Tie a long string to this bag and slip it up through each section of tile as it goes into place. As soon as one section of tile is in place and the masonry built up around it, pull the bag up a little so that it will smooth off the inside of the joint between the sections of flue-tile. This bag will also help you to remove any mortar or even tools that you may drop down through the

flue-tile. A good many otherwise perfect chimneys have been ruined because mortar or other debris was dropped down the flue and was caught in an off-set so that it could not be easily removed.

The Top of the Base

The base continues up until you are under the joists that frame the opening. When the base is level with the bottom edges of the floor joists, slip the edge of a strip of metal into the outside mortar joints all around the base and let the metal extend under the edges of the joists. The purpose of the strip is to provide a floor for the insulation that will be poured in later on between the masonry and the joists.

Sheets of rigid insulation board can also be used to insulate the masonry. Some type of insulation must be used so that if there is a crack in the masonry, the surrounding woodwork will be protected from the possibility of fire.

At 7½″ below the floor level, the front wall of the base is widened out forward. The bricks in the front wall are brought forward 1″. Two courses of bricks are laid thus, so that the front wall is about 6″ thick at the top instead of 4″.

When you reach a point 5½″ below the finished-floor level, level off the fore-wall or front wall of the base and notch out the rear wall 3⅓″ high and 1″ deep. See Fig. 2. The purpose of the notch is to provide a hold for the hearth, which will be poured later on.

THE FIREPLACE

FIREPLACE DIMENSIONS

	Finished Fireplace Opening	*Rough Brickwork*
Width	30″	42″
Height	28″ (basement, 24″)	
Depth	18″	22″
Back	16″	
Vertical back wall	14″ high	
Sloped backwall	20″ high	
Smoke chamber		25″ high
Slope of smoke chamber		14½″ high
Flue lining		8½″ x 13″ rectangular, or 10″ round
Throat		8¾″ wide

Now we are ready to go ahead and build the rough fireplace. To save time at this point, the rough fireplace will be built and the chimney finished off and you can then go ahead with other jobs and come back to finish off the fireplace later.

Before you start work on the fireplace, take a few minutes to study Fig. 3 in order to see exactly what must be done. You will notice that a well constructed fireplace is not square by any means. While the width of the fireplace opening that we are going to construct is 30″ at the front, it is only 16″ at the back. The distance from the front of the fireplace to the back is 18″. This will require that the two side walls of the fireplace gradually come together as they extend to the rear until they are 16″ apart. The back wall of the fireplace, which is 18″ from the front opening, is perfectly vertical for 14″ and then it inclines forward for 20 vertical inches until

it reaches the throat, which is 8¾″ wide. This, plus the nominal thickness of the finished front or breast of the fireplace, which is 4″, means that in 20″ the back wall has moved forward from 18″ to 12¾″. The result is a smoke shelf 9¼″ wide. Of course, these are the dimensions for the finished fireplace. To make the rough opening, we have to use other dimensions, because the interior will be lined with firebricks later on.

For the purpose of building the rough opening, the width is 42″ rather than 30″ (the finished width). The depth of the rough opening is 22″, rather than 18″ (the finished depth). At this time we do not have to worry about the height, because this will be taken care of later on when the finished brickwork and firebrick are added.

Build up the back and two side walls until you reach a height of 34″. The rough opening should measure

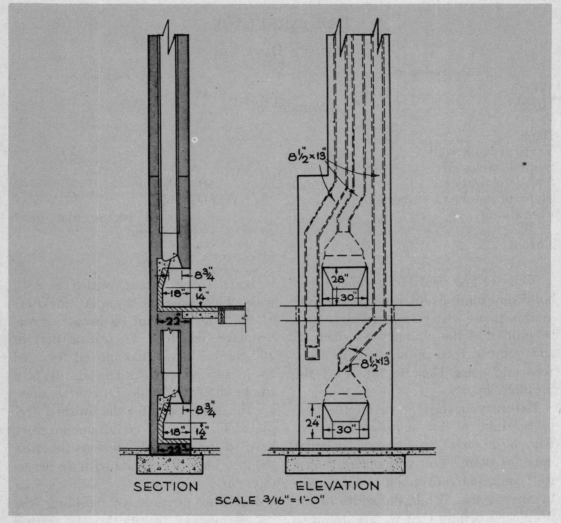

Fig. 3. Section and elevation of fireplaces.

42″ x 22″. The walls should be at least 8″ thick with at least 3¾″ of masonry around the furnace flue-tile, which is running up through one of the side walls.

The Smoke Chamber

At 34″, the two side walls start to come together gradually, so that a smoke chamber will be formed. The height of this smoke chamber is 25″ and the top should be the dimension of the chimney flue. If you are using rectangular flue-tile, use one 8½″x 13″. If you use a round tile, the inside diameter should be 10″. The best way to form the smoke chamber is to make a simple wood form as shown in Fig. 4.

The top opening of the form is equal to the size of the flue-tile that you are going to use. Set this form in place over the two side walls and then build up the side walls and the back. When you reach a height of 14½", put a piece of 3" x 3¾₆" angle-iron 36" long between the two side walls, embedding it in the masonry. The angle-iron supports the front of the chimney. Its distance away from the back wall of the fireplace should be the same distance as the width of the flue that you are using. If rectangular flue-tile is used, this distance will be 8½"; if round tile is used, it will be a little less than 10". Now continue up until the total vertical height of the smoke chamber is 25". Level off the four walls so that the first section of flue-tile can be put in place. Remove the forms that were used to get the proper pitch to the sidewalls and coat the masonry with a smooth covering of the cement mortar. This, by the way, is the only spot in fireplace and chimney construc-

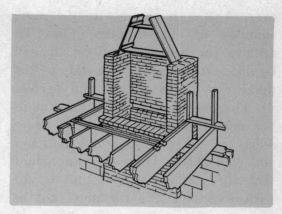

Fig. 4. Wood forms can be used to get the proper slope to the sidewalls to form the smoke chamber.

tion where mortar is preferred to brick or concrete chimney-blocks. Be sure that the two side walls have each the same amount of slope. If one has more than the other, you will have difficulty in getting a good fire burning.

Bringing the Furnace Flue Over

As the side walls come together to form the smoke chamber, it is also necessary to bring the furnace flue

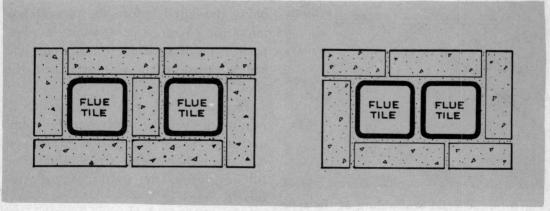

Fig. 5. Chimney made of masonry blocks with mortar and with block used between flues. The same arrangements can be used for a brick chimney.

over, so that it can go up the same chimney as the fireplace flue. To achieve the necessary off-set, it will be necessary to miter the ends of the flue-tile to get a smooth and perfect fit. This can be done in the same manner as cutting a hole in the tile, using a bag of damp sand and a hammer and cold chisel. It is very important that the joints between tile be cut with accuracy. The tile must *not* be given an off-set of more than 30° from the vertical. The furnace flue should be brought to within 4″ of the fireplace flue, and this is the closest they should ever be. The joints between the furnace flue and chimney flue should be staggered so that they are at least 7″ apart. The space between the two flues may be filled either with mortar and brick or with mortar alone. See Fig. 5.

Each of the four walls of the chimney should be at least 4″ thick.

THE CHIMNEY

From here on, it is just a matter of building the chimney up from the base that was made for it on the top of the fireplace. You will need a plumb line at all times to be sure that the chimney is going up perfectly straight and you will also want to be sure that all mortar joints and joints between sections of flue-tile are tight. Take the time to rig a sand bag such as was described earlier in this section, because if you drop mortar down the furnace flue, there is a good chance of its collecting at the off-sets.

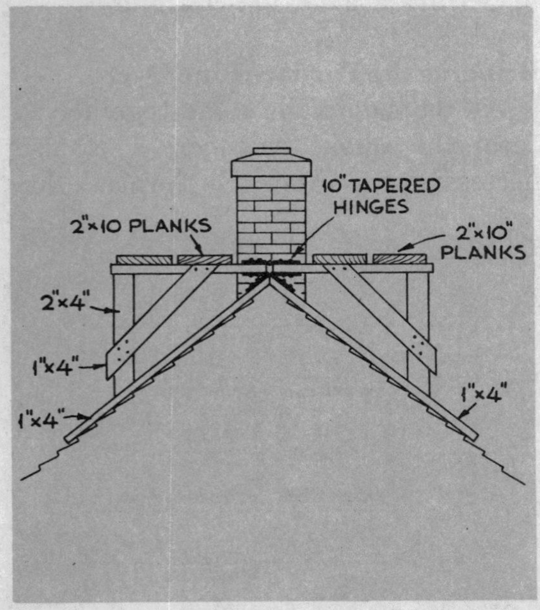

You are going to need some scaffolding as the work progresses, and it should be solid and should stand free and clear of the masonry, so that there will be no chance of the chimney's being damaged before the mortar has had time to set. Fig. 6 shows a platform-type of scaffold to use when you are working on the chimney from the roof.

Be sure that you have your 2″ minimum clearance between the chimney and the ceiling joists. Here you can use either metal strips and loose fill insulation or strips of asbestos board. See Fig. 7.

About 2′ below the point where the chimney passes through the opening

Fig. 6. Good solid scaffolding of the type shown above will be necessary when completing the chimney.

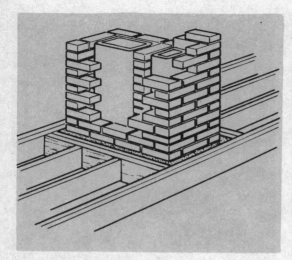

Fig. 7. Method of framing around opening in the floor or ceiling for the chimney. Double headers and double trimmers should be used. There should be a clearance of at least 2″ between the framework and the masonry. This space is filled with insulation.

that was framed in the roof, increase the wall thickness of the chimney from 4″ to 8″. This is done by off-setting four courses of bricks so that each course extends about 2″ beyond the wall surface. This is called corbeling. See Fig. 8. Although thickening the wall is not always essential, an 8″ wall is better for exposure to the weather and will enable you to do a better flashing job than with a 4″ wall. See Fig. 5.

The chimney should extend at least 2′ above the highest point of the roof. At the point where the chimney passes through the roof, there must be a 2″ clearance. See Fig. 9.

The joint between the chimney and the roof must be flashed with metal to make it watertight. See Fig. 10. A metal cricket in back of the chimney is also necessary, so that water running down the roof will not collect at this point. Fig. 11 shows the method of constructing a cricket with a wood base that is covered with copper. Figs. 12 and 13 show detail of metal cricket. At this time, only the cap flashing is installed. The base flashing will be added when the roofing is installed. The cap flashing should be bent at a right angle so that it can be fastened right into the mortar joints. It should extend in about 1½″.

Capping the Chimney

The top of the chimney should be given a good watertight cap; many

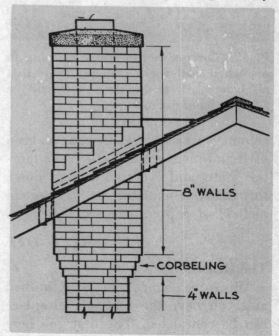

Fig. 8. Method of increasing the thickness of a chimney before it passes through the roof.

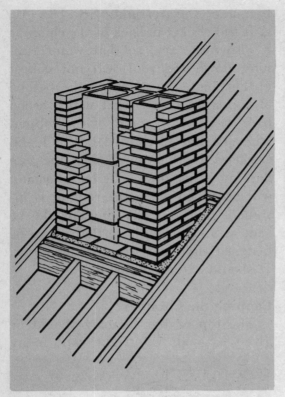

Fig. 9. Correct way to frame opening in a pitched roof for a chimney. Note that all framework is double and should be 2″ away from the masonry.

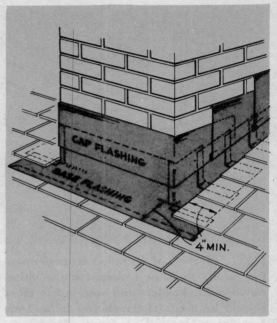

Fig. 10. Chimney base and cap flashing. The cap flashing extends into the mortar joints of the chimney. All flashing is overlapped 4″ and the joint between the metal is made tight with roofing compound.

chimneys leak because no cap has been used and moisture collects in the mortar joints and eventually seeps down through the masonry. A very good method of capping the chimney is to allow the tile to extend about 4″ beyond the last course of bricks or blocks. A wood form is then built around the top of the chimney brickwork, and a 3″ cap of concrete is poured over the bricks. The surface of the cap should be given a slight downward slope so that water will drain off easily.

FINISHING OFF THE FIREPLACE

The Hearth

When the chimney has been finished and you have the time, the fireplace can be completed. The first job here is to pour the hearth. The finished hearth should be more or less level with the finished floor, so that it will be easy to sweep. The hearth should project at least 16″ beyond the breast of the chimney and should be as long as the fireplace is wide plus 16″. These, of course, are minimum requirements. The hearth must be made out of some type of fire-resistant material,

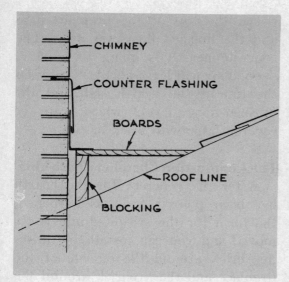

Fig. 11. Construction detail for the wood frame of a chimney cricket.

Fig. 12. How a metal cricket is installed in back of the chimney.

such as brick or concrete, and it should be 4″ thick.

The hearth must not be attached to the wood framework around the fireplace opening nor should it depend on any of the house framework for support. It must, in short, be supported entirely by the fireplace base.

There are two methods employed in building a hearth so that it will meet all the necessary requirements. One method, which has been in use for many years, is to build a supporting masonry arch under the hearth. This is a perfectly satisfactory arrangement except that building the arch is rather difficult and requires a good deal of time. The other method of construction is to use a cantilevered concrete slab. This type of hearth is made out of reinforced concrete 3½″ thick. It is anchored to the rear wall of the fire-

place base by means of the recesses or notches that were made when the

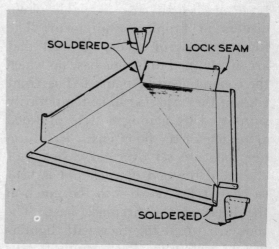

Fig. 13. Metal chimney cricket. The purpose of this device is to prevent snow and ice from collecting in back of the chimney and causing the roof to leak at this point.

Fig. 14. Fireplace rough opening completed.

base was constructed. The front of the hearth extends out beyond the front wall of the chimney base but, due to the method of construction, it will not require any support other than the fireplace base. Forms for making this type of hearth are available from dealers in fireplace equipment. The form consists of sheets of steel that are overlapped to form a base on which the concrete can be poured. The front edge of these sheets can be temporarily supported by nailing a strip of wood along one of the floor joists. Reinforcing rods are set over these sheets of steel and the end of each rod is bent so that it fits down into the notch at the back of the fireplace base. The rods are wired together with lighter-weight cross-rods. The opening for the ash-pit dump in the hearth can be made by installing a wood form of the same size as the outside dimensions of the dump. The distance left be-

tween the top of the fireplace base and the finished floor was 5½″. The concrete hearth is going to be 3½″ deep. This will leave about 2″ between the top of the hearth slab and the finished-floor level, which can be covered later with brick or tile.

The Combustion Chamber; Finishing

After the concrete for the hearth has been poured and has hardened, the form for the ash-pit dump is removed and you can install the finishing brick around the outside of the fireplace and the firebrick around the inside.

But before you get started, purchase the damper and the ash dump. The damper should be for a fireplace with a width of 30″. Read the manufacturer's instructions for installation carefully, because they may require slight modifications to the directions given here.

The combustion chamber of the fireplace is lined with firebrick rather than common or face-brick. See Fig. 14. It is the only material except metal that can withstand the high temperatures in this portion of the fireplace. Sometimes the firebricks are placed on edge to form a veneer 2″ thick. This is not the best type of construction to use because, unless special care is taken to install metal ties, the firebricks will eventually fall out of place. It is much better to set the bricks flat with the long side exposed. This produces a good, thick, solid wall of firebrick that should last the lifetime of the fireplace. The firebricks should not be set up with ordinary cement mortar; they must be set in fire clay. See Figs. 3 and 15.

The firebrick and the face-brick can be installed at the same time. To be sure that you get the dimensions of the fireplace correct, draw a line across the hearth to show the proper angle that the side walls must follow.

Now just to be on the safe side, let's run over the rough and finished dimensions of the fireplace opening. The present rough width at the opening is 42″. This is to be decreased evenly on each side until it is 30″. The rough depth is 22″ and this must be reduced to 18″.

Study Figs. 3 and 15, which show the plan, elevation and section of the fireplace and which also give the necessary rough and finished dimensions. You will see from these pictures exactly how the back wall of the fireplace is brought forward to form the throat and the smoke shelf. Note that the fireplace damper is located 6″ or so above the top of the fireplace opening rather than at the same height as the top.

Do not go ahead with the finishing off of the fireplace until you thoroughly understand these illustrations because while a slight error or so will not make too much difference, a serious one will spoil the chances of the fireplace's ever operating properly.

Draw a rough, large-scale plan and have it handy while you work.

Start out and lay the firebrick over the hearth, leaving the necessary size of opening for the ash dump. Now build up the side walls and the back walls. You will see that, as the side walls come towards each other, there is going to be an empty space between the firebrick and the rough opening. This space should be filled with mortar. When the back wall of firebrick is 14″ above the finished hearth, it should come forward. The inclined portion of the brick wall is going to extend upward for 20 vertical inches and thus it will form a throat opening of the correct size as well as forming the smoke shelf. Since the throat must be 8¾″ wide and the finished depth of the fireplace is 18″, the width of the smoke shelf will be 9¼″. It will save you a lot of time and work at this point if you build a rough wooden form or guide to use in laying up the back-wall firebricks. See Fig. 16. Mortar and rubble can be used in back of the firebricks to form the smoke shelf, which must be leveled off smoothly.

When the finished side walls are 28″ high, a steel angle-iron 42″ long is set across to support the top opening of the fireplace. The ends of this angle-iron also are embedded in mortar.

The top of the fireplace opening is 6″ below the top of the smoke shelf. The damper can now be installed and this is fastened into the mortar joints of the breast wall of the fireplace. If the damper has a rotary control— that is, of the type that can be operated from the front of the fireplace— it must be installed at this time so that

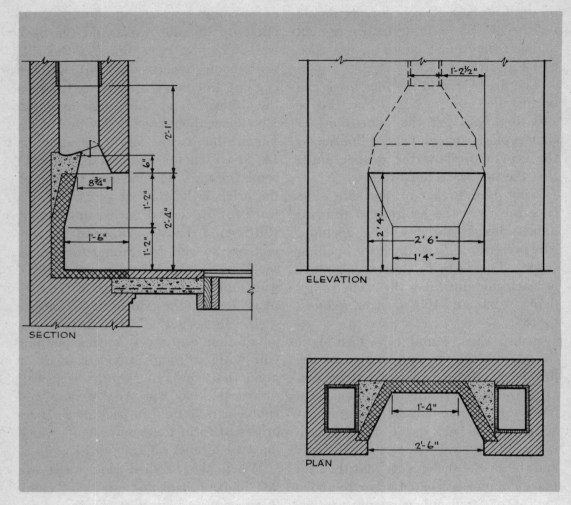

Fig. 15. Plan, section and elevation of fireplace.

the finishing bricks on the front of the fireplace can be put in around it. Now finish the front of the smoke chamber (this should be 14½″ high); then install the finishing brick or tile for the hearth.

CHIMNEY AND FIREPLACE CONSTRUCTION FOR OTHER TYPES OF HOMES

Second Fireplace in Basement

If you wish to have a fireplace in the basement as well as one in the living room, you can build it in with- out much added expense for materials. The basement fireplace will serve as a base for the fireplace in the living room. The dimensions for the basement fireplace and construction of the rough opening are the same as for the living room fireplace except that the height of the finished opening is 24″ instead of 28″ and that the outside walls of the basement fireplace are made square, so that when the construction reaches the first floor, there will be a base of sufficient size on which to build the upper fireplace. The flue of the basement fireplace must be off-set so that it can run up through one side of the living-room fireplace and will clear the hearth. This off-set will have to start with the *first* piece of flue-tile, because no section of tile should be off-set more than 30 degrees.

If the furnace is to be located in the basement, a flue for it will have to be installed in one side of the basement-fireplace rough opening. It should be installed in the side opposite to the side that contains the off-set fireplace flue.

When the work has arrived at a point just under the level of the first floor, you should have a rectangular base measuring 2′ 1″ x 5′ 2″, with the flue from the lower fireplace running up through one side, and the flue for the furnace running up through the other. The living-room fireplace is now built up on this base, and the basement-fireplace flue and furnace flue continue up straight until the work has reached the point above the hearth of the living-room fireplace where the furnace and first-floor fireplace flues are off-set to bring them together with the basement fireplace flue. The three flues then continue straight up in a common chimney.

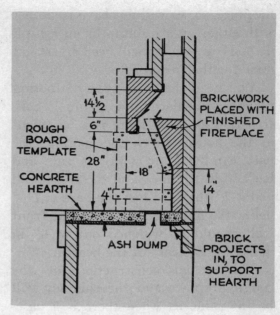

Fig. 16. Form for fireplace back wall.

You do not, by any means, have to complete the basement fireplace before the one in the living room. In fact, the best policy in most cases would be to leave the basement fireplace in the rough-opening stage until the living-room fireplace and chimney have been completed and construction work around the house has been finished.

If a house has no basement, but is set off the ground on concrete foundations, the method of building both the fireplace and the chimney is going to be slightly different. In the first place, the furnace is going to have to be located in the utility room, and this will mean that instead of starting the furnace flue in the fireplace base, you will not start it until the fireplace is well underway. Second, there will be no place to install an ash pit for the fireplace, so we will not have to bother with either an ash dump or an ash-pit door. However, we will need an ash-pit door for the furnace flue.

You need the same type of footing for this fireplace and chimney construction as when there is a basement in the house. From the footing, the base can be built with the side and back walls 8″ thick and the front wall about 4″ thick. When the base is 7½″ below the finished-floor level, the front wall should be widened out to 6″ in depth to take care of the hearth.

The actual construction of the rough fireplace and the chimney will be the same as when there is a basement except at the point where the furnace flue is brought in. The opening in the fire-clay flue must, of course, face into the utility room. The height at which the flue should start will depend on the type of heating equipment used. The main consideration is to allow enough width in the side wall so that you will be able to have 4″ of masonry around this flue on all sides. There should be a soot pocket of flue-tile 8″ below the opening in the tile, and you will want to have a furnace-flue clean-out door installed right under the pocket.

After the furnace flue-tile has been installed, the rest of the job can be done in exactly the same manner as previously described.

FIREPLACES ON CONCRETE-SLAB FLOORS

Fireplace and chimney construction in a concrete-slab-floor home is relatively simple compared to doing the same work when there is a basement to contend with.

First, a special footing is poured for the chimney and fireplace that is completely independent of the concrete floor of the house. Sufficient room is also left for the hearth, which does not require the same heavy construction as the footings for the fireplace but should also *not* be a portion of the concrete floor.

The construction of the rough fireplace can begin right on the footing after you have leveled it off sufficiently so that the fireplace hearth will be about the same level as the finished floor of the house. From here on, the work goes in the same manner as when there is no basement, but a base is required. The heating equipment must be located in the utility room, so you do not have to worry about the furnace flue until you have most of the rough fireplace put in. When the rough fireplace opening and the chimney have been completed, you can go back and pour the hearth right over a gravel or cinder bed.

The work of laying up the fire-clay around the combustion chamber and applying the finished brickwork is the same for this type of house as for the others.

A FURNACE CHIMNEY

If you do not wish to build a fireplace, the only requirement will be a chimney from the basement or slab for the furnace.

The minimum wall thickness of a chimney is 4″, but the over-all dimension of the chimney will depend on the size of flue-tile used. An 8½″ x 13″ flue should be sufficient for most systems.

The footing for the chimney should be at least 12″ deep and should extend 6″ beyond the chimney on all sides. If you are building without a basement and the house is on masonry piers, it is important to have the footing extend well below the frost line.

The same care with regards to keeping the masonry away from the house woodwork applies to a chimney as to a fireplace and chimney. Keep the masonry at least 2″ away from all the house framework.

The chimney should have a clean-out door located below the entrance of the thimble. Flue-tile should extend at least 8″ below the thimble, and the door should be located directly under the last section of flue tile.

TESTING THE WORK

Before the chimney is put into operation, it should be tested to be sure that it does not leak at any point. This test should be made for each flue. Build a small fire of wood and tar paper at the base of the flue or in the fireplace. When the smoke begins to pour heavily from the top of the chimney, cover the top with a heavy wet blanket. Now inspect the entire chimney carefully to see if you can find any smoke escaping through the masonry. If you do find any leaks, the cause must be corrected before the chimney is safe.

MATERIALS LIST FOR FURNACE CHIMNEY FOR THE BASIC HOUSE

Material	Quantity	Dimensions
Chimney blocks	64	7¾″ x 3¾″ x 12¾″
	64	7¾″ x 3¾″ x 14¾″
Clay flue-tile sections	9	2′ x 8½″ x 13″
Concrete chimney thimble	1	
Clean-out door	1	
Cement mortar	1.5 cu. ft.	
Copper flashing	1	10′ x 12″
	1	6′ x 8″
	1	4′ x 4′

Chapter 10

INSTALLING WINDOW AND DOOR FRAMES; INSIDE PARTITIONS; FLASHING

Types of Window Frame

There are three types of window frame that you can use. One is the knocked-down type, which you can get at any lumber yard. All the pieces are cut and fitted, you have only to assemble them. You can get a sheet of directions on just how this is done from your lumber yard, and you should have no trouble. In fact, even without directions the job is simple enough. If you want to pay just a little more, you can get frames that are already assembled from a local lumber concern. You can also make the frames yourself, but this is not recommended because of the time and skill required to make a really good frame by hand. Knocked-down frames and those that are already assembled are made by machine and are more precise than those that are made by hand.

Setting in Window Frames

The first part of the job in setting in window frames is to assemble the vari-

ous parts of the sash. In good construction, all joints between the members of the frame are set in white lead. This seals the joint against moisture and insures that the frame will have a good long life. You will have to tack a few temporary braces across the frame to hold it plumb until it is installed in the opening that was cut in the wall for it. Before the frame is installed, give it a good priming coat of white-lead paint. This is very important, for unless all the wood on the frame is covered with paint, it will absorb moisture and you will be troubled with sticking sashes and even rotting frames.

The two important points in setting the frames in the openings are to be sure that the frames are plumb and to be sure that there is no air space between the frame and the studding around the opening, which would allow air or moisture to get into the rooms. If the openings in the frame were cut accurately according to the dimensions given in the framing plans, tack a strip of waterproof building paper 8″ or 10″ wide all around the opening to the sheathing. If the opening is too large, install a false casing around it before putting the building paper on. This casing should come out flush with the sheathing.

If you used sheathing that is ¾″ thick, the frame can go into place without any additional work, but if you used a thinner sheathing, you will have to build onto the frame to make it fit properly. This can be done by tacking wood strips to the rear of the frame casing. The strips should be wide enough to make up the difference between the actual thickness of the sheathing used and three-quarters of an inch, which is the thickness of the sheathing that the frame was intended for.

Take plenty of time when placing the frame in the opening to see that it is properly centered and is plumb. Small wedges around the sides will help you get it just right. After this, nail it in place with 8d common nails. Sink the heads below the wood surface and fill the resulting hole with putty.

To make sure that you have a good, airtight joint between frame and rough opening, it is well worth taking the time to pack insulation between them. This takes only a minute.

The sashes can be installed now or later on. If you are going to use plaster on the walls, it is best to hold off installing the sashes, because you will need plenty of air circulating through the house to dry out the plaster. Also,

because of the large amount of moisture present in the plaster, the sashes are almost sure to absorb some of it and expand, which will cause them to stick.

Glazing

You can purchase sashes with the glass already in place, but there is a considerable saving in doing this work yourself. It is one of those jobs that you can do at odd moments—at the end of a working day perhaps, when you do not have time or energy enough to undertake anything big.

There are several grades of glass, but "A" and "B" are adequate for our purposes. The glass should be cut ⅛″ or 1⁄16″ smaller than the opening in the sash to allow for any irregularities.

Before the glass is put in, the entire sash should be given a priming coat of white-lead paint, just as was done with the frame. Be sure that the little recess that the glass fits against is well painted; unless it is, the wood will absorb the oil out of the putty and cause it to dry out and crack. Now apply a thin bed of putty along the shoulder of the recess and force the pane gently into place until the putty makes contact all along the edges of the glass. Now install the glazier points. You will need between 4 and 6 of these along each edge. They can be driven into place with a screwdriver, but be careful not to crack the glass. After they are in place, apply the triangular strip of putty that makes a tight joint between the glass and the sash. You can use an ordinary putty knife and, after you have done a few sashes, you will probably acquire considerable skill. If you wish, you can use a special little tool for this purpose that is a lot easier to handle than an ordinary putty knife. Give the putty a couple of days to dry and then give it a coat of paint.

Installing Exterior Door Frames

Just like window frames, door frames can be had all pre-cut and ready to be fitted together. The same care in regard to coating joints with white lead and giving the frame a priming coat of paint, should apply to these frames as to window frames.

The first step is to install a door sill, and this should be just thick enough so that it comes up flush with the finished floor. If you are going to lay a finished floor of hardwood, the sill should extend above the sub-floor for the thickness of the finish flooring. If you are going to use some other type of flooring, such as linoleum, figure out the thickness of this material, which will probably be $\frac{3}{32}''$ or $\frac{1}{8}''$, and add the thickness of the plywood or composition board that is going on over the sub-flooring. Once you have this figure, cut into the house sill to the necessary depth to allow the door sill to come even with the finished floor. Door sills, or thresholds, are usually made of hardwood. You can also get metal ones with a spring-loaded lip which engages into a recess cut along the bottom edge of the door, thus making a tight joint.

Take the same precautions to get the door frame on plumb that you did with the windows. Use tar paper or building paper around the edges to make a tight joint, and also pack in insulation.

There is no point at this time in hanging the outside doors; if you do, they are certain to be damaged as materials are brought into the house.

INSIDE PARTITIONS

The next job at hand is to put up the framework for the inside partitions. This is built in just the same way as that for the outside walls. A 2" x 4" sole plate is nailed to the floor and the studding spaced along this every 16". Be sure to get each piece of studding plumb. Along the top of the studding is a double 2" x 4" that serves as a top plate. Interior partitions can be made up in sections on the floor and then set up into position. Be sure that your measurements and cutting are accurate, so that the partitions come snug against the ceiling joists. The floor plans show interior partition framing along with the measurements for the door and closet openings. Fig. 15 in Chapter 8 shows a detail of how the interior partitions are joined to the outside wall.

You will note from the floor plans that one wall in the bath is framed with 2" x 6"s rather than 2" x 4"s. This is done to provide enough room inside the wall for the vent stack of the plumbing system. If ordinary 2″ x 4″'s were used, the wall would not be wide enough for the vent stack to pass through and you would have to build some sort of box around it. The extra thickness also allows recessed medicine cabinets and shelves to be built into the wall.

If you are going to use a warm-air system with wall registers for heating, openings for these must be left in the partition walls. The same holds true if recessed convectors are to be used.

Framing around the chimney and fireplace should be kept 2″ away from the masonry, and the space between the wood and masonry should be filled with a fire-resistant insulation.

Framing around door openings is double, and you can save yourself a lot of work right here by making these openings as accurate and plumb as possible.

Fig. 1 (right), illustrates how to frame the opening above the bathroom wash basin for the recessed medicine cabinet. This cabinet will be installed after the bathroom wall has been covered. You will find that when special horizontal studs have been installed between several of the vertical studs in the bath, these serve as bases to which you can attach the various bathroom wall fixtures, such as towel racks, soap dishes, etc. If plaster is used for the bathroom interior wall, these additional

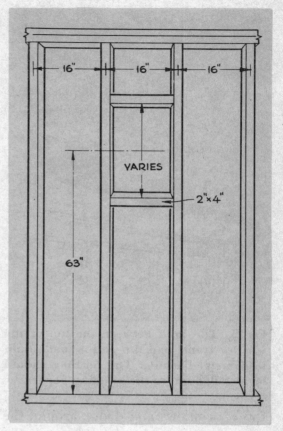

Fig. 1. Framing and opening in the bathroom wall for the medicine cabinet.

header-studs are not vital, because fixtures can be attached to the plaster with various types of anchor bolts. The studs are necessary, however, if wallboard is used, because wallboard alone is not strong enough to support these fixtures and it is not always practical to place the fixtures where they can be attached to the wall studding.

FLASHING

Metal flashing to make a watertight joint is required in a number of places about the house. For example, it is required around the chimney, at the

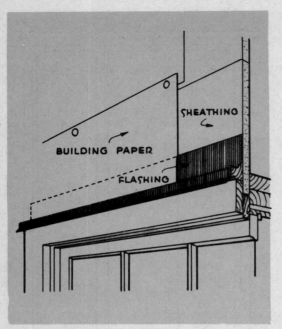

Fig. 2. The joint between the top of the window frame and the wall is made tight with metal flashing. The flashing should be installed under the building paper.

top of windows and doors, around the vent pipe where it comes through the roof, around dormer windows and at similar points. Either copper, aluminum or stainless steel can be used for flashing. Sometimes galvanized iron is used, but this is not too effective because, in time, the metal will rust, and replacing worn or rusty flashing can

be a difficult business. The same holds for tar paper, which is often used for flashing on cheap jobs. The best rule to follow when selecting flashing is to use a material that will last at least as long as the roofing or siding.

Copper makes excellent flashing, not only because it is long wearing, but also because it is soft and is easy to work with. Aluminum and stainless steel are just as good as but somewhat more difficult to work with than copper. Be sure that the nails you use with flashing are rust-proof and that they are made of the same material as the flashing. For example, don't use aluminum nails on copper flashing.

Flashing is applied to the top of window and door frames before the siding goes on. The flashing is nailed to the sheathing, is brought over the top of the window or door frame, and then bent under and nailed. In this way, after the siding is in place, the joint between siding and frame is quite watertight and all the nails used to hold the flashing in place are concealed and not exposed to the weather. See Fig. 2.

More details on flashing are covered as we arrive at various points where it is required.

Chapter 11

EXTERIOR SIDING

WHEN it comes to the siding for the outside walls of your house, you have a wide choice of materials to choose from. You can use some sort of wood siding, such as shingles, bevel or drop siding, or plywood. Then there are asbestos or asphalt shingles, or stucco, brick veneer or even aluminum siding.

Selecting the Type of Siding

The type of siding used on the walls is going to have a great deal to do with the over-all outside appearance of your home, so make your selection with care. For the man building a house by himself, it is best to stick to materials that he is more or less used to working with —wood or asbestos or asphalt. Stucco can be applied by the amateur but it calls for different skills than carpentry.

Brick veneer is something that calls for a really skilled brick-layer, because the veneer must be tied to the sheathing and, unless this is done correctly, the veneer may buckle or crack.

Every type of siding can be applied over diagonal or horizontal wood sheathing. If plywood was used for sheathing, special barbed nails must be used to install the siding since ordinary nails will not hold properly in the plywood. If composition sheathing was used, you can apply only bevel or drop siding because shingles cannot be nailed to it. Of course, if you wish to take the time, you can install furring or nailing strips along the sheathing, or recess them into the sheathing, and these strips will serve as a nailing base for shingles or other types of siding.

BUILDING PAPER

Before any sort of siding is applied over wood sheathing, it must be covered with building paper. The purpose of this paper is to keep air and moisture out of the house. Homes built without paper will be drafty on windy days. Also, rain or moisture is likely to penetrate through the siding and dampen the sheathing and interior wall. Building paper, on the other hand, should not be counted on to provide any great degree of insulation against heat flow.

There are a great many types of building paper on the market and some

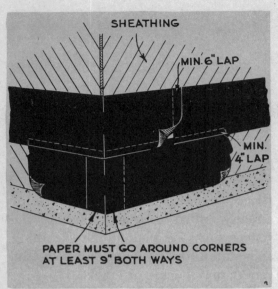

SHEATHING

MIN. 6" LAP

MIN. 4" LAP

PAPER MUST GO AROUND CORNERS
AT LEAST 9" BOTH WAYS

Fig. 1. Good quality of building paper and care in putting it over the wall will insure a tight exterior wall.

paper are no better than blotting paper—they are hard to put up because they are so soft that they tear, and rather than shedding water, they absorb it.

Use a good quality of paper and allow plenty for overlap at all seams. Do not have any joints come at the corners of the building because, as far as the siding goes, these are probably the first places that moisture will enter. The paper should be applied over the sheathing in horizontal strips, working from the bottom up. If you use a strong paper, it can be held in place with a few large-head rust-proof roofing nails or with a few wood cleats, which are to be removed as the siding is installed. See Fig. 1.

of them are worthless for our purpose. The best paper you can buy will be both moisture-resistant and airtight, and be strong enough so that you can put it up easily without its tearing. Some very inexpensive brands of building

Some types of composition sheathing come with a covering of waterproof paper; you do not need to put building paper over them. But be very sure that you have the proper sheathing before you decide not to use building paper.

WOOD SIDING

Fig. 2 shows several types of wood siding that are in common use today. Both bevel and drop siding can be had in various widths from 4" up to 12".

Corners

The first thing that must be done before the wood siding goes up is to decide how the corners are going to be treated. It is very important that you get a tight weatherproof joint between each piece of siding at the corners.

Figs. 3, 4 and 5 show three common methods of treating the corners. Fig. 3 shows the use of corner boards. This produces a very tight joint if the pieces of siding are all cut to the correct length. In Fig. 4 the pieces of siding have mitered joints. Such joints require a good deal of time to make up because each board must be cut and fitted with care or else you will have a seam that allows moisture to enter. Fig. 5 shows a corner made with metal corners, which can be purchased at lumber yards. They are very easy to install.

If you decide to use corner boards, they must be in place before the siding goes on. In some construction, the corner boards are put up after the siding is in place, but this is very bad practice. It leaves open seams between the edges of the boards and the siding that allow moisture to enter unless the time is taken to back each board with oakum and caulking compound.

One of the corners boards should be a little wider than the other so that, when they are overlapped to make a butt joint, they will be of equal width. If you have used composition sheathing-boards, you have another problem, namely, to avoid having the corner boards so wide that there is no place left on the corner posts to nail the siding to. You must remember that if siding is applied over composition sheathing, it cannot be nailed to the sheathing but only to the studs and corner posts.

The corner boards must be somewhat thicker than the siding.

Be sure these boards are on plumb. If they are not, aside from the fact that they will look poorly, you are going to have a hard time cutting the ends of siding at the right angle to get a tight fit.

The amount of lap given pieces of bevel siding will depend on the width of the siding. A 4″ siding is lapped ¾″; 5″ siding, 1″; 6″ to 12″ siding, 1½″. Of course, you can vary this

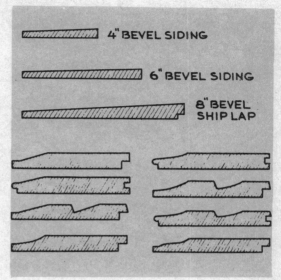

Fig. 2. Above: bevel siding; below: drop siding.

somewhat, especially to give a greater amount of lap, so that the top and bottom of the siding will come flush with the top and bottom of window and door openings. This will eliminate the job of having to notch out the siding

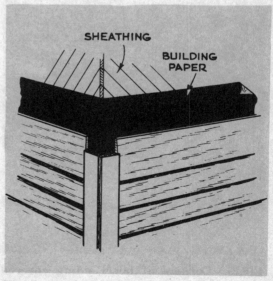

Fig. 3. Bevel siding with corner boards.

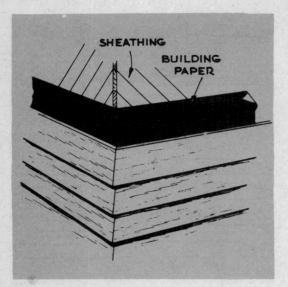

Fig. 4. **Bevel siding joined at the corners with a mitered joint.**

so that it can be fitted around these openings. See Figs. 6 and 7. In view of this, it would be wise to figure out the spacing of the siding before it goes

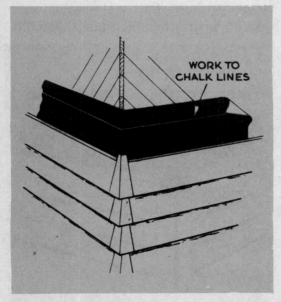

Fig. 5. **Corners of bevel siding covered with metal corner-plates.**

on, so that if a slight variation in the lapping is necessary, it can be distributed among several pieces rather than taken up by just one or two. It is also a good idea to mark the location of each piece of siding on the corner boards and at some other interval along the wall, so that you will know exactly where each piece is to go; in addition, you can string a line between these points to make sure that each piece is horizontal.

For best results, siding should be fairly well seasoned. The siding should be applied during dry weather and should never go on when wet or over wet sheathing.

Bevel Siding

The first step in applying bevel siding after the corner boards are up is to tack a strip of wood lath along the bottom of the sill, so that the first piece of siding will have the same slant to it as those that follow.

Some authorities claim it is wise to paint the back of each piece of siding before it is nailed in place. The purpose of this is to prevent moisture inside the house from penetrating the siding and causing the paint on the outside surface to peel. If the siding is dry and you are willing to take the time required, it is probably worthwhile doing this. On the other hand, if the siding is green or damp, it is best not to seal it up with paint; allow it to go unfinished so that it can dry out. The *ends* of the siding, however, should be given a coat of white-lead paint. It is at the edges mostly, that siding absorbs moisture.

The siding should be cut with a nice even joint and you want to have each piece fitting rather snugly against the adjoining piece and the corner boards. In very high class work, a diagonal cut is used where one piece of siding joins the next.

Siding nailed over wood sheathing can be nailed with 8d nails. These must be rust-resisting casing nails and should be spaced about every 16". The nails are driven through the overlap of each piece so that every piece is held with two nails at each point. See Fig. 8. If the siding is applied over composition sheathing, the nails should be driven in only where there is studding in back.

Fig. 7. Correct method of applying siding.

Fig. 6. Incorrect method of applying siding. Note that the shadow line of the siding does not come flush with the top and bottom of the window opening.

Ten-penny or even longer nails may be required to pass through the composition sheathing and penetrate the studding. If the nails tend to split the siding, drill holes for them a little smaller than the diameter of the nail.

The nails should be set into the wood and then puttied. This will prevent them from staining the siding.

Drop Siding

This type of wood siding is usually either tongue-and-groove or shiplap. This means that you will have more difficulty laying out the siding so that the tops and bottoms come flush with wall openings than is the case with bevel siding, where the amount of overlap can be varied. You can get some

Fig. 8. Correct method of nailing bevel exterior siding.

will have to be heated during the winter months.

Wood Shingles

Wood shingles are applied over building paper in the same way as wood siding. As mentioned before, they can be applied only over wood sheathing unless wood strips are first installed over or into composition sheathing to provide a nailing base. When applied over plywood, barbed nails must be used.

While it is best to use edge-grain shingles for walls, flat-grain shingles can be used with less chance of damage than when used on the roof—moisture runs off a wall faster than off a roof and there is less chance of the shingles absorbing it. Also, wall shingles are not exposed to direct sunlight for as long periods as roof shingles.

It is usually desirable to give wall shingles some sort of a finish. This can be either a stain or a paint. You can buy shingles that are already stained or you can stain them before or after application. As far as preserving the shingles goes, the stain should be applied by the dipping process before they go up, or if they are to be painted, this can be done after they are in place. If shingles are stained, however, they cannot be painted for a period of many years because most of the stains used contain creosote, which bleeds through oil paints.

Shingles for the wall come in the same sizes as those for the roof, namely, 16", 18" and 24" long. Because of their

leeway by not having the tongue fit all the way into the groove, but this may give a joint that will leak as the wood shrinks. See Fig. 9.

Drop siding is face-nailed with casing nails.

Drop siding is thicker than bevel siding and is often applied directly over the studs without any sheathing at all. In this case, the building paper is hung in vertical sheets between the wall studs. If the building frame has been properly braced with let-in braces and is not to be used for year-round living in cold climates, there is nothing very wrong with this practice. However, it should be used only on summer cottages, garages and other buildings of this type. Do not use it on a home that

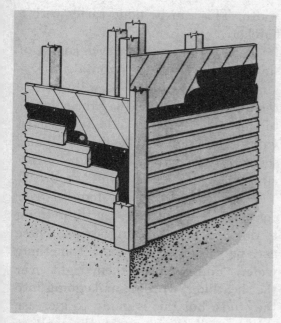

Fig. 9. Drop siding must always be applied with corner boards. The corner boards must be installed before the siding goes on.

location, wall shingles can be given a longer weather-exposure than those used for roofing. Use the following table for weather-exposure for wall shingles.

16″ long .... 7½″ to the weather
18″ ″ .... 8½″ ″ ″ ″
24″ ″ .... 11″ ″ ″ ″

At corners, you can either use corner boards, as for wood siding, or make the corners with shingles. Fig 10 shows how the lap in each course is broken to get a weathertight job.

Start the laying of the shingles at a corner at the base of the wall. As a rule, the first course is double and the butt of this course should be about 1″ below the house sill. Be sure that the vertical

joints do not fall right over one another. There should be a space of about ¼″ between each shingle. Before you lay up the rest of the shingles, figure out the spacing so that the shadow line of a course will fall flush with the top and bottom of window openings. This will save you time and a lot of cutting and fitting. You can usually get this shadow line to come out right by increasing or decreasing the weather-exposure of each course just a little. Vertical joints between courses

Fig. 10. One way to treat shingles at the corners. Note that the joints are staggered at each course.

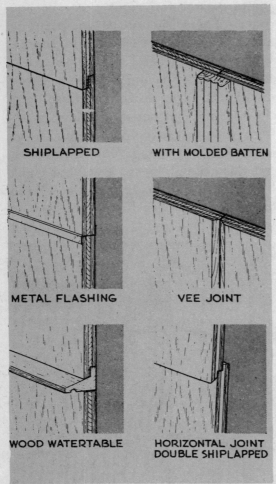

SHIPLAPPED   WITH MOLDED BATTEN

METAL FLASHING   VEE JOINT

WOOD WATERTABLE   HORIZONTAL JOINT DOUBLE SHIPLAPPED

Fig. 11. Left shows three methods of treating the horizontal joints between sections of exterior plywood. Right shows vertical joint treatment.

width. This can be done easily with a hatchet.

To be sure of getting each course of shingles absolutely horizontal, tack a strip of wood along the walls where the butts are to lie and lay the shingles to this. The board should be checked with a level. A chalk line will also serve, but it will not produce as accurate a job as the strip of wood.

If you want to lay shingles over composition sheathing, the first thing to do is to install nailing strips. These can be either 1″ x 3″s or something wider. You can nail them right over the sheathing, with the nails going into the studs, but this is going to increase the over-all thickness of the wall so that you will need special window and door frames. The other method of installing the nailing strips is to recess them into the sheathing. This takes a good deal of time, regardless of whether it is done before or after the sheathing is up, but in the long run it is probably better than having to use special frames for the openings. The nailing strips should be spaced at the same distance from one another as the length of shingle that is exposed to the weather.

Exterior Plywood

Plywood makes a very satisfactory type of siding, but you must be sure to get the exterior type that will not be damaged by moisture. If the plywood is applied over sheathing, you can use ¼″ stock. Plywood siding comes in widths running from 2½′ to 4′

should be broken so that there are 2″ or more of overlap on the side. Use 2 rust-resistant shingle nails on each shingle. The best position for the nails is an inch or two above the exposure line and about ¾″ from the edge. It is best not to use shingles that are too wide. Split any shingle over 8″ in and in lengths running from 5' to 12'. These sheets can be applied either vertically or horizontally to the house framework. They are nailed with 6d non-corrosive nails, which are spaced about every 6".

Fig. 11 shows several different ways in which the joints between sections of plywood can be treated. The edges of each sheet should be coated with a thick lead compound before the sheet is put in place. A compound made for this purpose can be obtained from your local dealer.

Figs. 12, 13, 14 and 15 show several ways to use plywood siding.

It is not necessary, of course, to use the same type of siding for the entire house. You may find it more interesting to use one type for the lower portion and another for the gable ends. This is a matter of choice.

① VERTICAL JOINT BUTTED, HORIZONTAL JOINT LAPPED. ② BATTEN JOINTS

Fig. 12. Exterior siding with different joint treatments can be used to very good effect.

ASBESTOS SHINGLES

Rather than use a wood siding, you may prefer one of the composition types, such as asbestos shingles. These shingles come in various sizes and colors and, if the plain shingle is used, can be painted. They are made out of asbestos fibers and Portland cement and are both fire- and decay-resistant.

Asbestos wall-shingles that are properly installed should last the life of the building.

These shingles are rather brittle, so care must be taken not to crack or break them. It will be necessary from time to time to cut a shingle; the best

tool to use is a shingle cutter, which you can probably rent from your local dealer. This machine also has an attachment for making nail holes. The shingles already have nail holes in them, but, of course, additional holes are necessary when a shingle is cut.

You run into the same conditions with asbestos shingles that you do with wood shingles—they can be put on directly over wood sheathing, but for composition sheathing, nailing strips have to be installed.

If you plan to use asbestos shingles for siding, be sure to get a full set of

① SHIPLAP - SHEETS ② METAL FLASHING
BETWEEN STRIPS

Fig. 13. Another method of using exterior plywood for exterior siding. The effect here is not quite as intricate as that shown in Fig. 12.

the installation directions put out by the manufacturer.

As with other types of siding, asbestos shingles are laid over waterproof paper. You can use the same sort of corner boards as for wood siding or the shingles can be joined at the corners with a butt joint. Alternate this joint for each course and use a rasp to smooth out the edges of the shingles so that you get a good tight fit. The corners should be flashed with a wide strip of asphalt paper or metal set vertically. See Fig. 16.

After you have decided how to handle the corners, tack a cant strip of 1″ x ¼″ stock along the base of the

wall. It must be perfectly level. The first course of shingles should overhang this strip of wood by ¼″. See Fig. 17. Tack a strip of wood or use a chalk line to indicate the position on the wall where the tops of the first course of shingles should be set. The exact location of this line will depend on what size of shingles is used. The corner shingle should be the first one installed. If you are using corner boards, place a joint strip (these should be purchased along with the shingles and are used under each vertical joint) vertically along side the edge of the corner board. If you are not using corner boards but are making the corners with shingles, bend this strip around the corner. The first shingle that is put on in the first course should be full length.

① SHIPLAP-SHEETS ② SCALLOPED EDGE
③ DOUBLE SHIPLAP-STRIPS

Fig. 14. Plywood siding wtih scalloped edges along the gables.

FULL SHEETS OF PLYWOOD HORIZONTALLY
SHIPLAPPED AND PAINTED

Fig. 15. A very plain but nevertheless attractive use of exterior plywood siding.

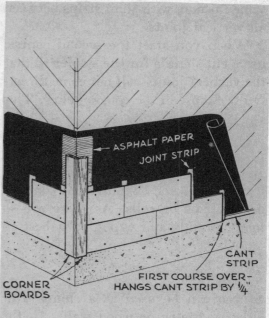

ASPHALT PAPER
JOINT STRIP

CANT
STRIP

FIRST COURSE OVER-
HANGS CANT STRIP BY ¼"

CORNER
BOARDS

Fig. 16. The use of corner boards with asbestos siding shingles.

It should be nailed with 1¼" rust-proof nails driven in through the holes provided in the shingles. Drive in the end and middle nails, leaving the far end of the shingle loose. Be careful when driving in the nails not to crack the shingles. Drive the nails in snugly but do not try to drive them tight against the shingle. Now slip a piece of joint strip under the free end of the shingle and nail the free end in place. The butts should be secured with special nails that are alloy-faced to prevent them from staining the shingles. The heads are small so that they will not show up. Be sure to use only this type of nail for the butt ends. The rest of the course can now be installed in the

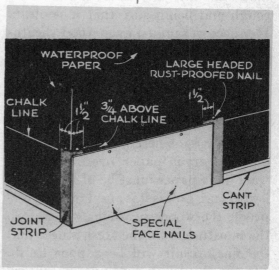

WATERPROOF
PAPER

LARGE HEADED
RUST-PROOFED NAIL

CHALK
LINE

1½"

3¾" ABOVE
CHALK LINE

1½"

JOINT
STRIP

SPECIAL
FACE NAILS

CANT
STRIP

Fig. 17. How the starter course of asbestos siding shingles should be installed. Note the felt joint strips at the vertical joints.

same fashion, with joint strips between all vertical joints.

When you start the second course, use a cut shingle for the starter so that the vertical joints will not come directly over those in the course below. This process of breaking the vertical joints in alternate courses should continue for the entire job. Be sure, however, that the cut shingles are secured with at least four nails, two at the top and two at the bottom.

ASPHALT SHINGLES

Asphalt shingles are also used for siding. These come as individual shingles or in strips or rolls. As there are so many brands and types, it is best to get a copy of the application instructions from your local dealer. Asphalt shingles are the least expensive type of siding that you can use.

STUCCO

Stucco can be used as a siding over either masonry or wood walls. In the case of masonry, the stucco can be applied directly over the masonry without the need of any preparation other than making the masonry surface rough and being sure that it is clean. If stucco is applied over wood sheathing, you will need a covering of waterproof paper and metal reinforcement lath.

Stucco Over Wood Sheathing

The first job here is to apply a layer of waterproof paper over the entire wall. This paper must be of high quality because unless it is absolutely waterproof, the wood sheathing will absorb the moisture from the fresh stucco and the final result will be a poor finish. (If the sheathing continues to absorb moisture from the stucco, there is a strong possibility of damage to the interior wall and to the sheathing.)

The paper is nailed securely with rust-resistant galvanized nails or some other type of rust-resistant nail. Lay the paper up from the base of the wall, overlapping the horizontal joints by 4″ or so and the vertical joints by 6″ or more. Double the paper around the corners. After the paper is in place, make sure that all seams around door and window frames are tight. Open seams should be packed with waterproof paper or caulking compound. This is important because the frames of windows and doors are also apt to absorb moisture from the fresh stucco and then they will expand.

If you want to have a good stucco job, be sure to use the right lath. There is only one type of lath to use for this job, and that is a non-rusting metal lath. Ordinary metal lath is not suitable—it will definitely rust in time. Wood lath is not suitable—if it should become damp it will expand and cause

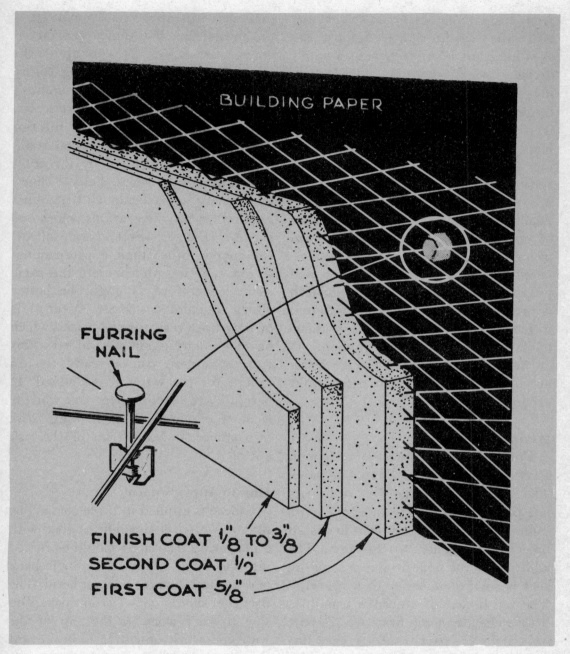

BUILDING PAPER

FURRING NAIL

FINISH COAT $\frac{1}{8}$" TO $\frac{3}{8}$"
SECOND COAT $\frac{1}{2}$"
FIRST COAT $\frac{5}{8}$"

Fig. 18. Detail of section of stucco wall showing furring nail, metal lath and three coats of stucco and their approximate thickness.

the stucco to crack. So be sure to get the rust-proof metal lath. You will

need special rust-proof nails for the lath, too. These nails, as you can see from Fig. 18, are designed so that the lath does not fit tightly against the sheathing but is, in fact, kept a slight distance away—about ¼″. This is done in order to allow the first coat of stucco to get in back of the lath, where, after it is hard, it will provide a strong bond between the whole stucco covering and the lath. The nails should be spaced about every 8″ along the lath in order to provide maximum support. Inadequate nailing can be the cause of much trouble later on in the form of bulges and so on. It must be remembered that three coats of stucco will weigh a great deal, and unless the lath is firmly attached, the stucco will pull it loose. Joints between the sections of lath should be lapped about 2″ or more and no joints should occur at corners. Let the lath come right around.

Mixing Stucco

Portland-cement stucco is made with Portland cement and clean fine sand. The usual mix for the first two coats is 1 part cement and from 3 to 5 parts sand. If you wish, 10 per cent hydrated lime can be added to this mix. The addition of the lime produces a plastic that is somewhat easier to work with. The finish coat of stucco is usually a little richer than the first two—1 part cement to 2½ parts sand. A very fine grade of sand should be used in this finish coat.

The stucco can be mixed either by hand or by machine. Remember that you do not want to mix more stucco than you can apply in 30 minutes— the normal time that cement mortar requires for setting. If you allow the fresh stucco to remain too long before it is applied or if you try to make it workable again by adding more water, you are going to produce an inferior stucco that may not be any good at all.

Stucco can be colored by the addition of certain powders. Table I shows the various ingredients and amounts required to produce various colors and shades. It is, however, very difficult for anyone other than a professional to get each mix of concrete the same shade. Therefore, it might be better either to paint the stucco after it is on or to use a ready mixed stucco, which has the coloring already added. This type of stucco comes ready to use except for the water to be added. It is sold by the 100-lb. bag, and while it is more expensive than making your own stucco, it takes a lot of the risk out of it.

How to Apply Stucco

Stucco is applied in three coats. The first or *scratch* coat can be applied with a plastering trowel. It should be forced into the metal lath until it gets in back of the lath to make a strong bond. The first coat should be ⅝″ or so thick. You should start work at the top of the wall and work down. It is important that once you begin to apply the stucco, the work go ahead until one complete coat has been applied to the entire surface. Before the scratch coat has time to set hard, score it so that you

TABLE I

TABLE FOR MIXING COLORED CONCRETE AND STUCCO

Color Desired	Commercial Names of Colors for Use with Cement or Stucco	Approximate Quantities Required in Pound Per Bag of Cement	
		Light Shade	Medium Shade
Greys, blue-black and black	Germantown lampblack	½	1
	or carbon black or	½	1
	black oxide of manganese	1	2
	or mineral black	1	2
Blue	Ultramarine blue	5	9
Brownish red to dull brick red	Red oxide of iron	5	9
Bright red to vermilion	Mineral turkey red	5	9
Red sandstone to purplish red	Indian red	5	9
Brown to reddish-brown	Metallic brown (oxide)	5	9
Buff, colonial tint and yellow	Yellow ochre or	5	9
	yellow oxide	2	4
Green	Chromium oxide or	5	9
	greenish blue ultra-marine	6	

Only first-quality lampblack should be used. Carbon black requires thorough mixing, being light in weight. Probably best for general use is either black oxide or mineral black. For black use 11 lb. of oxide for each bag of cement.

will have a rough surface for the next coat of stucco to bond to.

You should allow at least two days for the first coat to set before you apply the second. The exact time will depend, however, on weather conditions. If it is damp or wet, you might extend the time to three or four days. If the weather is dry and hot, dampen the stucco with water so that it will not dry out too quickly. Stucco exposed to direct sun should be kept covered while it is fresh.

The second or *brown* coat should be about ½″ thick. The main purpose of this coat is to even out any irregularities in the scratch coat so that when the finish coat is applied you will have a smooth even surface. For this reason, the thickness of the brown coat can be varied to suit the requirements. The brown coat should be worked over with a float so that you get it generally smooth and even but with a slightly rough surface. If you take plenty of time with the brown coat, you will not have too much difficulty with the finish coat.

The *finish* coat should not be applied for about a week after the brown coat. Keep the brown coat moist for two days or so. The finish coat can be colored and the surface can either be finished smoothly or be given one of many different textured effects. The simplest type of finish is the colonial. This is a finish coat applied over the rough brown coat and merely smoothed out.

The roughness of the brown coat is enough to give a slight textured effect. Other types of finish coat are obtained by using special tools and by using varying thicknesses of finish coating up to ⅜".

Stucco Over Masonry

To receive stucco, the masonry surface should be clean and free of oil or grease stains. Score the surface by brushing with a stiff wire brush. After this has been done the stucco is applied direct in three coats. No metal lath is necessary because the stucco makes a bond to the masonry.

MATERIALS LIST FOR SIDING FOR THE BASIC HOUSE

Material	Quantity	Dimensions
Corner boards	2	16'x1"x4"
Cant strips	2	16'x1"x6"
	10	16'x1"x2"
Beveled siding	1,200 feet	½"x6"
Exterior trim	220 feet	1"x3"
Building paper	5 rolls	500 sq. ft. each

Chapter 12

INSULATION

As soon as the shell of the house is complete and tight against the weather, the job of insulating the walls and roof can get underway.

The purpose of insulation is to reduce the passage of heat through the walls and roof. Heat always flows from hot to cold and, therefore, in winter the insulation tends to keep the heat in the house while in summer it protects the interior of the house by keeping out the heat of the sun. The value of insulation is so well established that it is taken for granted in all high-quality house construction. In the first place, a complete and properly applied insulation job will save as much as 35 per cent on heating costs per year. Considering the fact that the cost of the materials for insulating the basic house is only about $95, it is easy to see that the saving on fuel costs in just a few years will pay this entire sum. And after that, the yearly saving goes into the pocket of the home-owner.

But insulation does more than just cut down on fuel bills. It makes the walls proof against annoying and unhealthy drafts and it also helps to make the house more resistant against the sudden spread of fire. One of the basic flaws in our modern wall construction is the fact that there is an open space between the inner and outer wall surfaces. This space acts as a chimney for any fire originating in the basement or at the base of a wall. When this space between wall surfaces is filled with a fire-resistant insulation, the wall does not provide such a fire with a convenient chimney.

Another advantage of insulation is that it has certain soundproofing characteristics. While in most cases only the outside walls are insulated, as this is where a great deal of heat loss occurs, it is well worth the added time and cost to insulate some of the inner walls such as the bathroom or any other room where you wish to reduce the transmission of noise.

There are two types of thermal insulation. The first kind works on the principle that motionless air is a poor conductor of heat. This sort of insulation is made of vegetable or animal fibers or minerals. Between each particle of insulation is a minute air cell. The air in these pockets is held motionless by the matter that surrounds it. It is obvious that the greater the thickness of the insulation, the greater will be its insulating abilities. Once a certain point is reached, however, the fact that the thickness of the insulation is doubled does not mean that its insulating value is also doubled.

The other type of insulation is made out of thin sheets of shiny metal or metal foil attached to a paper backing. This insulation reflects the heat back toward its source. In winter, it reflects heat back into the house—in summer back toward the sun.

Many authorities feel that the most efficient insulation of all is a combination of the air-cell and the reflective types.

WHAT TO LOOK FOR IN INSULATION

The most important single item to look for in any type or brand of insulation is a low thermal conductivity. But this should not be the only consideration. A good insulation should also resist fire. Materials such as vegetable or wood fibers can be treated during the manufacturing process so that they will be fire-resistant. Mineral insulation does not require this treatment. Insulation should also be treated so that insects or rodents will not use it for a nesting place. A good insulation should not readily absorb and hold moisture because once insulation becomes damp, it loses its insulating qualities. Do not make the mistake of trying to save a few dollars by using such things as sawdust, hay or straw for insulation. While they will do the job to a certain extent, they are all highly inflammable and will attract all sorts of wild life.

VAPOR BARRIER

With the exception of reflective insulation, all types must be provided with some sort of vapor barrier. The reason for this is that the air inside a house during the winter months will contain a certain amount of moisture in the form of a gas or vapor. This moisture vapor passes through the interior wall, then through the insulation and finally strikes the cold, outside-wall sheathing, where it condenses into a liquid or, if the wall is cold enough, into frost, which in time will turn back into water. Moisture at this point may rot out the sheathing or be absorbed by the insulation, thus reducing its effectiveness. The solution to this problem is to apply a vapor barrier of treated paper over the inside or warm side of the insulation. This will prevent the water vapor from penetrating into the insulation. Many brands of insulation come with this paper barrier already in place. In other cases, after the insulation is in place, it is covered with a vapor barrier. Be certain that the paper used for this job is actually vapor proof; ordinary building paper is not satisfactory.

TYPES OF INSULATION

There are a great many types as well as brands of insulation on the market. One kind is flexible, and called roll or blanket insulation. It comes in rolls up to 100 feet in length. See Fig. 1. The width is made to fit between studding and varies from 16″ to 24″. The thickness of flexible insulation will run all the way from ½″ to a little over 3″. The insulating material may be either vegetable fibers or minerals. In either case they are encased in a heavy paper covering. On the edges of this covering is a small paper flange, which is used to attach the insulation to the studding or joists. Flexible insulation is very easy to apply, and the work goes very fast.

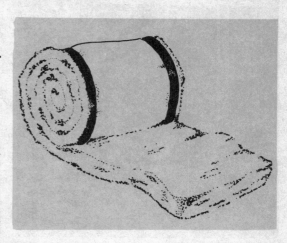

Fig. 1. Blanket or roll type of insulation without any vapor barrier of paper. Insulation of this type should be covered over with vapor-proof paper after it has been installed.

HOW TO INSTALL FLEXIBLE INSULATION

The most important point to keep in mind when insulating is that no sort of insulation will give satisfactory results unless it is installed according to exact specifications and the job is done in a workmanlike manner. When working with flexible insulation the first rule is to use as long runs of insulation as possible. Use the short lengths for patching and for small spaces, but avoid cutting and patching as much as you possibly can.

Flexible insulation is placed so that it fits snugly between the studding. It should not, however, be forced up against the outside wall sheathing. The reason for this is that a small dead air space between the sheathing and the insulation will act as additional insula-tion. Also, in the event that some water vapor does penetrate through the insulation and condenses on the sheathing, this air space tends to protect both insulation and sheathing from damage. If this air space is to be effective in aiding the insulation, the air in it must not move—it must be dead. That is why it is important that the insulation is tightly attached to the studding and that the joint between the studding and the flange on the insulation is covered over in some fashion. Flexible insulation comes with two types of flanges. In one case the flange is tacked to the side of the studding. If this type of insulation is used, it is wise to tack strips of lath over the flange so that you get a good tight joint. See Fig. 2.

Fig. 2. When insulation is nailed along the face of wall studding, the seam should be covered over with strips of wood lath to produce a tight joint.

Fig. 3. Blanket or roll type of insulation with an extra wide nailing flange that allows it to be nailed to the outside edge of the studding, thus eliminating the need for laths along the seams.

The other type of flange you may encounter is a little wider than the first one and has a right-angle bend. This bend allows the flange to be brought over to the face of the studding and nailed. See Fig. 3. No lath is required to seal over the joint between flange

Fig. 4. Applying insulation with a special stapling machine is a great time saver.

and studding. The interior wall material will do the job by itself. The insulation should not extend out so far that it will come into direct contact with the interior wall surface. A small air space here will help, just as the one between insulation and sheathing does.

Flexible insulation can be nailed to the studding with large-head roofing nails, but you will find that a stapling machine built especially for this sort of work will finish the job much quicker. See Fig. 4. It will also allow you to have one hand free and this is advantageous in centering the insulation and getting the flanges to line up along the studding. Stapling machines can be rented or borrowed from your local insulation dealer.

After all the long runs between studding have been filled, take the left-over pieces of insulation and fill in all small spaces. Do not leave any surfaces, no matter how small, uninsulated. You may find it necessary to cut up the material into very small pieces in order to fit it around the window and door framing.

BAT INSULATION

Fig. 5. Bat insulation with nailing flange of heavy paper.

This insulation is made from about the same materials as flexible insulation. It comes in short lengths measuring up to 48″ and the width varies so the bats will fit snugly between studding spaced on center from 16″ to 24″. The thickness of this type of insulation runs from 2″ to 3″. Bats are usually encased, or at least backed on one side, with paper. If bats without paper are used or if the paper is not vapor-proof, be sure to install a vapor barrier over the insulation after it is in place. See Fig. 5.

Installing Bat Insulation

There are several ways to install bats depending on the job and the kind

Fig. 6. Bat type of insulation.

Fig. 7. Insulating bats without a nailing flange can be held in place under the roof by means of wire.

of bat used. If there is no nailing surface provided on the bat, it can be wedged between the studding, joists or rafters. See Fig. 6. It is important to make sure that the bats are butted close together so there will be no air leaking through joints. When it comes to installing the bats on roof rafters, some device must be employed to hold them in place. A simple method of anchoring them in position is to drive some nails into the sides of the rafters on each side and then lace thin wire between these nails. See Fig. 7. Wood laths can also be used to hold the bats in place. When the bats are encased in paper and have a nailing flange, they are installed in the same manner as flexible insulation.

FILL INSULATION

This is also called granular insulation. It is loose, comes in bags and is poured into the area that is to be insulated. As it provides no vapor barrier, this must be installed before the insulation is poured in. In the case of a wall, the vapor-proof paper is tacked to the studding, or at least to a portion of it, and then some of the interior wall material is nailed up. The area between the vapor-proof paper and the wall material is then filled with the insulation, and the process is repeated until the entire wall area has been filled. In filling an attic floor, vapor-proof paper is placed between the floor joists over the ceiling of the room below. The insulation is poured in between the joists and leveled off. See Fig. 8. Fill insula-

Fig. 8. Loose fill insulation can be poured into the wall space after a section of vapor-proof paper has been installed.

tion is used most often on old work because it can be effectively blown into the wall spaces by means of a hose and air pressure.

RIGID INSULATION

This insulation is made out of wood or vegetable fibers that are compressed into sheets under heavy pressure. See Fig. 9. There are two basic types, one used on the outside of the wall and one used for interior work. The exterior type is called structural fiberboard insulating sheathing and is used in place of wood sheathing. The interior type is called insulating board and serves as an interior wall as well as providing insulation. Some of these insulating boards are extremely thin and do not offer the full amount of insulating value that may be required. For this reason, when you plan to use an insulating board for the interior wall material it is wise to use some additional type of insulation between the wall studding.

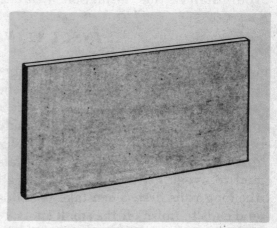

Fig. 9. Sheet of rigid insulating board.

The application of structural fiberboard insulating sheathing has been discussed in the section on sheathing. The application of the interior insulating board is covered in the chapter dealing with interior wall materials.

REFLECTIVE INSULATION

This insulation, as stated previously, differs from all others in that it prevents the transmission of heat through a surface by reflecting the heat back toward its source. It is made out of thin sheets of aluminum or heavy paper coated with aluminum. See Fig. 10. It is applied between the studding in about the same manner as flexible insulation. One of the most important things to remember when installing this type of insulation is that the sur-

face must be bright and shiny. If the surface becomes dirty or coated with dust, it will no longer reflect heat and the thin film of metal will be of little use as far as insulation goes. The second point that you must keep in mind is that there must be a space of at least 1 inch between the insulation and the inner and outer wall surfaces. If the insulation is placed tightly against the outside sheathing, it will have no insulation value at all. The best procedure when you install reflective insulation is to place it so that it comes right down the middle of the total space between inner and outer wall surfaces. If you install flexible insulation with one side coated with aluminum foil, put it up just as you would ordinary flexible insulation, keeping the side with the aluminum 1 inch away from the wall surface.

INSULATING THE HOUSE

Once the builder understands the purpose of insulation and how it works, the application is not difficult. It is just a matter of making sure that all outside walls and the roof surface are adequately covered. To conserve materials and to avoid joints and seams, do all the long runs first. Then take the odds and ends to finish off the small spots.

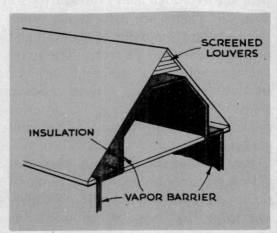

Fig. 11. When the attic of the house is to be used for living purposes, the side walls and the roof should be insulated as shown above.

Fig. 10. The reflective type of insulation should be installed as near to the center of the wall cavity as possible. It should never be placed up tight against the wall sheathing.

Insulating the walls should offer no great problems. But when it comes to the roof many persons run into difficulties. The first question is just where the insulation should go. Should it be placed under the roof between rafters or should it go under the attic floor between joists? The answer depends entirely upon what purpose the attic is to serve. If you plan to use the attic for living purposes—even as a den or study—then insulate along the roof rafters. See Fig. 11. If the attic is to serve only as a storage area, the insulation should go on the floor. When the attic is not to be heated during the winter, there is a definite advantage in insulating the floor rather than the roof. If the roof is insulated, the entire attic has to be considered as part of the total house area to be heated. But if the floor is insulated and the attic door kept closed, you have removed a good many cubic feet of space from the over-all amount that must be heated and this will help to further reduce your fuel bills. See Fig. 12.

Insulating the attic floor is not very difficult but the job must be done *before* the sub-floor goes on. If flexible or bat insulation is used, it can be tacked between the floor joists even if there is no ceiling on the room below. If the fill type of insulation is used, you will have to have a ceiling below to support it. Put down the vapor-proof paper first and then pour the insulation on over this.

After the insulation is down, a sub-floor is not necessary, but you should put down a few wide boards to serve as a surface on which to walk.

Insulating the roof is much the same as insulating the walls. The insulation is placed between the rafters and care should be taken not to let it come directly against the roof sheathing. The insulation should not be brought up along the rafters all the way to the roof-peak, however. There must be an air space between the insulation and the peak of the roof if the attic is going to be comfortable. The best procedure to follow is to bring the insulation up along the rafters until you come to the

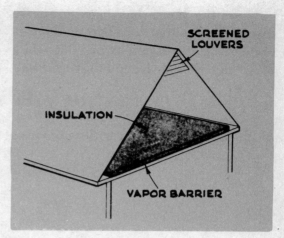

Fig. 12. If the attic is not to be used for living purposes, insulating the attic floor will eliminate heat loss and make the house more comfortable during the hot weather.

collar beams that tie the rafters together. Bring the insulation across between these collar beams and then down between the rafters on the opposite side. When you do this work with flexible insulation, you will be able to use long runs that will go from the base of the rafters on one side to the base of those on the other without a single seam or joint. With the insulation placed between the collar beams there will be an air space of several feet between the top of the insulation and the peak of the roof. This air space should be vented by means of louvres placed at each gable end of the house as near to the peak as possible. Because the collar beams are nailed to the side of the rafters it will be necessary to tack some 2″ wood strips to their sides so that the distance between these beams will be the same as that between the rafters.

Once the house has been properly insulated, see that as little damage is done to the insulation as possible while it is still exposed. Keep moisture away from it, and if holes must be cut into it for lighting or plumbing lines, make them as small as possible and do not disturb the insulation.

INSULATION FOR THE BASIC HOUSE

3″ thick roll insulation with vaporproof paper...................1600 sq. ft.

Chapter 13

THE HOUSE PLUMBING SYSTEM

ONCE you have the rough shell of the house completed, the job of roughing in the plumbing system should be done. This will consist of installing all the pipes through the walls and ceiling for the fresh-water supply and the drainage system as well as installing the various outlets for the plumbing fixtures. The fixtures themselves will be installed after the interior walls have been finished.

Considerations

As is the case with electrical wiring, plumbing for residential work is often regulated by local building codes, which vary greatly. In well settled localities, the plumbing codes may possibly insist that the entire plumbing system be installed by a master plumber. This is done to insure the health of the entire community. A faulty plumbing system in a built-up community can be a definite hazard to health. Other codes, not quite as strict, may demand only that the installation of the system be done in such a fashion that it will meet with the approval of local health and building inspectors. In rural areas there may not be any code

whatsoever and any sort of plumbing system can be installed by anyone who cares to do the job.

Because the comfort and, in most cases, the health of the various members of the household will depend on an adequate plumbing system, it is foolish to install any system that is not perfectly safe from the standpoint of health or will not insure the household an adequate supply of hot and cold water.

Not so very many years ago, installing a plumbing system was an almost hopeless undertaking for anyone except those who had had years of actual experience. Pipe joints had to be made by hand with hot lead, traps had to be made on the job by the plumber, and there were only a few basic fittings manufactured. Making up the various joints and fittings called for a type of skill that could only be acquired after long training. Today, thanks to the plumbing industry, there are fittings ready made to meet every requirement and the main trick involved in installing a system is to know which fitting to use and how to use it. But even so, many persons may not feel that they possess the necessary skill to do the entire job of installing a house plumbing system by themselves. To these we suggest calling in a plumber and working along with him on the job. There is a good deal of rough unskilled work to be done on a plumbing job and if you do this work while the plumber devotes his energies to the more involved problems, you will be pleasantly surprised to find how fast the work will go and how much can be saved. And helping to install the plumbing system is the best way to gain an understanding of how it works so that in the future, if something should go wrong, you will be in a good position to know where the trouble might lie and how it should be fixed.

But regardless of who does the work, be sure that a first-class system is installed. Do not take any short cuts or let anyone else take them on your house plumbing system.

THE WATER SUPPLY

There is no point in a plumbing system unless there is an adequate supply of fresh water. Hence, perhaps the best place to start when you think of plumbing is right at this factor. If you are building where there is a convenient city water main, your water supply is no problem. After the system is installed in the house, it is connected to the water main. The job of connecting the house line to the main is usually done by the city or the water company and there is a slight fee charged. If you do not live near city water, you have to think about some other source for the water supply—wells, rivers, lakes or springs.

Drilled Wells

By far the most efficient private water supply in most cases is that obtained from a drilled or artisian well. See Fig. 1. These wells are sunk deep into the ground to the point where they reach water-bearing stratum. This may lie many hundreds of feet under the surface. These wells are expensive and may possibly cost over $1000 before you have obtained a sufficient flow of water. They cannot be sunk by the home-owner, for the drilling requires special power equipment. But in spite of their high costs, drilled wells are usually the best, because they can be counted on to supply plenty of fresh water and they will not go dry during drought periods as will wells that are not very deep. Along with the well you will also need pumping equipment. This consists of a deep-well pump run by electricity and a storage tank.

Dug Wells

Dug or shallow wells can be dug by hand and cost far less than drilled wells. See Fig. 2. In soil where water is not far below the surface, this type of well may prove perfectly adequate for small homes and where the demand for water is not too great. The well need only be dug deep enough to insure an adequate flow of water. The inside of the well is lined with rocks or concrete tile, and it should be provided with a tight fitting lid to keep out insects and rodents. A shallow-well pump and a storage tank are required.

For years, dug wells provided an adequate water supply for most rural homes. The chief objection to them today is that, while they provided an adequate supply of water in the days when bathing was regulated to Saturday nights and the over-all water demand of a house was slight, they often are not able to keep up with the load imposed on them by regular daily bathing, automatic washing machines and garbage-disposal units.

If you plan to dig a well yourself, the help of another man is required. One does the digging while the other hauls up the dirt and rocks in a bucket. Great care should be taken in doing this work because in certain soil conditions there is the constant and very real danger of cave-ins.

Driven Wells

This type of well is common in sections of the country where it is possible to get down to the water-bearing stratum without running into hard rocks. The well consists of 2″ or 3″ extra-strength wrought-iron pipe. One end of the pipe is fitted with a drive-well point. The other end of the pipe is fitted with a drive head. The pipe is then sunk into the ground by striking the drive head with a maul. When one sec-

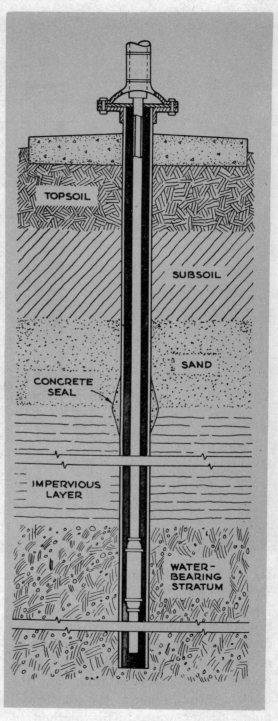

Fig. 1. A drilled well.

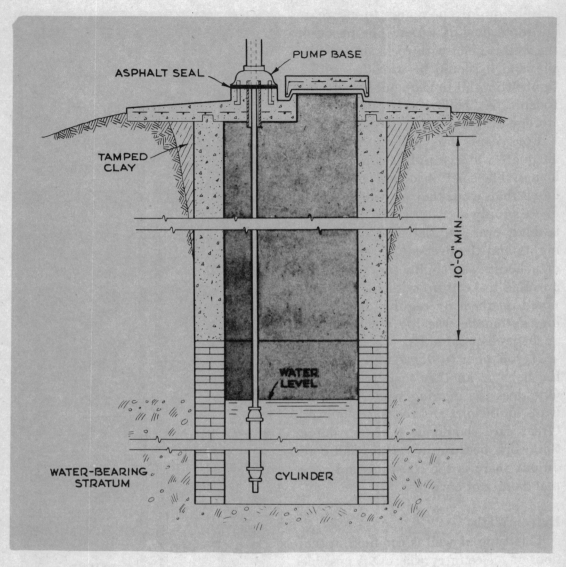

Fig. 2. A dug well. Unless conditions are very favorable, this type of water supply may have difficulties in meeting the water demands of modern housekeeping.

tion of pipe has been driven in, the drive head is removed, another section of pipe is attached, the drive head placed on the new section, and the work continues until the drive-well point strikes water. This method of making a well is impossible in soil where there is a lot of rocks because if the point strikes a rock, it must be pulled back out and started at some other point. The drive point cannot be driven through rock.

In spite of science, in spite of local characters with their divining rods, digging a well and finding an adequate supply of water at the bottom is still far from being a sure thing. It often happens that while your next door neighbor found an abundant supply of water with a 14-foot dug well, you may have to go 15, 20, 25 or even 30 feet and will end up with nothing more than a dry hole in the ground. The same holds true for drilled wells; where one will bring in an ample flow of water at 300 feet, another one in the next lot will have to go down 400 or 500 feet or even deeper.

Sometimes the various mineral conditions in the water will play a part in the decision of which type of well is best. There may be a vein of iron deep in the ground that affects the water coming from drilled wells and necessitates expensive filtering equipment before the water can be used for domestic purposes. On the other hand, a dug well in the same location might be free of iron but have the unfortunate habit of going dry at times. So before you select any particular type of well, get as much information regarding the local water conditions as you can. Check with neighbors, plumbers and local well-diggers, and find out which type of well seems to offer the best possibilities.

Lakes, Rivers and Springs

Many homes located near surface water draw their water supply for all purposes other than drinking and cooking from a lake, river or spring. Bottled water is used for drinking and cooking. Providing the supply is moderately pure, there is nothing wrong with this arrangement except that it is not always convenient.

Springs are often utilized for drinking as well as for the other purposes. Here again as in the case of dug wells, unless the spring has a very good flow it may not be able to keep up with the demands of the modern home.

Once you have a water supply, have the water tested before you do another thing. You not only want to have it tested so that you are sure it is pure for drinking, but you also want to know what minerals and chemicals it contains because this mineral and chemical content is an important factor in deciding which type of pipe to use for the house plumbing system.

TYPES OF WATER PIPE

In spite of what you may hear, be told or read, there is no one metal used for water pipes that is suitable for every water condition that you might run into. To be sure, certain types of pipe have definite advantages over others, but in so far as the pipe's ability to withstand the corrosive action of certain kinds of water goes, it is impossible to generalize.

Practically any water taken from the ground will have certain corrosive

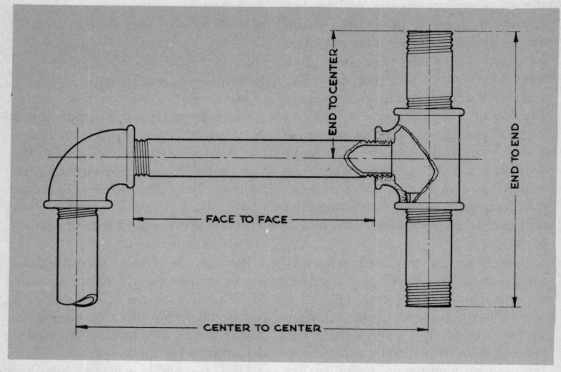

Fig. 3. When cutting and measuring iron pipe, be sure to take into account the fact that the pipe will extend some distance into the fitting.

characteristics. In the case of iron pipe, the corrosive quality of the water will cause rust. If the water is very corrosive, the rust inside the pipe will in time become so great as to completely clog up the lines and prevent water from flowing through. It will also cause the pipes to fail in time—usually at the joints, for here the metal is at its thinnest. In the case of yellow brass pipe, water containing certain specific corrosive elements will dissolve the zinc from the copper-and-zinc alloy and cause the pipe to fail. Red brass and copper are highly resistant to corrosion, but even they can be damaged by certain types of water.

Hard water, that is, water containing a high percentage of mineral salts, is usually less corrosive than soft water. On the other hand, these minerals in the water will attach themselves to the sides of the pipe, thus reducing the flow of water. This is more apt to happen in the hot-water system than in the cold supply because as the water is heated, it tends to release these minerals more readily than when cold.

Once you know what minerals and chemicals are contained in the water, select the pipe that will give the longest service. Even if this should be the most expensive type of pipe on the market, it will still be cheaper in the

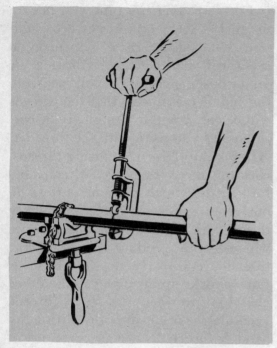

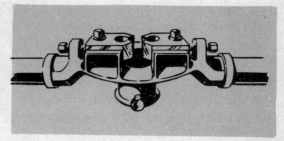

Fig. 5. Stock and die used for cutting threads on iron pipe.

Fig. 4. You will need a pipe vice and cutter if you use galvanized-iron pipe for the plumbing system.

long run than having to replace the plumbing system in a few years. On the other hand, when an inexpensive type

Fresh-Water Supply Pipes

The three most popular pipes used for the house fresh-water supply—and this includes the hot as well as the cold system—are galvanized steel, brass pipe and copper tubing. Of these three, galvanized steel is the least expensive and has been used for years in domestic plumbing systems. A somewhat similar type of pipe but one that is more expensive and more resistant to corrosion is genuine wrought-iron pipe.

will give as good service as the expensive, it is sensible to select the cheaper.

GALVANIZED STEEL PIPE

Making Joints

Galvanized steel pipe comes in lengths of 20 feet. Sections of pipe are joined together with threaded fittings. These threads will extend a certain distance into the fittings or couplings and this fact must be taken into consideration when measuring and cutting the pipe. To allow for the distance that the pipe extends into the fittings at each end, the pipe must be cut a little longer than the actual distance be-

tween the fittings. See Fig. 3. Allow about ½" for fittings such as valves, couplings and elbows at each end of ½-inch pipe. Allow ⁹⁄₁₆" for 1-inch pipe and ¹¹⁄₁₆" for the 2-inch pipe used in the drainage system.

To work with galvanized steel pipe you are going to need a pipe vice, a pipe cutter, (Fig. 4) a reamer, a die for cutting the pipe threads and two pipe wrenches for making up the pipe. See Fig. 5. If you do not have any of this equipment, don't buy it until you have at least tried to rent or borrow it from friends or hardware or plumbing stores. If you are an expert at measuring, you may be able to get by by having the plumbing-supply house cut and thread the pipe to your specifications, but this calls for very accurate measurement.

Much of the trouble found in plumbing systems with galvanized steel pipe is due to the fact that the pipes were not properly cut and threaded. Poor threads are almost sure to cause leaks at the joints. Unless the pipe is properly threaded, a good joint cannot be obtained, and unless the pipe is cut right, it is impossible to get it properly threaded. The tool used for cutting galvanized steel pipe must have a good sharp cutting wheel. Be sure that the cutter is properly centered and that the cut is made at the exact point marked on the pipe. The first cut must be square. If it is not, then make a fresh start. After the pipe has been cut, ream it out to remove the burr left by the cutting. This is an important step because if these little burrs are left inside the pipe, they will collect sediment and this may in time cause a serious stoppage.

For threading the pipe you need a die that is sharp and in perfect condition. Dull dies or those with nicks in them will not cut good threads. A guide bushing should be slipped into the end of the pipe so that the threads will be cut straight. Use plenty of cutting oil as you work with the threader. After each full turn of cutting threads, back off the die to clear it of chips before cutting further. Some cutters do not require this caution, but quality threads are the goal and this practice will help to produce them. If the threads are properly cut, when it comes time to make up the pipe you should be able to turn the pipe three threads (complete turns) into the fitting by hand before it is necessary to use a wrench. The explanation of this is that pipe threads are tapered so that the deeper the threads extend into the fitting the tighter the joint becomes. Actually, a well-cut threaded joint should be absolutely water tight by itself, but to take care of any small irregularities in the threads, it is wise to use pipe dope or pipe compound over the external pipe threads. Do *not* get any of this compound on the internal threads or it may cause an obstruction in the line.

BRASS PIPE

Brass pipe is somewhat more expensive than galvanized steel pipe. On the other hand, you can use brass pipe one size smaller and still get the same volume of water as with the larger galvanized steel pipe. This is because the inside of brass pipe is smooth while the interior of galvanized steel is rough. A rough interior causes a certain amount of friction as the water flows through and therefore produces a slow-down. Brass pipe is cut and threaded in the same manner as galvanized steel pipe. While it is possible to use the same cutter and dies for brass as for steel, special equipment is available that is intended only for work with brass and this should be used when possible. These cutters and dies, because they are made for work in brass which is a soft metal, should *not* be used on galvanized steel pipe. Ordinary pipe wrenches can be used to assemble brass pipe but they will leave burrs on the outer surface, which are a sign of less than perfect workmanship. For a first-class job, special friction vices and wrenches should be used with brass pipe so that the surface is not damaged.

In making up joints, use wicking as well as pipe compound. The wicking should be twisted around the external threads in the same direction that the threads are turned into the fitting.

COPPER TUBING

Copper tubing has one great advantage over either brass or galvanized iron and that is the ease with which it can be installed. See Fig. 6. Tubing comes in long rolls up to 100 feet in length. See Fig. 7. The tubing is strong enough to withstand handling but it is also soft enough so that it can be bent around obstructions, saving both time and the cost of various fittings. This is a great help for the amateur plumber because with rigid pipes it is necessary to have the exact measurements for a run of pipe between two fittings, but with copper the tube can be cut a little too long and then be bent slightly until it is just the right length. Copper tubing, like red brass, will withstand very well the corrosive elements found in most water.

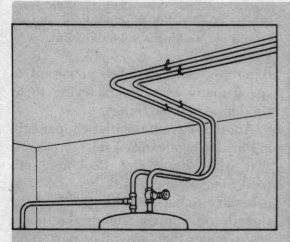
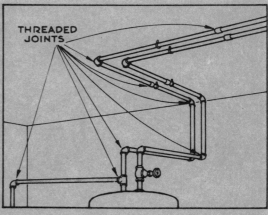

Fig. 6. Copper tubing (left) has a great advantage over rigid pipe (right) in that the copper tubing can be installed with a minimum of fittings.

Fig. 7. Copper tubing comes in rolls up to 100 feet in length.

One common mistake made about copper tubing, however, is the belief in its ability to withstand freezing. It is true that water inside soft-drawn copper tubing can be frozen several times before the tube itself is damaged, but repeated freezings will burst it eventually. Hard-drawn tubes will be damaged by freezing just like other types of rigid pipe.

Copper tubing is either hard drawn or soft drawn. There are also two wall thicknesses, type K for the heavy and type L for the light. Type L can be used in most instances, unless the water happens to be extremely corrosive, in which case the heavier type K should be used. Tubing comes in sizes from ⅛″ to 2″. Tubing can be used for the entire system, including the service entrance. In fact, if you had difficulty in digging a trench from the house to the source of water because of large rocks and it is impossible to get a straight trench, copper tubing is about the only

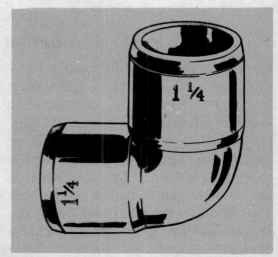

Fig. 9. Type of fitting used on copper tubing for making a soldered joint.

thing you can use unless you want to spend many extra hours trying to fit rigid pipe into the trench.

Another advantage that copper tubing has over galvanized steel or brass is that while brass and steel are both weakened at the joints because it is necessary to cut into the pipe to make threads, in copper tubing the joints are stronger than any other part. This is due to the type of fittings used with copper.

Fig. 8. Cutting copper tubing with a hacksaw and a simple wood jig.

There are two methods of making joints in copper tubing: one with a soldered type of fitting, and the other with a flanged compression type of fitting. Copper tubing can be cut with a hacksaw. Considering the fact that it is going to be necessary to do considerable cutting, it is well worth the effort to make a jig somewhat like a miter box so that the pipe can be cut with ease. See Fig. 8. There are also special tube-cutters that can be used for this purpose. Care must be taken when working with soft copper not to squeeze it in a vice or with a wrench so that it becomes dented, because this would act as an obstruction. If the end of the tubing is damaged in handling, it can be restored to shape with a sizing tool. After the tube has been cut, ream out the burr.

Soldered Fittings

As shown in Fig. 9, the fittings for soldered joints are made so that the openings at each end are slipped over the copper tubing. Before this is done, the ends of the tube should be carefully cleaned with steel wool or emery cloth until the metal is shiny. The inside of the fitting should be thoroughly cleaned in the same manner. See Fig. 10.

If the surfaces of both the tube and fitting that are to be soldered are not clean you will not get a good joint.

After the metal has been polished until it is bright, apply a non-corrosive soldering flux to the tube and the fitting where they have been cleaned. See Fig. 11. Slip the fitting over the end of

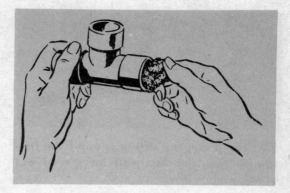

Fig. 10. Polish both fitting and end of pipe with steel wool until the metal is bright.

the tube and then turn it around several times so that the flux will be spread out evenly and all portions of the metal will be covered. See Fig. 12. The next step is to solder the joint. Some fittings are provided with a little hole in the side into which the wire solder is fed. Other types have no such hole, and the solder is fed in around the edges of the fitting. See Fig. 13. In either case, the

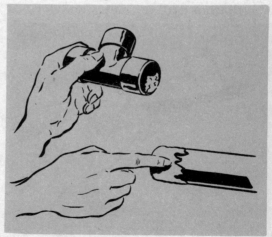

Fig. 11. Flux should be applied to the inside of the fitting as well as to the outside of the pipe.

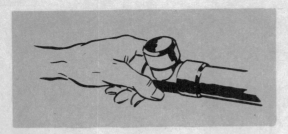

Fig. 12. Twist the fitting around the tubing so that the flux will be spread out evenly.

soldering procedure is about the same. The fitting must be heated and this can be done either with a gasoline blowtorch or an air-acetylene torch. See Fig. 14. There is some advantage in using the acetylene torch because it produces a more concentrated flame and, therefore, can be used more conveniently in close quarters where there is woodwork or other inflammable material present. But whichever type of torch is used, *be careful* about fire. The best plan is to put pieces of asbestos board around all near-by woodwork so

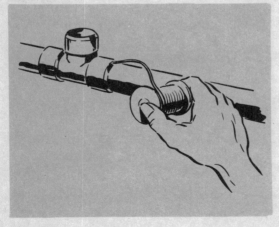

Fig. 13. If the fitting has been properly heated, the solder will be drawn into the joint until the joint is full.

that there will be less danger of setting something on fire. Hold the flame of the torch on the fitting and tube until the flux begins to boil. After this, remove the torch and start feeding in the wire solder either through the hole in the fitting or along the edges. If the joint is not hot enough, the solder will not be drawn into it, so be sure that both fitting and tube are properly heated. On the other hand, if you get the metal too hot, you will not get a

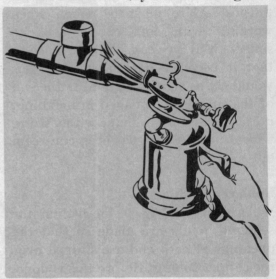

Fig. 14. The fitting must be heated so that the solder will run into the joint.

good joint. Feed the solder into the fitting and when no more is drawn up it means that the fitting is properly soldered. A ring of solder will appear around the edge of the fitting. Wipe the excess solder off with a brush. See Fig. 15. Give the joint time to cool, and then rub the ring of solder down with steel wool to make a neat job of it. Usually, you will have to make at least two joints at the same fitting. In such cases, it is necessary to wrap the joints that you have previously soldered with wet cloths so that the fitting can be

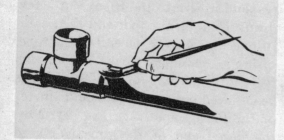

Fig. 15. A brush can be used to remove excess solder from around the edge of the fitting.

heated up again to make the succeeding joints. If this is not done, the first joint will melt when you re-heat the fitting for the second or third one. See Fig. 16.

Fig. 16. When it is necessary to make additional connections with soldered fittings, cover the soldered joints with wet rags so that the joints already soldered will not melt when the fitting is heated.

Flared Fittings

The other method of making up joints in copper tubing is to use the flared fitting. See Figs. 17 and 18.

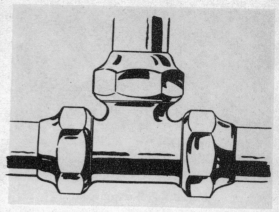

Fig. 17. A completed flared fitting.

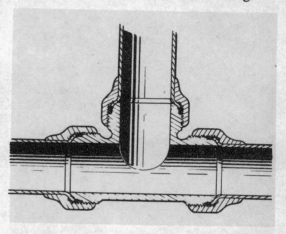

Fig. 18. The interior view of a flared fitting.

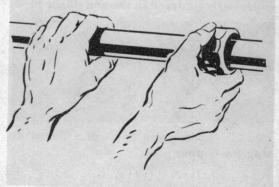

Fig. 19. Slip the union nut over the pipe before you flare the pipe.

Fig. 20. A flaring tool.

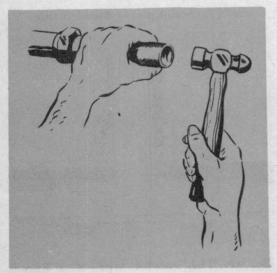

Fig. 21. Make sure that the flaring tool is properly centered in the end of the pipe.

Fig. 22. Component parts of a flared fitting for copper pipe.

After cutting the tube, which is done in the same manner as for soldered fittings, the first step is to slip a sleeve nut

on the section of tubing. See Fig. 19. Next, the end of the tubing is burred and then flared out with a flaring tool. See Fig. 20. This tool must correspond in size to the tube. Put a few drops of oil on the tool and then carefully center it over the end of the tube. Using a hammer, strike the flaring tool until the end of the tubing has been flared out to the outside diameter of the flaring tool. See Fig. 21. Now the flared end of the tube is placed (See Fig. 22) over the fitting and the sleeve nut is run up and tightened with a wrench. See Fig. 23.

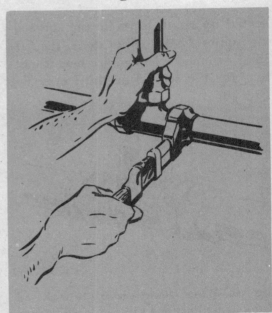

Fig. 23. Tightening up a flared joint with a monkey wrench.

The best practice is to use the same type of pipe throughout the fresh-water system. There is litle to be gained by using half copper and brass and half galvanized steel. In fact, connecting copper to steel may cause trouble. Brass and copper, however, can be used in conjunction with one another without harm.

PIPE SIZE

The size of pipe used for the fresh-water system will depend not only on the type of pipe used but also on the pressure of your supply.

If your water pressure is not very strong, the distribution mains should be 1″ or 1¼″. If the supply pressure is high, the mains can be reduced to ¾″, but this may not always be sufficient to take care of future expansion of the plumbing system, such as might arise if another bath were to be installed. In the long run, it is probably best never to use a supply main under 1″. Short branch-lines to the washstands, toilets, etc., may be ½″ pipe, and the kitchen sink and laundry should have ¾″ lines. These sizes are for galvanized steel pipe. If brass or copper is used, pipe a size smaller can be used.

CAST-IRON SOIL PIPE

Cast-iron bell and spigot pipe over 2″ is used for the drainage inside the house and for the vent system. These pipes come in standard lengths of 5″ and up to 6″ in diameter. For most purposes, a 4″ pipe will be sufficient except for the kitchen sink-drain, where a 2″ pipe is used.

Cast-iron pipe is cut with a cold chisel. See Fig 24. First of all, the pipe should be lightly scored around the point where the cut is to be made. Make this line as square as you can. Now, with the pipe supported on some 2″ x 4″′s, start making deeper cuts along the line with the cold chisel. Turn the pipe after each blow. After you have gone around several times the pipe will break clean at the cut line. Before you assemble the pipe, strike it at each end with a hammer. If you get a clear ring, the pipe is sound.

Vertical Joints

Making up the joint in cast-iron pipe is a complicated business, but with a little practice you should not find it too

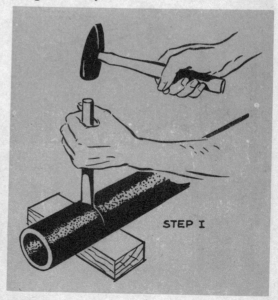

Fig. 24. Cutting soil pipe with a cold chisel.

difficult. The ends of pipe to be joined should be clean and bone dry. When working in a vertical line, the bell end of the pipe should face up. Insert the spigot end of the next section of pipe into the bell end and then secure this length of pipe to a framework with metal strips or by some other means so that it will not fall over. Now pack twisted oakum into the bell until it is about 1″ from the top. For a 4″ soil pipe, you will need about 5 feet of oakum for each joint. The oakum should be solidly packed into the bell with a tool called a yarning iron. See Figs. 25 and 28. If any of the fibers of the oakum protrude, they should be burned off with a blow-torch. After the oakum is well packed into place, the joint is ready to be caulked with lead.

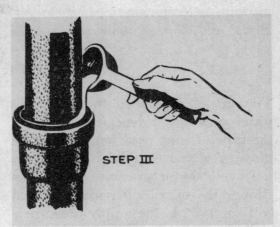

Fig. 26. Pouring in the hot lead.

You will need about 3 pounds for 4″ pipe. Needless to say, enough lead should be melted at one time for several joints. Lead can be melted in a gasoline-fired melting pot. When the lead is molten, pre-heat the ladle that is used to carry the lead so that it will not chill the molten lead before you get it to the joint. Take the hot ladle and push back some of the dross or slag that lies on the surface of the lead and then scoop up a ladleful of lead. Do not disturb the molten lead in the pot any more than is necessary. The lead must be poured into the joint in one operation. Move the ladle around as you pour so that the joint is filled uniformly. See Fig. 26. Do not pour hot lead on a wet joint because the moisture will cause the hot lead to fly out. It is wise to keep your face away from the joint while you pour so that if any of the lead does fly out it will not hit you. The joint should be completely filled until the lead is a little above the rim of the hub—about ⅛″ or so.

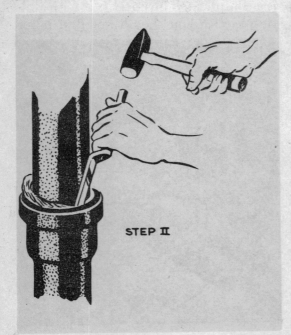

Fig. 25. Packing in the oakum with a yarning iron.

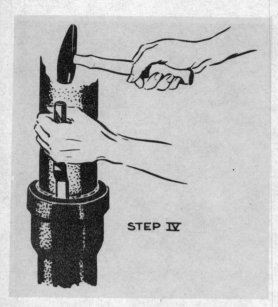

STEP IV

Fig. 27. Caulking a vertical joint.

The next step is the final caulking of the joint and this can be done just as soon as the lead is cool. Caulking backs the lead firmly inside the joint. See Figs. 27 and 28. It must be done because lead will shrink slightly as it cools and, therefore, unless the joint is caulked it will not be tight. The first step in caulking is done with an outside-caulking tool. Place the end of this tool on the lead and then strike it gently with a hammer. If you strike it too hard, you may jar the lead loose from the joint. Tap all around the leaded joint and then change to an inside-caulking tool. Heavier blows can be struck with this. Finish off the caulking with a caulking tool that fits into the space without binding.

When working with a section of pipe that has been cut, great care must be taken to be sure that the cut end is properly centered in the bell of the section below. See Figs. 29 and 30. If the end is not properly centered, you will not get a good joint.

Some codes permit joints in cast-iron pipe to be made with a commercial jointing-compound that requires no caulking or with shreaded lead, which is calked cold.

Horizontal Joints

For making horizontal joints, the same general procedure is used as for the vertical joints. The joint is first packed with oakum. To introduce the lead, a contraption called a joint-runner is required. See Fig. 31. It is made of asbestos and is wrapped around the pipe just above the hub. Get the runner on as tightly as possible; the clip that holds the runner together should face up. This is the point at which the lead is poured in. Tap the runner after it

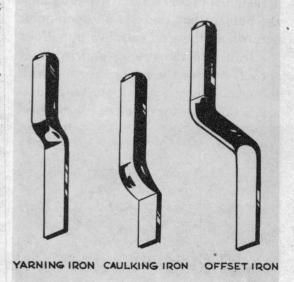

YARNING IRON CAULKING IRON OFFSET IRON

Fig. 28. Three tools you will need to make up joints in cast-iron soil pipe.

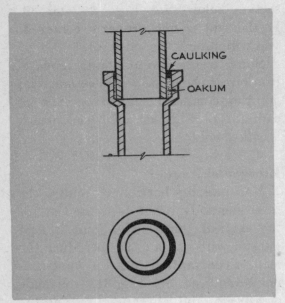

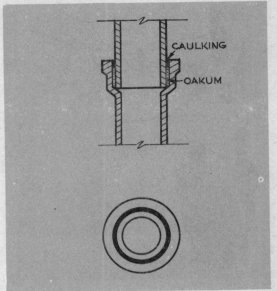

Fig. 29. Care must be taken in making up a joint with a section of pipe that has been cut, to get the end properly centered in the bell end. The joint shown above is off center and may cause trouble.

Fig. 30. Correct method of centering the end of cut pipe for making a caulked joint.

joints so that the underside of the joint can be caulked.

is fastened in place and drive it against the hub so that there is no open joint here where the lead can flow out. Pour the lead into the runner and, when it is cool, remove the runner for use with the next joint. Special caulking tools are available for use on horizontal

Threaded Joints

If you wish to save yourself the job of having to make up caulked joints in cast-iron pipes, you can use special pipes of this type with threaded joints. They are especially designed for drainage work so that the interior of the pipe at the fitting or joint will be perfectly smooth and free from shoulders that might catch solid matter passing through the line. Of course, this type of pipe is more expensive than the bell and spigot type and more care is required in cutting and fitting the sections together. On the other hand, the same degree of skill is not required in making the joints, the work goes faster and is much neater.

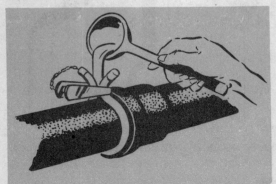

Fig. 31. Pouring lead for a horizontal caulked joint by means of a joint runner.

Wiped Joint

This joint is used when it is necessary to join lead pipe to lead or to brass or copper. The first step is to prepare the two sections of pipe as shown in Fig. 32. This can be done with a rasp. The ends of the pipe should then be painted with plumber's soil for 4″ or so. After the soil is dry, the

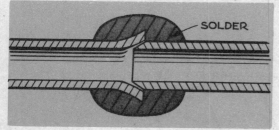

Fig. 32. How the ends of pipes should be prepared for making a wiped joint.

pipe should be shaved about 1¼″ back until the metal is bright. Rub candle wax over the shaved portion to prevent it from tarnishing. Both ends of pipe should be treated in this manner.

Solder used for wiping joints should be 60 per cent lead and 40 per cent tin. The solder should not be overheated.

Before the solder is poured, put the two sections of pipe together and support them above the floor so that there are at least 4 inches under the joint.

The cloth used to make the joint is herringbone ticking, and it should be folded until you have a pad with 16 thicknesses of ticking. This should be warmed and then rubbed with mutton tallow without salt. The pad is held under the joint while the solder is poured slowly back and forth over the top of the joint. The solder that runs off the sides can be caught in the cloth and patted against the underside. The pouring continues until the solder on the joint becomes plastic. When the solder over the entire joint has become plastic, the pouring ceases and the plastic is worked into a joint that has the shape of an egg.

Solder that runs off the joint and onto the floor can be reheated and used again.

INSTALLING THE PLUMBING SYSTEM

Before you can do much in the way of getting the plumbing system installed, you must obtain the roughing in measurements for the type of fixtures that you are going to install. These roughing plans will give you all the dimensions of the fixtures, their minimum height from the floor and distance from the wall, and the location of the holes in the wall and floor for the supply lines and waste pipes. You can get these measurements from your dealer when the fixtures are purchased.

If your first floor is made of wood, the first thing you should do is to make the openings in the floor of the bathroom and kitchen so that waste lines to the fixtures can be brought in. Holes can be made by first drilling through the flooring with a brace and bit and

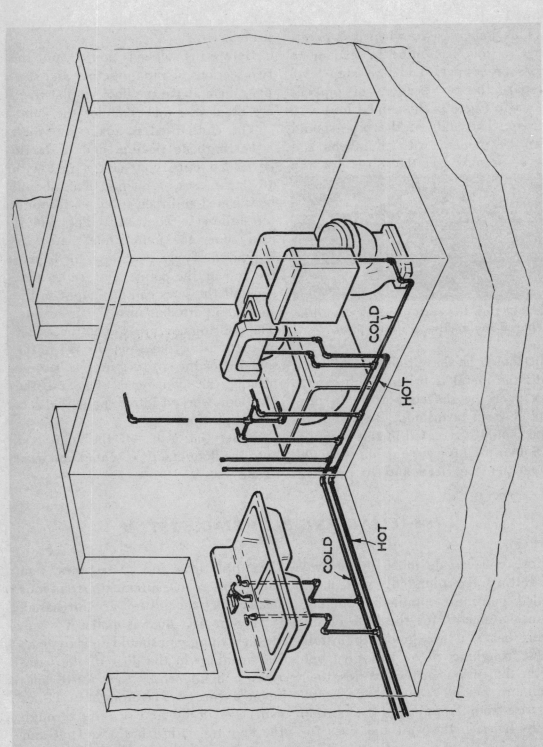

Fig. 33. Layout for the fresh-water supply system.

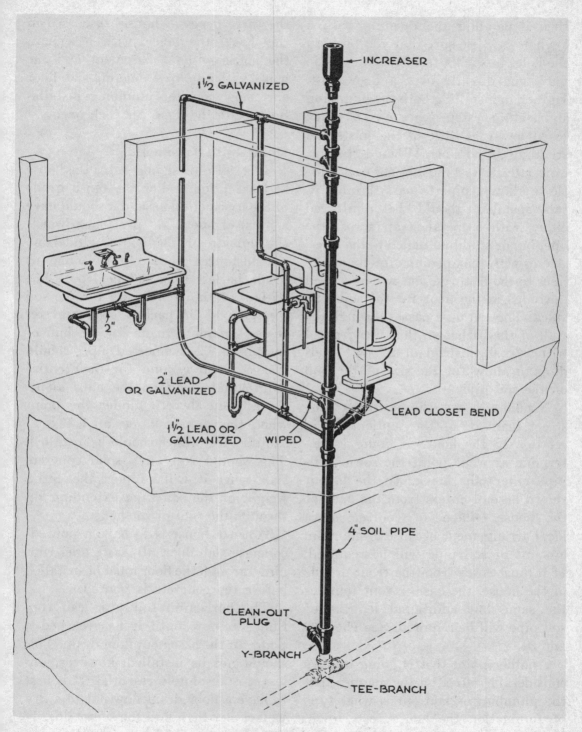

Fig. 34. Layout for connections to the soil stack.

then expanding the opening with a keyhole saw. Be sure that you position the holes in such a fashion that you do not come directly over a floor joist. In fact, in installing both the plumbing and heating systems, care must be taken to cut away as little of the joists and studding as possible. When a stud or, especially, a joist must be cut back a little to allow a pipe to pass through it, this member should be reinforced either with a metal strap across the opening or studding nailed to the sides. Along with the openings for the waste lines to the fixtures, you will also need openings in the floor for the soil-pipe stack. The soil pipe passes through the wall of the bathroom that was framed with 2″ x 6″ instead of 2″ x 4″ studding to allow for the size of the hub on the soil pipe.

' Needless to say, the location of the street main or of the septic tank in relation to the house is going to determine at what point the sewer soil-pipe enters the house. In the layout shown here, it enters from the back of the house, which, of course, is an ideal arrangement because a minimum amount of soil pipe will be required. If it must enter from the front or side of the house, the basic layout remains the same but additional lengths of soil pipe will be required. See Figs. 33 and 34.

Another point that is going to have considerable effect on the manner that the plumbing is laid out is what type of foundation the house rests upon. For the purpose of clarity, let us take the three types of houses discussed in this book, the house with basement, the house without basement and the house with a poured concrete-slab floor and show how the plumbing installation should be done for each one.

Homes with Basements

The soil pipe should enter the house at least 1 foot below the finish grade of the basement floor and it should have a pitch of about ¼″ per foot towards the outside of the house. Under no circumstances should this pitch or grade be less than ⅛″ per foot. The bottom of the trench dug for the soil pipe should be packed solid and recesses should be made for the hub of the pipes. The connected pipes should rest on solid ground for their entire length and never on the hubs alone. At a point directly under the point where the vent stack goes up, a 4″ x 4″ sanitary tee-branch should be installed. This should rest on a solid concrete slab, since it will support the entire weight of the soil pipe extending up through the roof of the house.

When a house is to have a poured-concrete-slab floor, all waste lines running through the floor must be installed before the concrete is poured.

The horizontal soil pipe can continue on now until it has reached a point for the basement floor drain. This should not be installed, however, unless it is absolutely essential. It is best to have a floor drain flow out to a dry well rather than into the sewer line. If the drain must discharge into the sewer line, the drain should be fitted with a deep-seal trap.

The first vertical piece of soil pipe coming off the sanitary tee-branch is a Y branch. One side of this is fitted with a brass clean-out plug so that, in the event the sewer line should become clogged, there will be an opening into it at a convenient location. If you are not going to have a basement floor drain, the end of the sanitary tee-branch can be plugged to serve as a clean-out.

The vertical stack can continue up again until it arrives at the spot for installing the branch to take care of the toilet, bathtub and washbasin drains. This branch is a double-topped T with a 2″ tapping. The next section is a 4″ x 2″ tapped sanitary tee.

The soil stack continues up farther until you reach the point where a 4″ tapped sanitary tee is installed for the vent line from the fixtures. The exact location of this tee will depend on what future plans you have for the attic. If a bathroom is going to be installed later on, this fitting should be installed above the highest fixture in the attic bath, and you will also need a double-topped sanitary tee at the bathroom floor level for the future additional fixtures. The openings in this tee should be capped until it is ready to be put into use.

In cold climates, special care must be taken with the portion of the soil pipe that is above the roof in order to prevent frost from forming inside the pipe and blocking it up. One

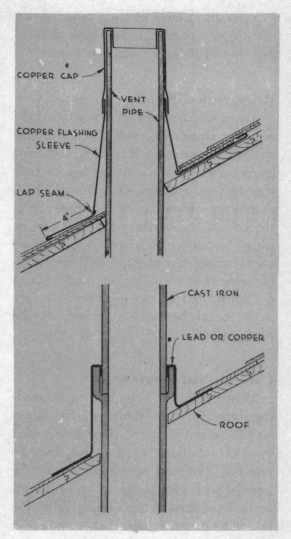

Fig. 35. Several methods of flashing around the soil pipe and roof.

method of doing this is to increase the size of the pipe by means of an increaser. The increase in size should take place at least 12 inches below the roof.

The opening between the roof and the soil pipe must be carefully flashed to prevent leaking. Fig. 35 shows several methods of flashing. The flashing should extend at least two courses of shingles above the soil pipe. Flashing should be either lead or copper.

Basementless Houses

The main consideration when installing the drainage system in a house without a basement is to have sufficient headroom under the first floor so that the various fittings can be installed. As there will be no need of a floor drain, the end of the sanitary base tee can be plugged for a clean-out. As the horizontal runs of soil pipe will probably be somewhat above grade, they should be supported at least every 10 feet with metal hangers attached to the floor joists.

Concrete-Slab Houses

When a house is to have a poured-concrete-slab first floor, all the pipes and fittings below the floor level must be put in place before the floor is poured. The top openings should be packed with something to prevent concrete or debris from falling into the line. The pipes must be held securely in place so that there will be no chance of their being moved out of position by the fresh concrete. The pipes themselves should not be encased in the concrete. Slip loosely fitting metal sleeves around them before the concrete is poured. Pipes and fittings that are to be covered with concrete must be especially durable as it will be almost impossible to replace them. Cast iron, copper, brass and lead are suitable.

Fixtures

Once the soil stack has been completed, you can go to work and install the waste lines to the various fixtures. The first one to take care of is the closet bowl and this is the most difficult one you will run into. As the closet bowl is going to rest on the floor, there is almost sure to be a slight amount of movement between it and the cast-iron waste pipe. The joint between the bowl and the pipe must, therefore, be flexible enough to take up this movement without cracking the bowl and yet be tight enough so that it will not leak. A more flexible type of joint is required when the bowl is set on a wood floor than on a concrete slab because of the relatively large amount of expansion and contraction that is to be expected.

A type of closet connection that is suitable for both concrete and wood floors consists of a 4″ lead bend that is attached at one end to a brass ferrule by means of a wiped joint. The other end is soldered to the closet-bowl floor plate, which is of brass. See Fig. 36. The joint between the bowl and the floor is made tight with an asbestos gasket and the bowl is secured to the flange by means of hold-down bolts. The brass ferrule is caulked to the hub of the cast-iron soil pipe.

As soon as you have completed the connection to the closet bowl, pack the opening with old rags and cover up the work so that it will not be damaged if something heavy drops on it. The bowl itself will not be installed until the bathroom walls have been completed. In fact, the installation of all the fixtures should be put off to the very end of the job. This should be done not only because you will find it much easier to complete the walls if the fixtures are not in place but also because the fixtures are very easily damaged and to have them lying around out of their crates while you are doing heavy work might result in serious harm to them.

The next job is to rough in the drain and vent system for the lavatory, bathtub and kitchen sink. Refer to your roughing-in dimensions and locate the position of the lavatory trap. Start here with a tee fitting and run up the vent line for the lavatory and bathtub traps. This will be made out of 1½" galvanized pipe. As you will note, a short distance above the lavatory this line is offset to allow room for the medicine closet, which is going to be installed directly over the lavatory. The top of this line is fitted with a tee and then one side continues on to the tapped sanitary tee in the vent stack. The other side of the line continues on over to the kitchen sink, where it drops down and will be connected later on to the kitchen-sink trap.

All joints in the galvanized pipes should be made up with pipe compound so that they will be tight.

Fig. 34 shows how the bathtub and the lavatory are connected into the soil stack. In this particular case, 1½" galvanized pipe with drain fittings has been used, but the job can also be done

with lead. You may find that lead, in spite of the wiped fittings involved, will be less difficult for this job because of the fact the lead is flexible and easier to work with. If lead is used, it will have to be connected to a brass tee under the lavatory. The waste line from the bathtub and lavatory are connected into the soil stack at the double-topped fitting to which the closet is also connected.

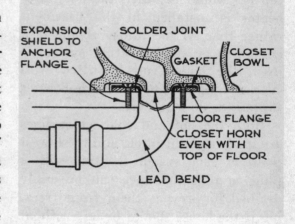

Fig. 36. How the toilet bowl is connected to the drainage system.

The waste line from kitchen sink to soil stack can be galvanized steel or lead. There should be no trouble in getting the right measurements and cutting the pipe to exact size.

Slip joints on fixtures should only be used on the fixture side of the trap. They should not be used on the sewer side because they are not tight enough to prevent the passage of sewer gas through the joint. All joints on the sewer side of traps must be either threaded, soldered, wiped or caulked.

THE FRESH WATER SUPPLY

You will find that installing the fresh water system is a simple business compared to the drainage system.

Fig. 33 shows the layout of these lines for houses with first floors and those with concrete slab floors. There will be no radical difference in the lines between houses with basements and those without basements. The only exception would be when the hot-water heater is installed in the basement rather than in the utility room. If a hot-water or steam-heating system is used, the boiler can be fitted with special equipment to heat the hot-water supply for domestic use.

Both the hot and cold water lines are given a slight pitch, and the lowest point of each system is fitted with a plug so that the lines can be easily drained to prevent them from freezing if the house should be left without heat. Considerable fuel can be saved if the hot-water pipes are insulated.

When bringing the supply lines to the bathroom lavatory, the cold-water line should be placed so that when the fixture is connected up, the faucet on the user's left will be the cold water.

All lines should be given proper support in the manner described earlier in this chapter. Pipes that are not secure will vibrate when water under pressure flows through them, and in time the joints will open up and leak.

As soon as the lines are in, the rough walls around the bathtub can be put in and the tub installed. The lavatory, kitchen sink and water closet will go in later, after all the walls have been completed. The lavatory should stand about 30 inches off the finished floor.

There is no fixed standard as to how high off the floor the kitchen sink should be. The main point to watch out for is not to have the sink too low so that someone working in it will have to bend over. The women of the house should have the deciding voice in exactly how high the kitchen sink should be.

The water-closet bowl is attached to the floor plate with bolts and the heads of these bolts are covered with porcelain caps, which are fastened in place with plaster of paris. The line between the flush tank and the bowl is made up with slip joints.

HOT-WATER HEATERS AND STORAGE TANKS

An adequate supply of hot water is a "must" in any modern home, and it will certainly pay to get the very best type of equipment for heating it. The domestic hot water can be heated by the furnace boiler or by means of an inde-

pendent hot-water heater. Of course, if you use some sort of warm-air heating system, you must have an independent heater. Many persons have the idea that water heated by the furnace boiler is not costing them anything. This is not correct by any means. Additional fuel will be required to heat the hot water in winter, when the system is in full operation, as well as in summer, when the system only goes into operation long enough to heat the water for the plumbing system. The only type of furnace that is suitable for heating the hot-water supply all year around is one that is fully automatic, such as a gas or oil burner.

Independent hot-water heaters run on either gas or electricity. Both types are very efficient and are fully automatic. The deciding factor as to which one to use is the local gas and electric-power rates. These heaters have a built-in, insulated, hot-water storage tank. The tanks are made of galvanized iron, copper, or steel lined with glass.

The size of storage tank required will depend on the number of persons in the household.

Fig. 37 shows the method of connecting up a gas or electric hot-water heater. A tee is attached to the hot-water line at the top of the heater, and to this is attached a hot-water relief valve. A line is run from the relief valve to the floor, where it empties into a bucket, or is run outside of the house. The purpose of the relief valve is to prevent the hot-water storage tank from exploding if the pressure inside becomes too great. The line to the floor is necessary to prevent anyone's being burned by the hot water and steam escaping from the valve. When the local water supply has a very lime content, the relief valve should be

placed on the cold-water entrance pipe to the heater because it will not become coated with minerals in this location as readily as if it were installed on the hot-water line.

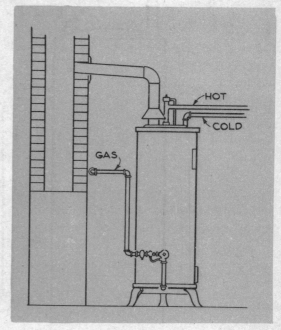

Fig. 37. Method of connecting lines to gas or electric hot-water heater.

Gas-fired heaters should be equipped with a vent from the top to allow the fumes from the heater to be carried outside. The vent stack can be of metal, but this type is not always suitable because of the condensation of the fumes on the inside of the line. It is better to use special asbestos vent pipes.

Fig. 38 shows the method of connecting a hot-water storage tank when the water is to be heated by the furnace boiler. A horizontal tank is used rather than a vertical one, and the tank should be insulated to prevent heat loss.

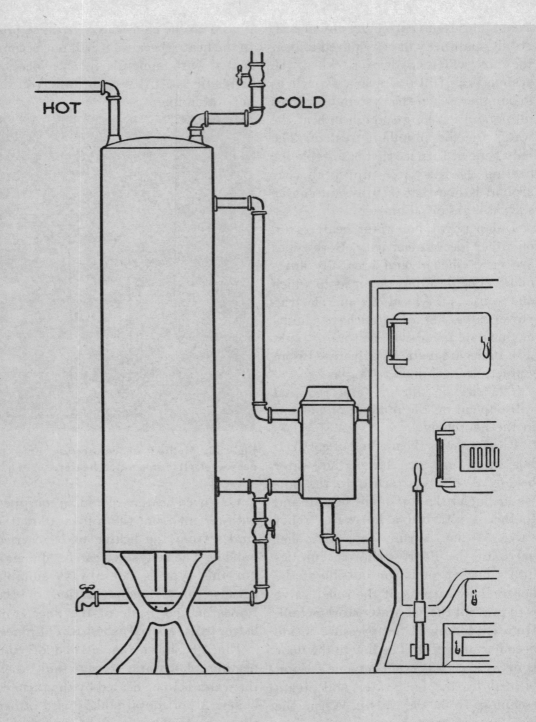

Fig. 38. Connection of hot-water storage tank to furnace hot-water heater.

TESTING THE DRAINAGE SYSTEM

Before fixtures are connected into the drainage system, the work should be checked over to be sure that it is perfectly tight. The simplest way to do this is to fill the system completely full of water. To do this all the openings in the system except one must be closed tightly. You can get a special test plug with a rubber ring that can be placed in an opening and then expanded by means of screws so that it will make an air-tight fit. After all the openings have been closed with these plugs, the system is filled with water. This can be done by pouring water down the top of the vent stack. When the system is full, allow it to stand for a while and then see if there is any drop in the water level in the stack. If there is a drop, go over the work carefully until you find the spot where the water is escaping. If it is a threaded fitting, it may be that the threads were not properly cut or perhaps you neglected to use pipe compound on the threads. In the case of a caulked fitting that leaks there is no easy way to make repairs. The job should be done over again. The joint can be freed by holding a blow-torch to it until the lead melts out.

If water is escaping through cracks in the cast-iron soil-pipe hub, this entire section will have to be removed.

A test on the fresh-water system is not absolutely vital, but it is a wise precaution to take. It can be made by plugging up the openings and running water through the line. The chances are that you will not need any additional pressure in the line to expose any flaws in your work. Sometimes a special pump is used to increase the pressure in the line a little over and above that found in normal fresh-water systems.

THE HOUSE SEWER LINE

The cast-iron soil pipe should extend for at least one section (5 feet) beyond the house. After this, you can use either cast-iron soil pipe or vitrified-clay pipe to carry the waste to the sewer line or cesspool. Clay pipe is the least expensive, but it has the drawback that seepage through the pipe joints will attract tree roots, which in time may clog up the line. This danger can be eliminated to a great extent, however, by installing copper washers inside each joint. The copper will kill any tree roots that come in contact with it. Clay pipe can be joined with cement mortar. The sections are placed together and oakum is packed into the bell to prevent the mortar from getting into the line. The mortar is then worked into the joint, either by hand or using a joint runner. Cast-iron soil pipe can be joined with caulked joints or with special threaded joints. It will last indefinitely.

SEWAGE DISPOSAL

If you are building your home on a lot where there is a near-by city sewer line, you do not have much to worry about as far as sewage-disposal goes. There will probably be a slight charge involved for opening up the main so that your line can be attached and you may find that you will not be able to lay the sewer pipes from your house to the main yourself, but your worries are few compared to those of building in outlying districts where each house must have its own private sewage-disposal plant.

Cesspools and Septic Tanks

There are two types of private sewage-disposal systems that you can use. One is the cesspool and the other is the septic tank. Of the two, the septic tank is by far the superior, and in many localities it is the only system that may be used. The cesspool is more or less out of date today, and its main advantage is the fact that it is a very simple and inexpensive system to install. It consists of a large hole in the ground that is lined on the inside with rocks or concrete blocks set up without mortar. The sewage from the house flows into this tank and the liquids pass through the openings in the rocks or blocks and are absorbed into the earth. The top of the cesspool is provided with a tightly fitting concrete lid to keep out insects and vermin.

The first great drawback to this type of system is that it can easily contamin-ate wells or near-by water supplies. The liquids that are absorbed into the ground are by no means pure and slowly but surely the earth around the cesspool becomes contaminated.

Even when the cesspool is below a well, there is still a chance that, due to rock formations, the seepage from the cesspool will reach the water supply.

Cesspools are of little use in ground that is low-lying and wet because the earth will not absorb the liquids from the cesspool and you will have to have it pumped out repeatedly.

The septic tank works on an entirely different principle from the cesspool. The waste from the house flows into a watertight tank. It remains there for twenty-four hours or so while the bacteria reduce many of the solids to a liquid state. At the end of this interval, the liquids flow out of the tank into a leaching field made of tile. These tiles are placed fairly near the surface and this allows air to get to the liquids and evaporate them before they have a chance to get very far.

There are several misunderstandings about a septic tank. In the first place, not all the solids that enter the tank are reduced to a liquid state and flow out into the tile field. Some of these solids remain inside the tank as sludge. In time the sludge will accumulate to such a degree that the tank will not operate properly until it has been pumped out. Second, the liquids that flow out of the tank are by no means

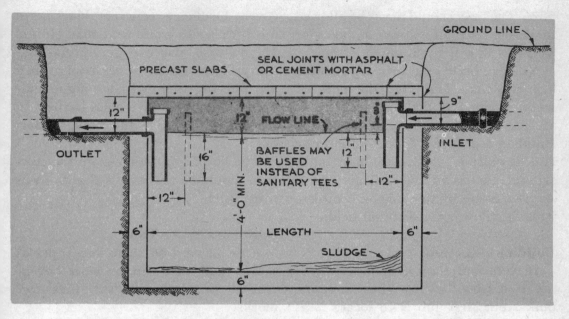

Fig. 39. Detail of the construction of a single-chamber septic tank.

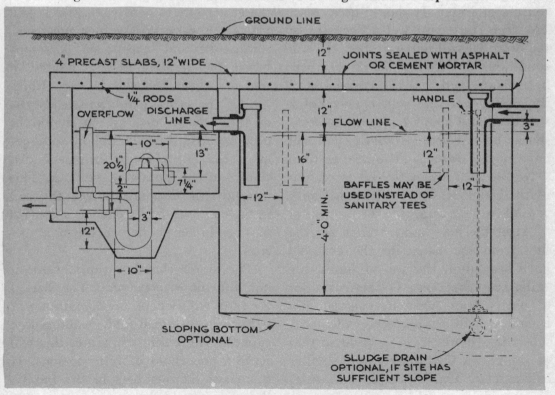

Fig. 40. A septic tank with a dosing chamber.

pure. The tank should never be allowed to empty out into streams, lakes or rivers as it will contaminate them.

You can build your own septic tank, but you may find that the ones of metal or concrete that are ready-made are more practical for your purposes. Building a properly functioning septic tank is quite a job. Ready-built tanks are not expensive and will give good service. Some of them come complete with the tile for the disposal field.

Building a Cesspool

If you find that it is practical to use a cesspool rather than a septic tank, your first job is to locate it as far as possible from any wells or other sources of water. It should be at least 100 feet from any well. The size of the cesspool will depend upon the soil conditions and the number of members in the household. For the average family and in average soil, a cesspool 7 feet deep and about 7 feet in diameter should be sufficient. Actually, you will have to dig down a little deeper than 7 feet so that when the lid is on top of the cesspool, you can cover it with topsoil for planting.

After the hole and a trench for the line from the house to the cesspool have been dug, the job of lining the walls is undertaken. If there is a lot of native stone around, you can use it and it will be perfectly adequate. The trick, however, is to build so that as you go up, the tank becomes smaller in diameter. This is necessary in order to provide a small opening for the cover. Ordinary concrete blocks are much easier to work with than stones. If you wish, you can get special masonry blocks made for cesspools. They are put together with a tongue-and-groove joint and have holes in them to allow liquids inside the tank to flow out.

The line from the house to the cesspool should be laid with a slight downward pitch.

Building a Septic Tank

Figs. 39 and 40 show two types of septic tank that can be built out of poured concrete or concrete masonry-blocks.

The tank shown in Fig. 39 is by far the easier one to construct, and it will provide a very satisfactory means of sewage-disposal except in locations where the disposal field is limited in size or where the soil is very tight. Under the latter conditions, the type of tank shown in Fig. 40 should be used because it has a siphon arrangement that provides intermittent discharge of the liquids in the tank. This intermittent discharge gives the soil in the disposal field a chance to get rid of one discharge before the next occurs.

The single-chamber septic tank is not difficult to construct. The size of the tank will depend on the number of persons in the household. A 500-gallon capacity is the minimum, and this will serve a household of four persons. If there are six members in the family, the size should be increased to 600 gallons. For a 500-gallon tank, the width should be 3', the length 6' and the depth 5'. The inlet should be 9" below the top of the tank and should be fitted with a sanitary tee. The outlet line to the disposal field is placed 12" below the top and this also has a sanitary tee.

Fig. 41 shows how the tank is laid out on the site before the excavation work is done. Forms for the tank should be constructed sufficiently level and solid so that they will not be forced out of place by the weight of the concrete. See Fig. 42.

Fig. 43 show how the top of the tank can be cast in sections out of con-

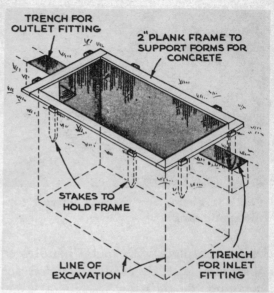

Fig. 41. Laying out a septic tank.

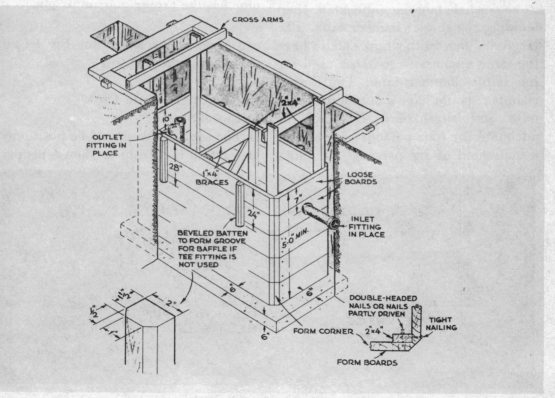

Fig. 42. Construction of forms for septic tank.

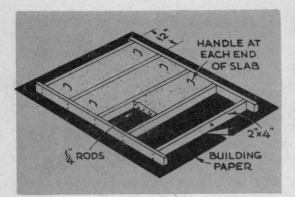

Fig. 43. Forms for making precast tops for septic tank.

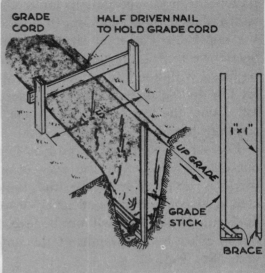

Fig. 44. Laying sewer soil pipe. A simple grade stick is used to insure that each pipe has the proper amount of pitch.

crete, complete with metal handles so that they can be easily removed for cleaning the tank.

Building a septic tank with siphon is somewhat more complicated than building the single-chamber tank. The large chamber in this tank should have the same dimensions as those used for the single-chamber tank. The dosing chamber should have a minimum width of 3′ and length of 6′. This will be adequate for four persons or less. For a household of six persons, the width can remain the same but the length should be increased to 7′.

Laying Out a Septic-Tank Disposal System

The septic tank should be positioned at least 50 feet from the house proper.

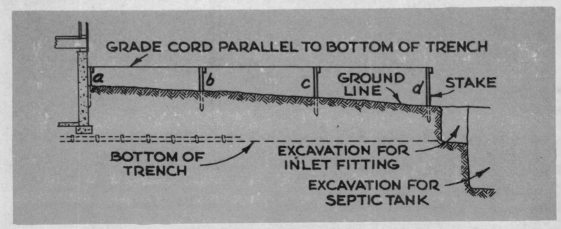

Fig. 45. Use of grade cord to get the proper pitch to the sewer line.

Clay pipe can be used to connect the tank to the house drainage system. The first section of tile can be joined to the cast-iron soil pipe extending from the house with cement mortar, which is also used for the following sections of clay pipe. But be sure that you pack oakum into the bell ends first to prevent the mortar from seeping into the line, and make your connections as tight as possible because if you do not, you will be troubled with tree roots that get into the line and clog it up.

The septic tank cannot be constructed in accordance with the plans given earlier in this section. From the outlet side of the tank, a line of clay soil-pipe with cemented ends is run for about 15 feet. This line, as well as the line from the house, should have a slight downward pitch. The house line should be pitched 1″ in every 10″, while the line coming out the outlet side of the septic tank should be pitched 1″ for every 20″. See Figs. 44 and 45. The end of the outlet line from the septic tank is connected to a distributing box

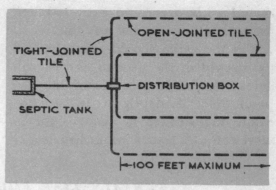

Fig. 47. Suggested layout for septic tank distribution field.

as shown in Fig. 46. This box can be constructed with extra openings that are plugged for the time being but can be opened up at some future date if additional lines in the disposal field are required. The feed lines coming out of the distributing box should be pitched 1″ for every 20″, and it should be made with caulked joints.

Fig. 47 shows the arrangement for a disposal field on level ground. The number of feet of tile and the number of branches will depend on soil conditions and on the number of persons in the household.

For the average-size household and where the soil is not too sandy or clayey but is medium as far as drainage goes, there should be four branches to the line and the total number of linear feet of 4″ drain-tile should be about 350. The disposal field can be made with ordinary 4″ clay tile with open joints or you can use special perforated drain pipes that come in standard 4-foot lengths. Each branch of the line should be given a slight slope, but this

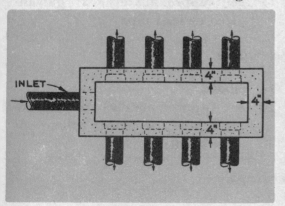

Fig. 46. A distribution box made out of concrete.

should not be over 6" to every 100 feet, the maximum length of any line.

The drain-tile should never be laid too deeply in the ground as this will defeat the whole purpose of the disposal field. A depth of 18" to 24" below the surface is about right in most cases. A trench six inches deeper than this should be dug and a layer of gravel 6" deep put down for the tile to rest upon. Pieces of tar paper are placed over the joints between the tile sections, which are then covered with another layer of gravel. Finally, straw is placed on top of the gravel and the soil is put back.

MATERIALS LIST FOR PLUMBING SYSTEM FOR THE BASIC HOUSE

Drainage System

1 4" x 4" sanitary tee branch
1 4" x 4" Y branch
1 4" clean-out plug
1 4" x 4" sanitary tee branch with 2" tapping
2 4" sanitary tees with 2" tappings
8 5-foot sections of 4" cast-iron soil pipe. Exact number of sections depends on location of sewer and whether basement floor drains are connected into sewer line
1 Increaser for top of vent stack
1 4" lead closet bend with brass ferrule and floor flange

1 Kitchen sink with fittings
1 Bathtub with shower and fittings
1 Lavatory with fittings
1 Water closet with flush tank and fittings
4 Drain traps for kitchen sink, bathtub and lavatory
6 1½" drain tees
5 1½" elbows
30 feet (approximately) 1½" galvanized pipe
11 feet (approximately) 2" galvanized or lead pipe

Fresh Water System

7 Tee fittings
50 feet (approximately) ½" galvanized pipe (or copper tubing one size smaller)

14 Elbows
10 feet (approximately) ¾" galvanized pipe (or copper tubing one size smaller)

Hot Water Supply

1 30-gallon hot water heater, gas or electric

Chapter 14

THE ELECTRIC WIRING

THE rough electric wiring, like the plumbing system, should be installed before the interior walls are covered with plaster or wallboard.

How much, if any, of the electrical wiring can be done by the home-builder himself will depend on local regulations. Practically all well settled communities have their own codes governing the installation of electric wiring. Some of these codes will insist that this type of work be done only by a licensed electrician. Other codes, not quite so strict will allow any one to do the wiring providing it passes inspection by a building or housing inspector. Your electric power company will be interested in how the house is wired, and unless the wiring meets with its approval, the power company will not bring in and connect their lines. Last but not least, home fire-insurance concerns may refuse to insure a home that is not, in their opinion, adequately wired.

Checking Up

All this means that you have quite a lot of checking up to do before you can go ahead with the installation.

This business of who is to do the wiring should be looked into well before you reach the point of doing the actual work because if the work must be done by an electrician, you may not be able to get one at short notice and then you are going to be held up all along the line.

First of all, check with your local building authorities and find out if you are allowed to do this work yourself. If you find that you can, get a copy of the local wiring codes, because wiring methods that meet the approval of one community will not necessarily meet with approval in others. If there is no special local code, the wiring should conform with the National Electric Code, which contains the minimum requirements for safe residential wiring. Wiring methods outlined in this chapter meet with these requirements and, therefore, can be used in all cases where there is no local code that supersedes the National Electric Code.

After you have found out about local codes, check with your local power concern and your local fire-insurance agent. You may find that their only requirement is that the final installation must be checked over by a licensed electrician before the power is connected.

WIRING METHODS

While there are many materials used for wiring, the three that are usually accepted for residential wiring are rigid conduit, armored or **BX** cable and nonmetallic sheathed cable.

Rigid Conduit

This type of wiring is approved by almost every code but it is also the most expensive type and requires the most work to install. It consists of steel-pipe conduits, which are fastened together in the same fashion as water pipes. See Fig. 1. After these conduits are installed, electric wires are pulled through them. The conduits are soft enough to permit bending. Local codes will often require the use of conduits in damp locations, such as basements.

Rigid conduit comes in 10-foot sections. It has a finish that is either black enamel or galvanized. The galvanized type should be used where there is the possibility of moisture. The conduit can be cut in the same manner as steel water-pipes and with the same type of equipment. After a length has been cut to size, the cut end should be reamed out to remove any sharp burrs left by the cutter. This is a very important step because if these burrs are left inside the pipe, they may damage the insulation on the wires as the wires are pulled through the conduit. Unlike water pipes, the threads on conduits do not taper but are perfectly straight.

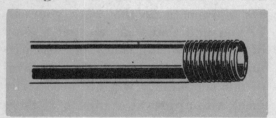

Fig. 1. A piece of rigid conduit.

Fig. 2. A bender that is used for bending conduit.

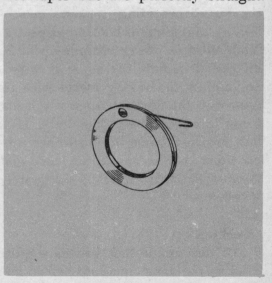

Fig. 3. Fish tape.

Therefore, special thread-cutting dies should be used and not the ones intended for plumbing installation. There are special elbow bends that can be used and the conduit can also be bent with the aid of a conduit bender. See Fig. 2.

The threaded end of the conduit is attached to the outlet box by means of locknuts and bushings. Rigid conduits should be supported by means of pipe straps placed every 5 feet or so.

After a length of conduit is installed, the wires are run through. On short runs it is often possible simply to push the wires through, but on long runs or where there are bends this probably will not work. What you need in such cases is fish tape, which is a length of steel wire that can be easily pushed through the conduit and around bends. There is a loop at one end of the tape so that the wires can be attached and then pulled through the conduit. See Fig. 3.

There is another type of conduit called "thin-wall" conduit, which is the same as the rigid conduit except that, as its name implies, it is somewhat thinner. Connections between lengths of this type of conduit are not made with threaded joints. Because of the thinness of the conduit, a special coupling is required.

Armored Cable

This type of wiring, often called by the trade name "BX cable," is approved by most local codes for residential wiring. It is less expensive than the rigid conduit and does not require as much work to install. It consists of two or more wires encased in heavy kraft paper, which in turn is covered with flexible steel armor. See Fig. 4. As it comes in long lengths, the only cutting and fitting necessary is where the cable is attached to an outlet or junction box. Armored cable is usually run through wall and ceiling framework. Holes ⅝" in diameter are cut through the studding and joists so that the cable can be passed through. A

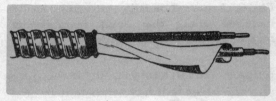

Fig. 4. Section of armored cable showing anti-short bushing in place and heavy paper over wires.

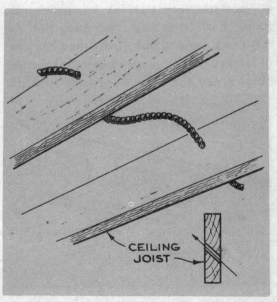

CEILING JOIST

Fig. 5. How BX cable can be run through studding and joists.

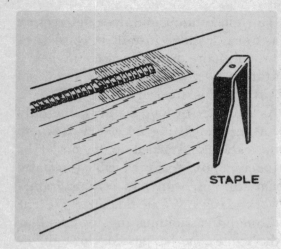

Fig. 6. Armored or BX cable can be easily installed along the wood framing by means of large metal staples.

long electrician's bit is best for this job, and the holes will have to be cut in at a slight angle. See Fig. 5. Drill the holes at the approximate center of the studding and joists. The cable should be supported every 4 feet or so and at not more than 12 inches from each outlet. You can use any one of the many types of straps for this purpose, but large staples are the least expensive and do

not require more than a moment to install. See Fig. 6.

Fig. 7 shows three methods of running a cable across a ceiling. Note that in *B*, where the cable is unprotected, a running board is used to provide it with adequate support and protection. These running boards should always be used when cables are run across attic floor joists where no flooring is to be used.

Armored cable can be cut with an ordinary hacksaw, but there is a trick in just how to cut the material to get a clean break. Hold the saw so that the blade cuts through the strip of armor that runs around the cable. See Fig. 8. Cut through the steel strip but do not cut so deep that the saw damages the

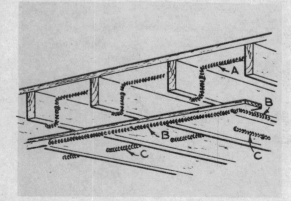

Fig. 7. Three methods of running cable over a ceiling.

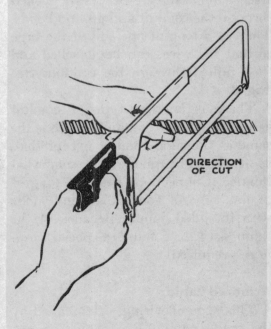

Fig. 8. Correct angle at which to hold the hacksaw when cutting BX cable.

kraft paper or insulation over the individual wires. Now take hold of the two ends of the armor and twist the cable apart at the point cut by the saw. Once the armor has been separated, the wires inside can be cut with a pair of snips. Next, make a second cut about 6 inches from the end of the cable. Twist off the 6 inches of armor and kraft paper, leaving 6 inches of wire exposed for making connections. Cutting the cable will invariably leave a series of sharp burrs on the end of the armor and these can easily damage the insulation on the wires. To prevent this possibility, a small fiber anti-short bushing should be inserted at the end of the cable to protect the wires from the burrs. See Fig. 9. The kraft paper covering should be removed from the wire for a short distance underneath the armor, so that this bushing can be inserted into the cable.

Armored cable is attached mechanically to the outlet boxes by means of special fittings. See Figs. 10, 11 and 12. It is important that a good mechanical connection be made, not only because it will prevent the possibility of any strain being carried by the individual wires, but also because it provides the system with a continuous ground. A metal connector is slipped over the end of the cable and secured there by tightening a screw. One end of this fitting is threaded and is slipped through one of the knockout holes in the outlet box. A locknut is then placed inside the box over the fitting and tightened by means of a screwdriver. See Fig. 13. Some types of outlet box

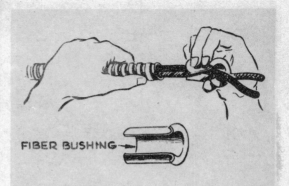

Fig. 9. A fiber anti-short bushing should be placed over the wires to protect their insulation from the rough ends of the metal cable.

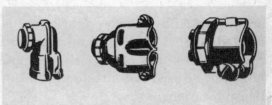

Fig. 10. A type of connector used to secure cable to outlet box.

Fig. 11. Cable outlet box connector.

Fig. 12. Cable outlet box connector. This type of connector is secured to the cable by tightening up the screw at the side.

are provided with built in clamps, which take the place of the separate connectors for the cable.

Armored cable should not be used in damp locations unless it is a leaded type, that is, one that has a lead sheath inside the armor.

Nonmetallic Sheathed Cable

This type of wiring is somewhat similar to armored cable except that instead of a covering of steel the wires

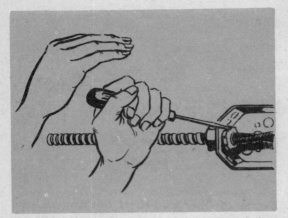

Fig. 15. Metal bracket used to support nonmetallic sheathed cable. Metal staples should not be used on this type of wire.

Fig. 13. Armored cable is secured to the outlet box by means of a lock nut, which can be tightened with a screwdriver.

are protected by a heavy fabric that is treated so that it is fire and moisture resistant. See Fig. 14. It should not, however, be used for outside work or in damp locations.

This particular type of wiring is very popular wherever it is permitted by codes. It is less expensive than the rigid steel conduit or armored cable and is very easy to work with.

For the most part, nonmetallic sheathed cable is installed in the same manner as armored cable. Metal straps, rather than large staples, should be used to fasten the cable to woodwork. See Fig. 15. Staples are not satisfactory because of the possibility that their sharp points may damage the

cable's fiber covering. The cable should be supported every 4 feet or so and 12 inches from each outlet box.

The outer covering of this type of wire can be removed by slitting it with a knife and then ripping it back as far as desired—at least 6 inches when connections are to be made. The ends of the insulation can then be cut off with a jacknife. Be careful not to damage any of the insulation around the individual wires when cutting off the outer insulation.

Nonmetallic cable can be fastened to an outlet box with a type of fitting similar to that used with armored cable. The connector is first attached securely to the cable and then inserted in the box. A locknut is then run up to secure the connection.

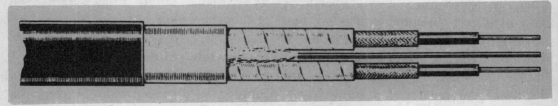

Fig. 14. Nonmetallic sheathed cable.

One type of nonmetallic cable has a third wire—an uninsulated wire—for grounding purposes. If the local code requires this method of wiring, the un- insulated wire should be attached to the frame of the outlet box. In this way the entire system is grounded through the ground wires connected to the boxes.

WIRE SIZE

The size of wire required for the various circuits throughout the house will depend in each case on the circuit.

There are three different kinds of circuit. The first is the general purpose branch circuit. This requires a 15 ampere fuse and the wire size is No. 14. The maximum safe load for this circuit is 1725 watts, a figure arrived at by multiplying amperes (15) by volts (115). This type of circuit is used for lighting, and the like.

The second type of circuit is the appliance branch circuit. It is fused with a 20 ampere fuse and the wire should be No. 12. It has a safe load of 2300 watts and is required for the various electrical appliances used in the kitchen, dining room, workshop, etc. These appliance branch circuits should *not* be used for lighting purposes—they are for appliances only.

The third type of circuit is the individual branch circuit and here the wire size will vary depending on the particular piece of equipment it serves. Each individual branch circuit serves one piece of equipment only. Fuel-fired heating equipment, electric garbage-disposal units, automatic washing machines, home freeze units, water pumps, and power equipment for the home workshop should all have individual 20 ampere, No. 12 wire branch circuits. Heavier equipment such as electric kitchen ranges or electric clothes dryers will require even heavier wiring. Kitchen ranges usually require a No. 6 wire and a 50 ampere fuse on a three wire 115/230 volt system.

NUMBER OF CIRCUITS REQUIRED

As a general rule, there should be one general purpose branch circuit for every 500 square feet of finished floor area or fraction thereof. All these circuits are of No. 14 wire with 15 ampere fuses. In addition to this, there should be at least two appliance branch circuits for the kitchen, for the workshop, and so on. These require No. 12 wire. After these come any individual branch circuits that may be required. Fig. 16 shows the wiring diagram for the basic house. It contains 3 general purpose branch circuits, 2 appliance branch circuits and 3 individual branch circuits. Adequate wiring should not only contain a sufficient number of circuits to meet present requirements but should also provide for expansion of the house or an increase in various types of elec-

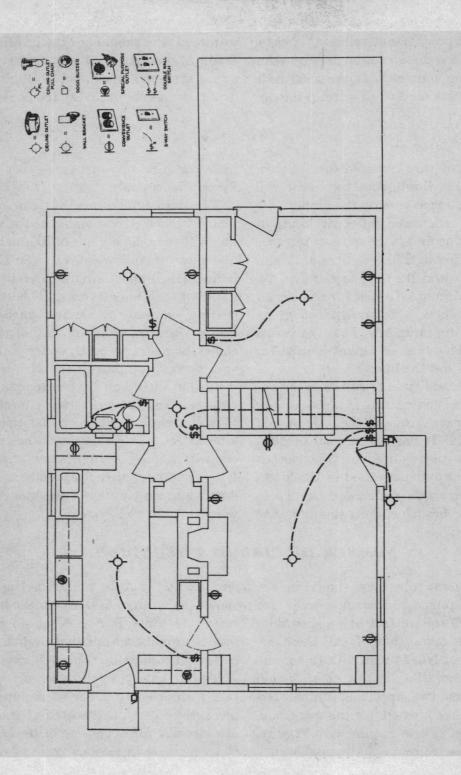

Fig. 16. Wiring diagram for house.

trical equipment. It is a lot simpler to put in additional circuits for future needs when the main wiring is being done than to have to do this work at a later date when the walls and ceilings have been finished and wires have to be run in back of the walls and fished out through openings.

WIRING THE HOUSE

The Service Entrance

The first step in wiring the house is to locate the position of the service entrance. This is the point where the power is brought into the house and its exact location will depend on the location of power lines. The local power company should be consulted in this matter. The service entrance will include the wires that bring the power into the house as well as the meter and service switch.

The meter and switch can be placed indoors, but there is a definite advantage in having the meter outside which is that this allows the meter to be read without disturbing the household. Also, if there is no basement, it is just one less piece of equipment that you have to find wall space for.

Service insulators must be installed on the outside of the house, where they serve as a base for the power lines running to the house. See Fig. 17. Three of these insulators will be required, and they can be installed individually or as a unit. The insulators must be placed at least 6 inches apart and must be solidly attached to the building. They should be placed as high on the building as possible. If the power lines have to cross a road or driveway, there is usually a regulation in the local code

that states just how far off the ground they must be. In the event that there is no regulation in the local code, be sure to keep the insulator at least 18 feet off the ground. The power lines are attached to these insulators and the service cable that brings the power into the house is spliced to them.

The service wires should be No. 4, wire, and you will require 3 of them. They can be run through conduit or you can use special service-entrance cable that does not require a conduit. If the service wires are to be run underground, a lead-sheathed cable is used that is run through a conduit.

Where the service wires leave the conduit or cable in order to be attached

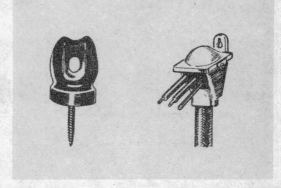

Fig. 17. Insulator used to attach entrance wires to building.

Fig. 18. A service head for a service entrance cable.

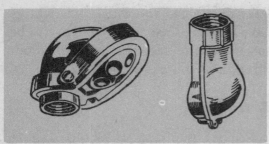

Fig. 19. Service head for service entrance conduit.

Fig. 20. Type of fitting used at bottom of conduit to bring entrance cable into building.

to the power lines, a special type of fitting is required so that moisture will not get into the cable or conduit. This fitting is called a service head. When rigid conduit is used still another special fitting is required at the point where the wires enter the building. See Figs. 18 and 19.

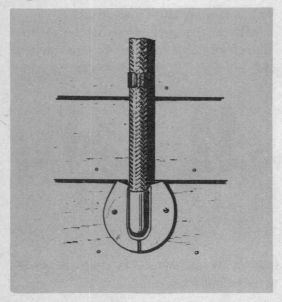

Fig. 21. Sill plate used to bring service entrance cable into building.

A similar type of service head (Figs. 20 and 21) is required for service cable where it enters the building to prevent moisture from following the wires indoors. Rigid conduit is attached to the side of the building by means of metal straps. The cable is attached with special clips containing screws.

If an outdoor meter is used and the service wires are run in rigid conduit, the conduit is mechanically attached to the meter box. This will produce a weathertight joint. In the case of entrance cable, a special waterproof type of fitting is used to make the joint between cable and meter box watertight.

Main Switch and Fuse Box

From the electric meter, the service cable runs to the main switch and fuse box. In old installations there was usually one piece of equipment containing the main fuses and main switch and another containing the various circuit fuses. Today there are a great many pieces of equipment that combine all these various operations in one small compact box.

The switch and fuse box should be located where it is readily accessible. If there is a basement in the home, it is the usual location for this equipment, but the basement is not necessarily the best location. It may be much more convenient to have the equipment where you can get to it easily when a fuse blows—not having to locate a flashlight and stumble down to the basement. The kitchen and the utility room are both good spots to locate the switch and fuse box. The box, recessed into the wall and with a hinged door, can, in fact, be located in any room of the house—wherever it is most convenient and still near the service entrance.

The type of service switch and fuse box to use will depend upon your pocket book and the local codes as well as on the location of the equipment. If you plan to have it recessed into one of the room walls, you want something that is compact and takes up no more room than is necessary.

Fig. 22 shows a pull-out type of switch and fuse box. The main fuses are held in clips mounted on plastic blocks. There is no over-all main switch, but when the blocks are pulled out of the cabinet by means of their handles, the power to the house circuits is cut off.

Fuses for the house circuits are located under the main fuses.

Fig. 23 shows another type of switch and fuse box. In this piece of equipment, when the door of the box is opened the current is automatically cut off. It also contains fuses for the house circuits.

Another type of equipment is the circuit breaker. This unit does not contain the orthodox type of fuse. When there is an overload or a short circuit, the mechanism inside the circuit breaker automatically breaks the flow of current and cannot be set back until the cause of the trouble has been removed. The main switch mechanism inside the box is operated by a small mechanical switch. See Fig. 24.

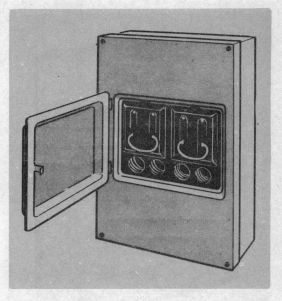

Fig. 22. A pull-out type of main switch and fuse box.

The great advantage that the circuit breaker has over the ordinary type of fuse box is that when there is a short circuit, you do not have to worry about whether or not there is an extra fuse around to replace the one that has blown. Once the cause of the trouble has been corrected, the circuit breaker

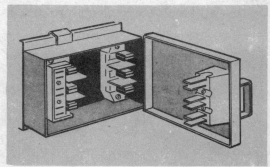

Fig. 23. The switch in this type of switch and fuse box is operated by opening and closing the switch-box door. When the door is open the house circuits are broken.

Fig. 24. Circuit breaker.

tion should be removed than is necessary to make a good connection—electrically as well as mechanically. Be sure to clean the wires at the point of contact so that no insulation is left on them.

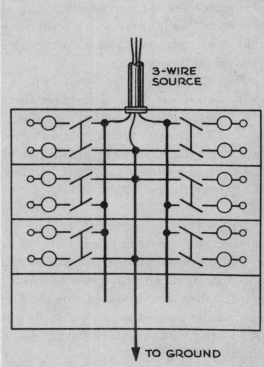

can be reset. Some local codes do not permit circuit breakers.

All connections on the service entrance equipment must be of the solderless type. See Fig. 25. Lugs are provided in the units so that the various wires can be attached. No more insula-

Fig. 25. Lug used for making connections at service entrance.

Fig. 26. Internal wiring for typical switch box. Note that no soldered connections are used inside the switch box. Also note the ground wire from the switch box which is connected to the house plumbing system.

Fig. 27. A single uninsulated wire in an armored cable is used to ground the house electrical system.

Service switches and fuse boxes usually have an internal wiring diagram attached to them so that there will be no chance of a slip-up when making the connections. Fig. 26 shows a typical switch box with internal wiring. This wiring will apply for the basic house. Note that the third wire of the service cable, the neutral wire, is grounded to a metal plate. This plate in turn is grounded by running an armored ground wire to a cold-water line. See Fig. 27. The one wire inside this cable is not insulated. The connection should be made to the cold-water supply rather than to the hot-water lines because the cold offers a better ground. The type of clamp used to connect the ground wire to the pipe should be of the same metal as the pipe. See Fig. 28. If you have brass pipe, use a brass connector. If the pipes are steel, then use a steel connector. The reason for all this is that if dissimilar metals are used, you will get an electrolytic action between the metals that will prevent an adequate ground.

In case you make the ground on the house side of the water meter, there should be an electrical connection made around the meter. This is necessary because if the meter should be removed for one reason or another, you will still

Fig. 28. Ground clamp used to secure ground wire to plumbing line.

want your electrical system and it must be adequately grounded. Fig. 29 shows the type of hook-up used for this purpose. Of course, if you ground the wires on the far side of the meter, this procedure is not necessary.

The rating of the service equipment will depend on the number of circuits and the load required. For our purpose, the switch should be rated at 100

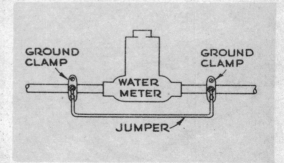

Fig. 29. If the house has a water meter, a wire jumper should be put around it so that if the meter is removed, the electrical system will remain grounded.

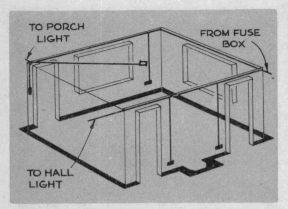

Fig. 30. Wiring diagram for living room.

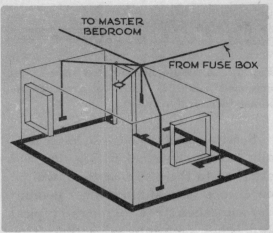

Fig. 32. The wiring diagram for small bedroom.

amperes and the main fuse at 70 amperes. If a circuit breaker is used, it should have a 70 ampere rating.

The next project is to install the various outlet, switch and junction boxes. Figs. 30, 31, 32, 33 and 34 show approximate locations for these boxes in the various rooms. The solid lines are general branch circuits that are rated at 15 amperes and made of No. 14 wire. The dotted lines are 20 ampere appliance circuits made with No. 12 wire. Shaded lines are individual circuits.

Installing Outlet Boxes

Metal outlet, switch and junction boxes serve several purposes. See Fig. 35. First, they provide a base for mounting fixtures or switches. Second,

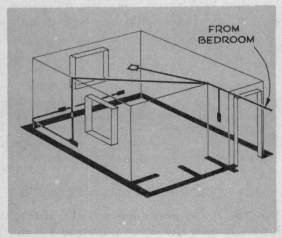

Fig. 31. The wiring diagram for master bedroom.

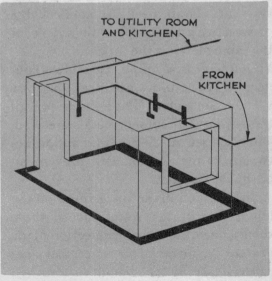

Fig. 33. Wiring diagram for bathroom.

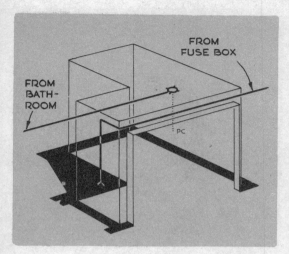

Fig. 34. **Wiring diagram for utility room.**

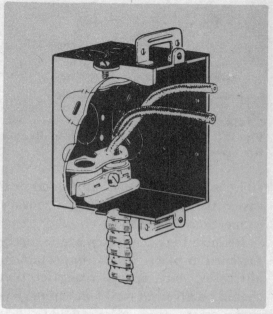

Fig. 35. **Outlet box showing clamps used to secure the cable to the box.**

they provide a means of splicing wires. No splices should be made, under any circumstances, except in boxes. The reason for this is that there is usually enough inflammable matter, such as dust or sawdust, in back of a wall or ceiling to start a fire if there should be a short-circuit spark in the wiring.

These metal boxes can be had with brackets attached to them so that they can be attached to the studding or joists. Some types have small metal lips suitable for the same purpose. See Fig. 36. When a box must be placed between two pieces of studding or joists, metal hangers can be used or the opening can be framed with odd bits of studding. See Figs. 37 and 38.

The various boxes are provided with several little round knockouts, which can be removed so that the wires can be brought into the box. See Fig. 39. Just give the circular piece of metal a sharp jab with a heavy screwdriver and it can then be easily removed. Do not re-

move any more of these knockouts than there are wires entering the box. Each box has a metal face-plate, which must be replaced after all the connections have been made.

You will find that it is better to use the larger sizes of boxes whenever pos-

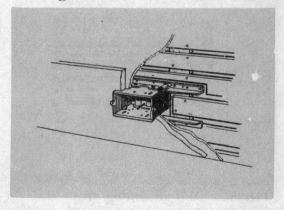

Fig. 36. **Outlet box with metal bracket for fastening to wall studding.**

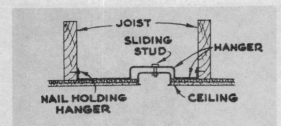

Fig. 37. Outlet box with built-in hanger for use on ceilings.

sible, as they will make it a good deal easier for you to handle the various connections inside the box.

Be sure that the boxes are securely fastened in place. This is important in all cases, but special consideration should be given to wall and ceiling fixtures where the entire weight of a rather heavy fixture will be carried by the outlet box. Do not forget to allow for the thickness of the plaster or wall-board that is going to make the interior walls.

No matter what type of wiring method is used, it is most important that there is a strong mechanical con-

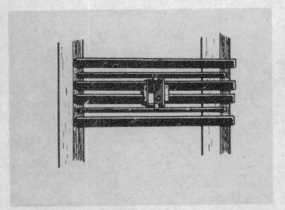

Fig. 38. Steel mounting strips used to fasten outlet box between wall studding or ceiling joists.

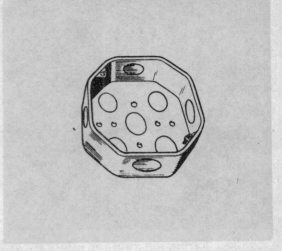

Fig. 39. Outlet box showing knock-outs.

nection between the conduit or cable and the box. Allow the wires to extend into the box for about 6 inches, as this much free wire will be required for making connections.

Black and White Wire

One of the wires used in wiring is covered with black insulation. The other is covered with white or grey insulation; sometimes it has a white tracer instead of a solid color. The black wire is always the "hot" wire and the white wire is always the neutral wire. When the wires are connected to the fuse box, the black wire should be connected so that the current to it is broken by the fuse. The white wire is connected to the metal neutral-strip, which is grounded. Throughout the entire wiring system, this difference between the two wires must be respected. The black wire is always broken by a switch, the white one never. See Fig.

40. The reason for this is that if the white wire were to be broken by the switch and the black wire run directly to the fixture, then, even though the switch were off, current would be flowing to the fixture and if someone were to touch it and be grounded at the same time, he would get a shock. The black wire should never be connected to the white wire except in one special circumstance, mentioned later.

Three-Wire Cable

Cable containing three wires—black, white and red—should be used on all three-way switches, that is, when a fixture is to be controlled by two switches at different locations. While not absolutely necessary, three-wire cable should also be used for fixtures controlled by wall switches since this will eliminate an extra run of cable.

Fig. 41. A pigtail splice. The wires should be soldered and then covered with rubber insulation tape as well as friction tape.

From the main fuse box, the various circuits run to the portion of the house that they serve. If there is a basement in the house, the logical place to run these sub-feeders is along the basement ceiling and then up through the floor into the wall area. If there is no basement, the lines can run either through the wall or along the ceiling.

The best way to insure a wiring job that will pass the most critical inspection is to do it as neatly as you possibly

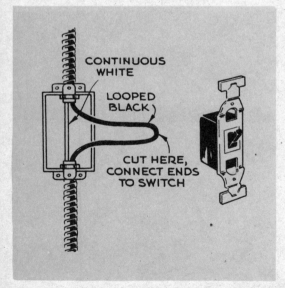

Fig. 40. When a switch is installed, it should always be wired through the black wire rather than the white wire.

CONTINUOUS WHITE

LOOPED BLACK

CUT HERE, CONNECT ENDS TO SWITCH

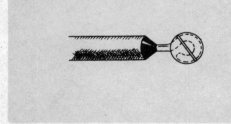

Fig. 42. How wire should be fastened around terminal screw. The wire goes around the screw in the same direction that the screw is turned to tighten.

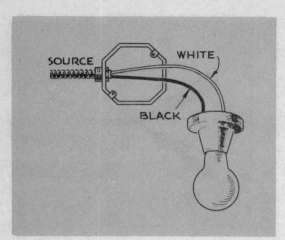

Fig. 43. The simplest type of hook-up. The supply of current to the fixture is controlled by a switch and pull chain built into the fixture.

can. Be sure that all connections to outlet boxes are secure. When it is necessary to splice a wire—and splices should only occur in metal boxes—use a pigtail splice as shown in Fig. 41.

Remove the insulation from the ends of the wire and then scrape the wire clean with a knife. Twist the wires together and then solder the connection. Unlike connections in the service entrance, connections in the house wiring should be soldered. You can save yourself a lot of time by making all the connections first and then going around and dipping each one in a small ladle filled with molten solder. This is considerably faster than trying to solder each connection with a soldering iron.

After the connection has been soldered, the exposed wires should be covered with a layer of rubber tape. Over this goes friction tape until the insulation around the splice is at least as thick as the insulation on the rest of the wires.

When connecting wires to terminal screws on wall switches or on fixtures,

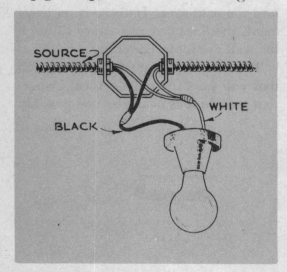

Fig. 44. When the source is to continue on to another fixture, splices in the wires must be made inside the first fixture outlet box.

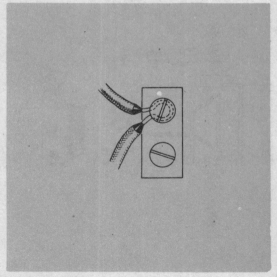

Fig. 45. When a wire continues on to another fixture, it is not necessary to cut it at a terminal screw.

remove only enough insulation to allow the wire to be twisted around the screw. The wire should go around the terminal screw in the same direction that the screw is turned to be tightened. See Fig. 42. If the wire goes on in the opposite direction, as the screw is run up it will have a tendency to force the wire away. A pair of long-nosed pliers is a "must" for making tight and neat electrical connections.

The simplest type of wiring that you will run into is that for an outlet with a pull-chain, such as will be required in the basement, closets, etc. Wires running directly from the source are connected to the fixture without any other problem involved. See Fig. 43. If the wires are to continue on to another outlet, a splice must be made inside the first fixture-outlet box. See Fig. 44. The same thing applies when wiring to convenience outlets. In this case, however, it is often not necessary to make a splice because the terminal screws on the outlet itself will allow you to make the connection between the two wires here. See Fig. 45.

When a fixture is to be controlled by a wall switch, the wiring becomes a little more complex. Fig. 46 shows one method of taking care of this matter. The cable running from the fixture box to the switch box contains ordinary black and white wire. The white wire of the source cable is attached to the white wire of the fixture. The black wire of the source cannot be attached to the black wire of the switch cable because this wire is going to have to be attached

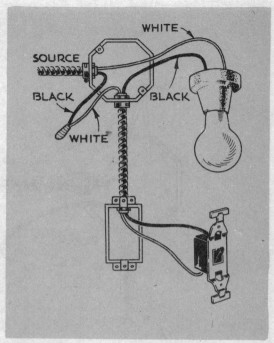

Fig. 46. How a wall switch should be wired to a fixture. Note that because a standard black and white wire cable is used from the fixture to the switch, the black source wire is connected to the white switch wire.

to the black wire of the fixture. The only thing to do then is to attach the black wire of the source to the white wire of the switch cable. (This is the *only* case where black wire is attached to white.) Of course, if the location of the source cable is such that it can easily be run through the switch on the way to the fixture, all this is not necessary. The connection can be made as shown in Fig. 40.

Another way of wiring in a wall switch so that it will control a fixture but not the one beyond is shown in Fig. 47. Here the source is brought into the switch on a regular two-wire cable.

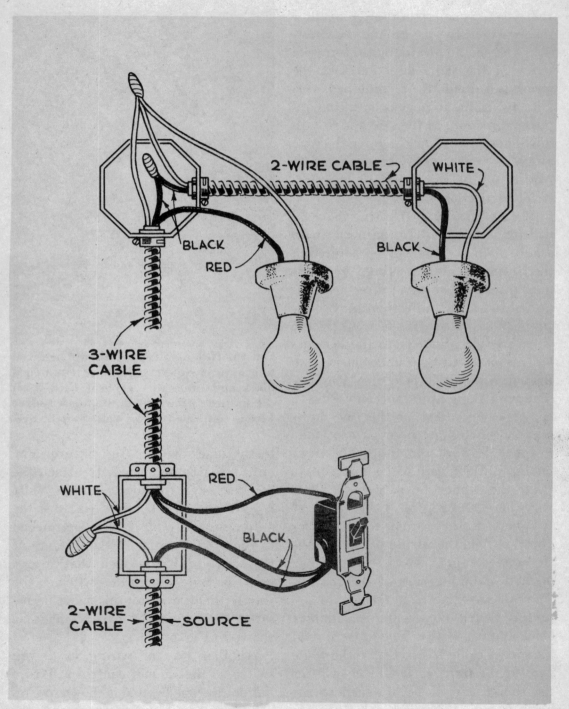

Fig. 47. The above illustrates how a switch should be wired to two fixtures when it is only to control the first and not the second fixture.

The white wire is not run through the switch but is connected to the white wire running to the fixture. The black wire of the source is connected to one side of the switch and then continues on to the second fixture that is not to be controlled by that particular switch. The red wire is connected to the opposite side of the switch from the black, and the red wire is then run to connect to the black wire of the fixture that you want to control from that switch. If you want the switch to control both fixtures, use the hook-up in Fig. 48.

In some cases it is convenient to have one fixture controlled by two switches. This is particularly useful in the living room, since it allows lights to be turned on at either entrance, and in the case of basement and attic stair-lights and in the garage. The hook-up required will depend on the location of the switches

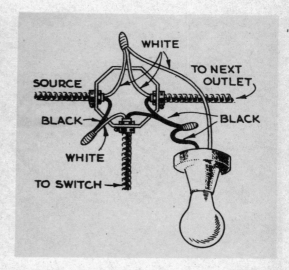

Fig. 48. This type of hook-up should be used when you wish one switch to control two light fixtures.

in relation to the fixture. If both switches—and they must be special three-way switches—come before the fixture, the hook-up in Fig. 49 can be

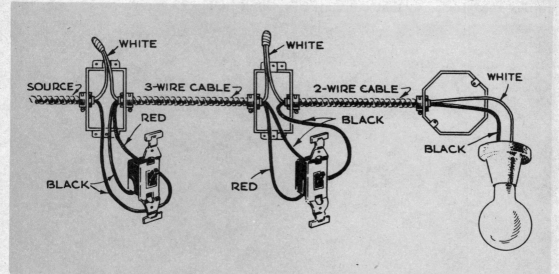

Fig. 49. The above illustration shows the hook-up used when source enters one of the three-way switches and both switches come before the fixture. Three-wire cable is needed only between the two switches and not throughout.

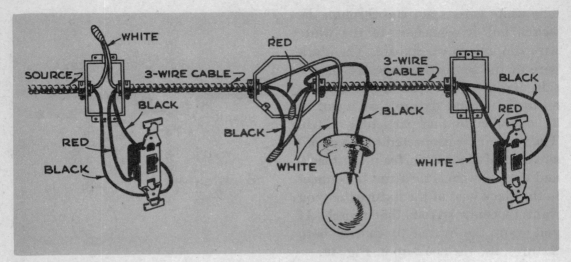

Fig. 50. As depicted above, when the fixture is located between the two three-way switches, three-wire cable must be used throughout.

used. If the fixture is between the two switches, then Fig. 50 shows the correct connection. If the source comes into the fixture first, use Figs. 51 and 52.

In some cases it is desirable to wire duplex receptacles so that one half of the outlet can be controlled by a switch while the other half remains permanently connected. The wiring diagram for this hook-up is shown in Fig. 53.

Convenience outlets are usually located about 12 inches or so from the

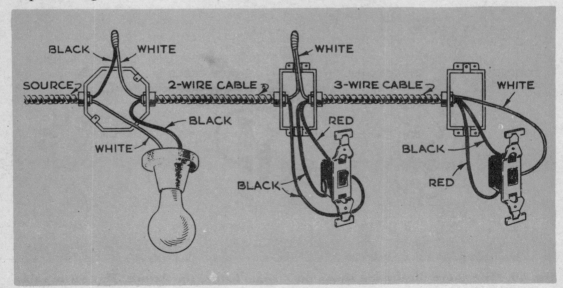

Fig. 51. Hook-up used when the source enters at the fixture but the two three-way switches are located past the fixture on the same side.

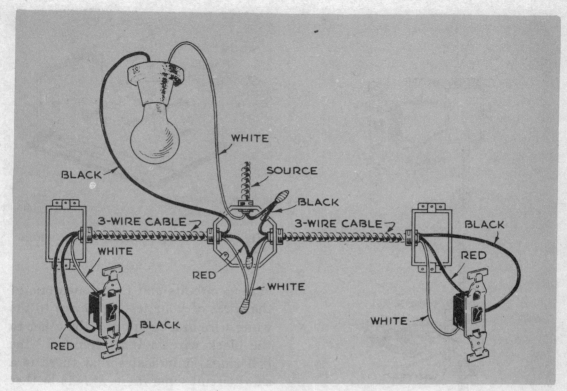

WHITE

SOURCE

BLACK

BLACK

3-WIRE CABLE

3-WIRE CABLE

BLACK

WHITE

RED

RED

WHITE

WHITE

BLACK

RED

WHITE

Fig. 52. The above diagram illustrates a hook-up used to control fixture from two three-way switches when the source enters at the fixture.

sub-floor. Wall switches should be about 4 feet from the floor. Appliance outlets in the kitchen should be placed where they will be readily accessible for plugging in various pieces of kitchen equipment, irons, etc. The final say on this matter should come from the lady of the house. It is her kitchen, so put the outlets where she wants them. The location of these outlets shown in Fig. 54 is only a suggestion.

The location of junction boxes should be such that they can be examined without having to remove any of the wall or ceiling. They should be covered with removable metal plates.

Testing the Wiring

Once the rough wiring has been done, it should be checked over to be sure that it is free of short circuits or any other wiring mistakes. This should be done before switches or outlets are installed and, of course, before the system is connected to the power lines and before the interior wall and ceiling material goes on.

There are special testing devices you can use for this job, but two ordinary dry cells connected in series with a door bell will prove perfectly adequate.

First of all, twist together any wires in the system, such as those in the

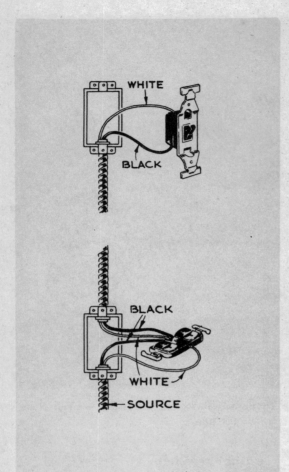

Fig. 53. The switch in this illustration will control one-half of a duplex outlet. This type of connection is very useful in the living room or bedroom when there are no wall or ceiling fixtures.

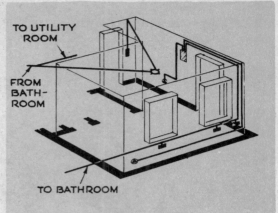

Fig. 54. Wiring diagram for kitchen.

switch boxes, that would ordinarily be attached together either directly or by means of a switch. Wires that are to be connected to fixtures later on should not be connected—they should be spread apart so that there is no chance of their coming together.

The first part of the test is made at the switch box. Insert fuses for the various circuits and then touch one of the wires of your testing device to the white wire in a circuit and the other to the black wire in that circuit. If the bell rings, it indicates that there is a short circuit somewhere. It may be that the black and white wires are touching each other somewhere in the system or, if you are using flexible armored cable or steel conduit, that a black wire is touching the metal of the conduit, cable or metal box. Each circuit should be checked through in this manner. The next check is made by removing the bell from the batteries and connecting one wire from the battery to the white wire, and the other to the black wire. Now take the bell and go around and connect it to the black and white wires of the various outlets. If all is well, the bell will ring. If it does not, go back and check first any wall switch outlets in that particular circuit. It may be that the wires you twisted together are not making a good contact. If this is not the case, there is an open circuit someplace and you can find it by moving back along the circuit towards the fuse box until the bell rings. Once you have found the approximate location of the open circuit, it will have to be hunted out and corrected.

If armored cable or conduit is used for the wiring, there is one other test that can be made. With the same hookup just mentioned, touch one terminal of the bell to the black wire and the other to the metal box. If the bell rings, it means that the system is adequately grounded. If it fails to ring, it means that at some point in the system you do not have a good mechanical connection between the armor cable or conduit and the box. This test is not used on non-metallic sheathed cable unless it has a ground wire, because with the two-wire cable, you do not have any connection between the various boxes.

As soon as you have your system checked out, you can go ahead and wire in the switches and outlets. Ceiling and wall fixtures cannot be attached to the outlet boxes until the ceiling and walls themselves have been completed, but be sure that there is a sufficient amount

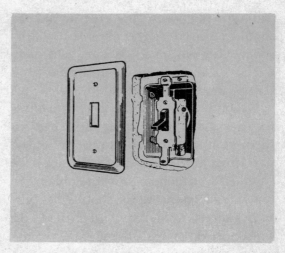

Fig. 55. Wall switch installed in box and the cover plate that is installed after the finish wall is in place.

of wire in each box to allow these connections to be easily made.

From this point on there is nothing more you can do with the final wiring until the walls and ceilings have been finished. But you can, if you wish, install temporary fixtures and tape up any wires not required so that the power can be connected into the house and you will have adequate lighting for interior work as well as having power for machine tools.

FINISHING THE WIRING

When the walls and ceilings have been finished, the last step in the house wiring can be completed. This will include mounting and attaching the various fixtures, in addition to installing plates over switches, outlets, etc. See Fig. 55.

Electric fixtures are of standard design and every brand is equipped with some sort of device so that it can be attached to an outlet box.

Fixtures used in damp locations should be of porcelain rather than metal as this reduces the shock hazard. For ordinary purposes, this type of fixture should be used in the basement, bathroom, kitchen and garage. Outdoor fixtures should be of some special type that is weathertight.

Certain types of wall and ceiling fixtures have two wires attached to them that are to be connected to the two wires in the outlet box. White wire should be attached to white, black to black. All connections should be pigtail splices, soldered and taped. If there are no wires on the fixture, the outlet wires can be attached to it with the terminal screws. The white wire should be attached to the white terminal screw, the black wire to the bronze or gold screw. Wall switches and convenience outlets are attached to the wires by means of terminal screws on the body of the switch or outlet.

Do not allow a fixture to be hung so that only the wires support it. It must be solidly attached to the outlet box.

You will find when fastening wall switches in place, that the holes on the outlet box are elongated so that even if the box is not quite straight, it is still possible to position the switch itself so that it sits plumb.

WIRING FOR KITCHEN RANGES

Wiring for kitchen ranges differs from the ordinary house wiring in that a three-wire system is used instead of a two-wire system. Ranges operate on 115/230 volts, while the rest of the house system operates on 115 volts and a two-wire system.

The reason for the three-wire system for ranges is to provide the necessary span of temperature control. When the range is turned up as high as it will go, it operates on 230 volts. When cut down low, it operates on 115 volts.

Many persons are confused as to just what volts and amperes are. Such confusion can cause a good deal of trouble when it comes to installing electrical equipment. *Volt* is a term used to indicate the electrical pressure in a line. It does not indicate how much current is actually flowing through the line. The unit used to measure the actual flow is the *ampere*.

The practice today is to bring a three-wire 115/230-volt system into the house when the service entrance is installed. This eliminates the need for doing any great amount of extra wiring if you should decide to install an electric range at some later date.

Most of the electrical equipment on the market today is made to operate on a 115-volt system. If this equipment were to be wired directly into a 230-volt system, the pressure of the current in the lines would be too great and the appliance would be ruined.

Ranges rated above 12 kilowatts should be fused with a 50-ampere fuse to take care of the heavy flow of current required by such appliances. The wiring from the switch box to the range must also be heavy enough to carry the current without the wire's overheating and burning up the insulation.

When a 50-ampere fuse is used, a No. 6 wire is suitable. The type of wiring can be the same as that used for the house electrical system. BX cable, non-metallic sheathed cable and conduit are all suitable.

The electric range cannot be wired directly to the house system but must be wired through a plug that provides a means of disconnecting it from the system. This plug is a heavy-duty three-wire receptacle. It must have a rating in amperes adequate for serving the equipment, as must the wiring and the fuse. The receptacle is usually placed in back of the range so the range can be plugged right into it.

The frame of the range must be grounded. This is accomplished either by an independent ground or by connecting the frame right to the neutral wire.

MATERIALS LIST FOR ELECTRICAL EQUIPMENT FOR THE BASIC HOUSE

1	3-wire service entrance cable (length depends on location)		1	Outside wall fixture
1	Service entrance head		6	Single wall switches
1	Service entrance ell or sill plate		2	Double wall switches
1	Switch and fuse box or circuit breaker		2	3-way switches
1	Grounding bushing		14	Duplex convenience outlets
1	No. 6 wire ground cable (length of run from fuse box to water pipe)		3	Special purpose outlets
			12	Wall-switch plates
			14	Duplex convenience plates
30	4" or 3¼" outlet boxes		3	Special purpose outlet plates
29	2½"-deep switch boxes		9	Offset metal hangers for ceiling fixtures
100	Cable connectors			
100	Fiber bushings (for flexible armored cable only)		350	feet (approximately) of No. 14 two-wire cable
7	Ceiling fixtures		50	feet (approximately) of No. 14 three-wire cable
2	Ceiling fixtures with pull chain		50	feet (approximately) of No. 12 two-wire cable
2	Wall fixtures		2	Door bells and buttons

Chapter 15

THE HEATING SYSTEM

THERE are relatively few sections of this country where it is possible to get along without some sort of heating system. In the cold northern climates, a good central heating system is as important as any other part of the house. In fact, real estate agents, banks and others engaged in buying and selling homes attach a good deal of importance to an adequate heating system, and they are certainly right, because few things will ruin a house as fast as a heating system that is not efficient, that fails to make the house comfortable to live in during cold weather, or that never seems to work very well for long periods and requires constant attention. You may not care, or be allowed, to install your own heating system, but that does not mean that you should not put ample time and thought into selecting adequate equipment.

TYPES OF HEATING SYSTEMS

There are two main points that must be decided. First, what type of system to use, and, second, what kind of fuel to burn. There are three main types of heating system in use today. They are warm air, hot water and steam.

Warm-Air Heating Systems

The simplest type of warm-air heating system is the pipeless furnace. It consists of a furnace that is fired by either gas, coal or oil. At the top of the furnace is a heat drum that is warmed by the fire in the furnace. Cold air circulates around this drum and, when heated, rises through a register and into the room above. As the air becomes chilled, it drops back down to the floor and is drawn down through the edges of the register to be reheated. There is only one register used in this system and it is located in one of the main rooms of the house, usually the living room.

This is a very inexpensive system and is very easily installed. There are no pipes, ducts or registers other than the main one, which is actually a part of the furnace. The only work involved in installation is setting up the furnace and making the hole in the floor for the register.

There are, however, several drawbacks to this kind of system. First of all, it is not very efficient. A large amount of the warm air that flows up through the register remains in the room where the register is located. This means that to get the other rooms in the house comfortable in very cold weather, it is often necessary to have the living room too warm. Another point is that the heating is more or less uneven. The warm air remains around the ceilings and drops to the floor as it becomes cold. This means that when you are standing up there will be a considerable temperature difference between the air around your head and that around your feet. People who live in homes heated by pipeless furnaces usually complain that their feet are always cold. Another point against the pipeless furnace is the fact that the warm air depends on doors for circulation to the other rooms in the house. When a door is closed, no heat will enter that particular room unless wall registers have been installed. Also, housewives complain bitterly about the amount of dust and dirt that comes out of the register along with the warm air, and there is no effective remedy for this because it is impossible to install an effective filtering device on a pipeless furnace. Lastly, because it depends entirely on gravity and the fact that warm air rises, a pipeless furnace must be installed in a basement. It cannot, like other types of warm-air heating or hot-water systems, be installed in the utility room unless it is a certain type of pipeless furnace—usually called a space heater—that does not have to be put in a basement. Space heaters are very compact in design and can be used in the utility room, in an interior wall partition, or hung through the floor from the room above. A fan operated by electricity, is used to force the warm air from these heaters to various points in the house. Good space heaters will work very well in a small compact house. They do not require much space and are fully automatic. In some cases, two heaters are used to provide the necessary amount of heat. But even then, if they are hung through the floor, they do not take up too much space. If you do not plan to use the attic space as living quarters, a good space heater with the required BTU (British thermal unit) output will prove perfectly adequate.

The Gravity Warm-Air System

A more advanced type of warm-air heating than the pipeless furnace is the gravity system. This employs the same sort of furnace as the pipeless system but metal ducts are used to bring the heat from the furnace to the various rooms in the house. Other ducts and registers are used to return the cold air from the rooms to the furnace for reheating. Before the air is heated, it passes through a filter, which removes any dust or dirt that may have been picked up.

A gravity system when properly installed will prove quite adequate for even two-story homes. The heating is even and the flow of warm air to the various rooms can be governed by opening or closing the individual room registers. But like the pipeless furnace, it must be installed in a basement.

Forced Warm-Air Systems

The most efficient as well as most modern type of warm-air system is the "forced" system. This has little or no resemblance to the old pipeless system. It consists of a furnace that warms the air, an electric blower, and ducts and registers. Air heated by the furnace is forced through the ducts to the various registers. Additional registers and ducts are used to bring the cold air back to the furnace to be reheated. Filtering devices are used to remove dust and dirt particles from the air, and a humidifying system adds sufficient moisture, when required, so that the air does not become too dry. The heat output to the various rooms in a house can be governed by the dampers in the ducts or at the registers in the rooms.

Because the warm air is forced through the ducts in this type of system rather than just flowing through them by its tendency to rise, a forced system does not have to be installed in a basement. It can be installed in the utility room and will give just as good service, or it can be installed at some other point.

If you are looking for the best in warm-air heat, a forced system is your safest bet and will provide excellent heat.

Hot-Water Systems

So far we have considered only heating systems where air is heated and sent directly to the rooms in the house. Now we take up systems in which a medium for heating air is sent to the rooms and the air in the rooms is warmed by circulating around it. In the case of a hot-water system, hot water is obviously the medium used to warm the air. The water is heated in a boiler and then flows through one of various devices. In the rooms, the heat in the water is diffused, either through radiation or convection. The old-fashioned hot-water system consisted of a furnace and a boiler to heat the hot water. From the furnace the water flowed through pipes to the radiators in the rooms. Hot water, like hot air, will rise and, therefore, there was a natural circulation of water through the system, the hot rising and the cold returning to the boiler to be reheated. This type of system, in which the boiler has to be located below the lowest radiator, is seldom used today. Modern hot-water heating systems use small pumps to force the hot water through the radiators. This means that the furnace and boiler do not have to be installed in a basement. They can be installed in the utility room. Another improvement in hot-water heating is the replacement of the large bulky radiators with convectors that can be set into walls and take up practically no room, or baseboard panels or radiant-heat floor panels set in a concrete-slab floor such as is used in the basic house.

A hot-water system gives very even heat. Moreover, just as soon as the water becomes warm, it begins to warm the room and, therefore, the heating is easily controlled. The main drawback is the fact that the entire system is full of water and if you wish to close the house during the winter or if, for some reason or another, the furnace goes off for a long time, the entire system must be drained.

Steam Systems

As hot water was the medium used to heat the air in a hot-water system, steam is the medium used in a steam system. This system requires a furnace and boiler along with radiators or some other means of allowing the heat to be absorbed by the air in the rooms. Steam systems must be installed in a basement. Another disadvantage is the fact that when the system is turned on, you do not get any heat in the radiators or panels until the water in the boiler reaches 212°, which is the temperature at which steam forms. You do not have quite the same control over a steam system as you do with forced air or hot water because of this very reason. When the water is hot enough to form steam, the radiators are very hot, when the water is below 212°, the radiators are cold.

Once you have made up your mind as to which type of heating system you want to install, the next point that has to be decided on is what sort of fuel you are going to burn and what sort of equipment you are going to burn it in.

FUELS

The three main types of heating fuels generally used are coal, oil and gas. As a rule, coal is the least expensive, followed by oil and finally gas. You should not, however, make your choice on this factor alone. In the first place, you may build in a location where, for one reason or another, some type of fuel other than coal may be the least expensive. In the second place, you may find that one kind of fuel is much more readily available than the others. In these changing times, it is risky to prophesy that coal, for example, will continue to be the cheapest or most available type of fuel to burn. You will be wise to check with local distributors and find out which fuel is the cheapest in your section.

As far as heating values go, all three fuels will produce excellent results if they are burned in good equipment.

Coal

Coal can be used in either hand-fired or automatic equipment. This makes it, from the standpoint of the cost of equipment, the cheapest. A hand-fired furnace is far less expensive than the automatic types that are required for gas and oil. Another point in favor of the hand-fired furnace is that a power failure will not interrupt the heating. But there are some drawbacks to a hand-fired furnace—even one with various automatic controls. Someone must be on hand at least once a day to add coal and remove some of the ashes. Automatic coal-stokers, however, require very little attention. When they draw the coal from a large bin, about the only maintenance required is the removing of a small accumulation of ashes. Other than that these stokers are completely automatic.

The main drawback to coal as a fuel is the large amount of space required for storage. This can be off-set to a certain extent by building an underground fuel bin outside the basement. Another point in favor of storing the coal outside of the house is that it removes most of the dust and dirt evil and makes the basement more usable.

Oil

Oil is a very satisfactory fuel for the home heating system. It can be stored in tanks located either in the basement or underground outdoors. It is clean and free of any dust and dirt. All oil-burning equipment, with the exception of some small space-heaters, is fully automatic.

Gas

Gas is the cleanest of all fuels to burn. If it were not for its high cost, except in some areas, it would undoubtedly be the best type of fuel to use.

FORCED WARM-AIR HEATING SYSTEM IN THE BASEMENT

Fig. 1 shows the layout for a forced warm-air heating system when the furnace is located in the basement.

The furnace is installed first and then the hot- and cold-air ducts are run from it to the various outlets in the rooms. Rectangular ducts rather than round ones are used where the ducts pass up through wall surfaces or along ceilings that are to be covered with wallboard.

Warm-air ducts should be installed in interior partitions only. If they are installed in the exterior walls, they must be insulated to reduce heat loss. The cold-air ducts, on the other hand, can be run through the exterior walls.

The warm-air outlets should be located near interior partitions and they can be either at floor level, in the baseboard or any where up to 6 feet off the floor. The best location in most cases is at baseboard height. This will give you an unbroken floor surface.

Cold-air outlets must be placed at floor level.

INSTALLING RADIANT HEATING

This job must be started before the concrete floor slab is poured. The insulation around the slab where it joins the concrete foundation is the same as

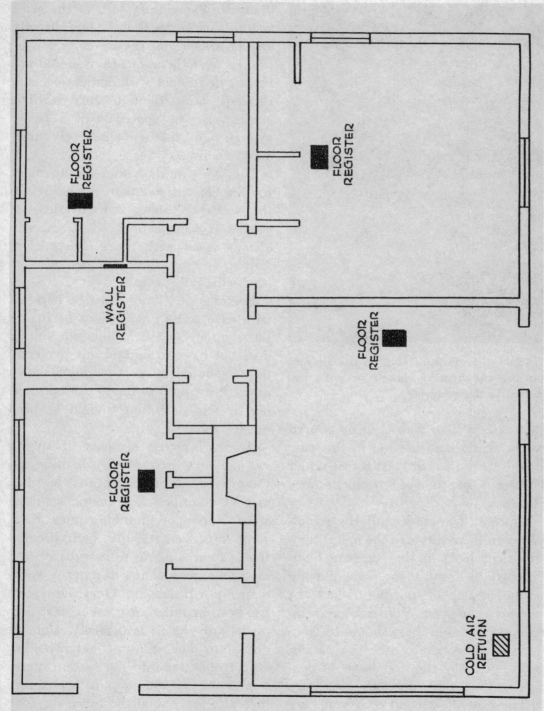

Fig. 1. Location of hot and cold registers in a house heated by forced warm air.

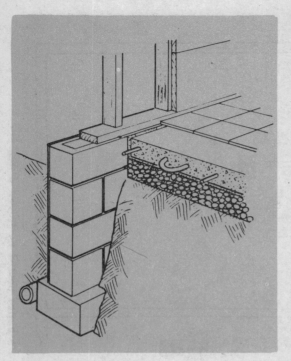

Fig. 2. Concrete floor slab on the ground showing the heating panels or coils imbedded in the concrete.

when only a floor slab is to be poured except that the insulation in this case should extend for at least 3 feet under the floor rather than only 18 inches. See Fig. 2.

The best way to install the panels is to wire them down to the metal reinforcement used in the concrete floor. This will prevent them from moving too much out of position when the concrete is poured. You must remember, however, that there should be from 2″ to 4″ of concrete over the panels, so do not make the first layer of concrete so thick that to get the necessary thickness in the second coat you have to bring the floor higher than you had

planned. The copper coils of the radiant-heating system can be laid directly on the gravel and the concrete can be poured over them, but they should not be put in contact with cinders because this will cause them to corrode. The cinders can be coated with a heavy asphalt paint that will effectively insulate the coils.

Fig. 3 shows the panel arrangement for the various rooms in the house. In this case ½″ tubing is used and it is spaced at 9 inches, but ¾″ tubing can also be used with the same spacing. Either ¾″ or 1″ tubing can also be used with 12″ spacing.

Sections of tubing must be handled with care so as not to dent or injure them in any way. While the tubing does not have to be laid out perfectly flat, it should have the design shown in the drawing and the indicated number of feet of tubing should be used in each room.

Joints between sections of tubing are made up with soldered fittings and the method employed here is the same as that described for making soldered joints in copper plumbing lines. Each joint must be carefully made because this system is going to be subject to a high pressure and any flaw in the workmanship will show up. Once the system has been installed, it must be tested to make sure that it is perfectly tight at all points. The usual method of testing is to run water into the system under a pressure of 200 pounds per square inch and leave it in the tubes for four hours. If all joints are tight after this

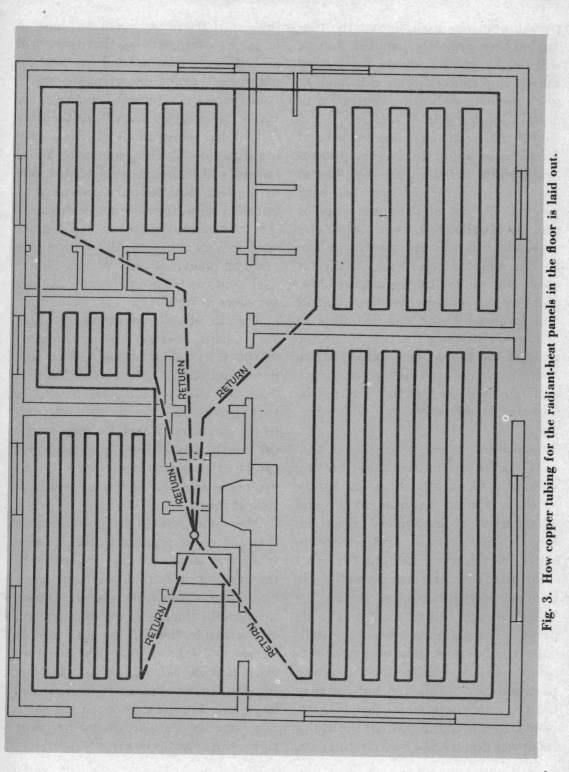

Fig. 3. How copper tubing for the radiant-heat panels in the floor is laid out.

period, you may assume that the tubing has been properly installed. As you will not have the facilities for testing the system yourself, you will have to get a plumber or heating contractor to do this job for you.

Once the system has been tested and found to be sound, take every precaution possible not to injure the pipes in any way until the concrete has been poured. Do not step on the lines or run a wheelbarrow over them. Be especially careful when spading or hoeing the fresh concrete that you do not strike the copper tubing a hard blow.

After the concrete has been poured and leveled off and has had time to set, build small wood boxes around the ends of the tubing that extend above the concrete or cover them with a larger section of pipe so that they will not be damaged in any way.

The Boiler

If the boiler for the house heating system is to be located in the utility room, it should be brought in and placed in its approximate location before the interior-wall partitions are installed. If this is not done and the boiler is installed after the interior walls have been completed, the job of getting the boiler into the utility room and in its proper location may prove very difficult. Another important reason for getting the boiler in before the inside-wall partitions are installed is that you may have to purchase a boiler that is somewhat larger than the one that the utility room was designed to hold. In this case,

the size of the utility room will have to be increased slightly so that there will be sufficient room around the heating plant for normal maintenance work. Another consideration as to the exact size of the utility room will be the type of fuel that is burned. A gas-fired heating plant is extremely compact. An oil burner will run somewhat larger, due to the fact that the burner element is installed on the outside of the furnace. An automatic coal-stoker will require considerably more room as allowance must be made not only for the stoker itself, but for the hopper and container for ashes as well.

The size of boiler recommended here for radiant heating has a rating of 96,000 BTU. This rating will be sufficient not only to take care of the first floor but also to handle the attic if it should eventually be finished off into living quarters. Panel heating is not used in the attic. Risers from the boiler can be extended up to radiators or convectors in the attic bedrooms and bath to heat them.

The boiler should be positioned so that the stove pipe from the furnace will run in as direct a line as possible to the opening made for it in the chimney flue. The stove pipe should extend through the thimble in the chimney and to the inside face of the flue tile. It should not extend past this point because if it should project into the flue tile, the furnace draft will be seriously impaired. The joint between the stove pipe and the thimble should be made tight with asbestos cement.

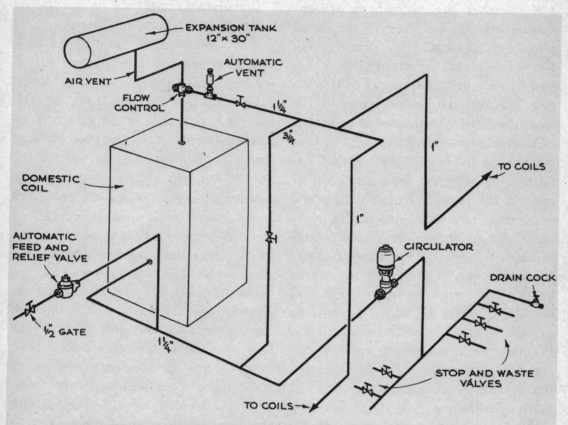

Fig. 4. Hook-up of pipes for boiler used on radiant-heating system.

The stove pipe should be adequately supported by means of metal brackets from the ceiling joists and it should be kept as far as possible from any woodwork. If it is necessary to run the pipe close to woodwork, cover the wood with a fire-resistant board.

The furnace must sit solidly on the floor in order to prevent any great amount of vibration when automatic equipment such as an oil burner or coal stoker is used. Excessive vibration when the system is working will not only be annoying to the members of the household but in time the pipe connections will loosen up and begin to leak.

Fig. 4 shows the layout for hooking up the coils to the boiler. The house water supply is brought to the boiler near the base and a ½″ gate valve is installed between the supply and the boiler. During the operation of the boiler this valve is left open. Between this valve and the boiler, an automatic feed valve and a relief valve are installed. The purpose of these is, first, to allow water from the supply to flow into the boiler when needed and, second, to prevent excessive water pressure in the house plumbing system from flowing in. From this point, the supply line is carried to a tee fitting. One end of this fitting is connected to the boiler at the base, the other is connected in by means of a second tee fitting to a ¾" line that runs up to the top of the boiler. Continuing on with the horizontal run of pipe at the base, the next fitting is a circulator. This is an electrically operated pump that forces the water through the coils in the floor. The circulator is one of the most important parts of the entire heating system, and it is well worth the added expense to get the best. The first consideration is that both pump and motor are well constructed so that they will give years of uninterrupted service. As this unit will be in operation a good deal of time, a self-lubricating type of pump and motor are most desirable if you wish to eliminate constant maintenance. Another factor that must be considered is vibration. Excessive vibration during operation on the part of the circulator will be transmitted throughout the entire heating system. The best type of circulator, from this standpoint, has a flexible connection between motor and pump, and the motor is mounted to the pump by means of springs. This arrangement reduces any possibility of vibration.

You will note that the circulator is installed in the return line of the heating system rather than in the supply.

Circulators can be had for either horizontal or vertical mounting.

The circulator is connected into a line that, in turn, is connected to the return lines from the various room-panels. Each return line from the various room-panels is fitted with a stop-and-waste valve. The purpose of these valves is to allow you to control the flow of hot water through the various rooms and so get varying temperatures according to your own taste. If you wish to keep the bedrooms a few degrees cooler than the living room, the stop valves at the return end of the bedroom panels are partially closed off. This reduces the flow of water through these panels without any effect on the flow of water to the other panels. The valves should be located in the utility room where they will be easily accessible. Each valve should be tagged with the name of the room of the house that it controls.

At some point where the return lines come together, a drain cock should be installed so that the coils can be drained of water when the heating system is closed down during cold weather. Air pressure will be required to clear the lines of all water under these circumstances. The drain cock should, however, be located at a low point in the system.

The next step is to install the 12" x 30" expansion tank. This tank should be installed above the highest point in the system and, therefore, if the attic is ever to be used for living quarters, the tank should be installed above the attic ceiling. It is best to cover the tank in this unheated portion of the house with insulation to eliminate any possibility of water in the tank freezing.

Connected directly under the tank is a special type of vent valve that is used to allow any air that may be in the pipes to escape up into the expansion tank.

From this fitting, the line drops down to the flow control valve. This is a type of check valve that closes off the flow of water through the system when the circulator is not in operation. It is automatic. If it were not for this valve, you would have some circulation of water through the coils regardless of whether the circulator were working or not. This might not be desirable as it would tend to overheat some of the rooms. The valve can, however, be hand operated so that it will remain in the open position and allow a gravity circulation of water through the coils if this is desirable at certain times of the year.

This check valve, as you will note from Fig. 4, has three openings for lines. One line, as was just mentioned, is connected to the expansion tank. A line at the bottom of the valve is run to the top of the boiler. The third line is connected to the coils. Flow-control valves have the various openings clearly marked so there should be no difficulty in getting the right pipe connected to the proper opening in the fitting.

From the flow-control valve, the flow line is connected to an automatic vent. This vent is necessary in order to re-move any air that may collect in the system. Pockets of air in the lines or coils will keep the system from operating properly. A gate valve is installed in the line after the automatic vent.

After the pipe has passed through the gate valve, a tee with a ¾″ opening is connected in. Attached to the ¾″ side is a line that runs back down to the base of the furnace and is connected in to the line that runs from the base to the circulator. A gate valve should be installed somewhere along this line.

The flow line continues off the tee until it is connected into the individual heating coils. Branch lines from the supply to the various coils can be one-inch pipe. These, as well as the other lines, can be copper tubing, which will make the installation work much easier.

You will note from the room-coil layout that there are two branch lines leaving the boiler. One line extends over to the kitchen wall where a tee fitting is installed. One side of this tee is connected to the living-room panel. The other side is connected onto the kitchen panel. The second line from the boiler runs directly over to the bathroom and from here on to the two bedrooms. In each case, a return line from the room is brought back to the boiler through the stop-and-waste valves. There is no control valve of this type on the flow side of the lines. You will see, however, that if the return from a particular coil is shut off by means of the stop valve, there can be no flow of water through that particular coil and the water coming from the boiler will by-pass that coil and flow on to another.

Automatic Control System

For a radiant-heating system to function properly, it must be equipped with a set of automatic controls. All types of automatic-heating equipment, such as gas, oil burners and coal stokers, are provided with a thermostat that can be set for a desired temperature and that will start the burner or the coal consumption when the temperature inside the house falls below a predetermined point. This is a very simple type of system to install since modern thermostats come as complete units ready to be hooked up to the electrical wiring running to the furnace.

Some thought must be given to the location of the thermostat, however, for a thermostat in the wrong place can decrease the efficiency of the heating system. The best place for a thermostat is on an inside wall four feet or so from the floor level. It should not be located near electric light fixtures because the heat from these fixtures may prevent the thermostat from starting the heating equipment when the room temperature falls below a comfortable point. At the same time, it should not be installed directly in front of or near outside doors because when the door is opened, a cold blast of air striking the sensitive thermostat will start the heating equipment going. The best room in the house in which to locate the thermostat is the living room because this is the room where the temperature is most likely to be kept at an even point. The temperature of the air in the kitchen and bath will vary, due to the kitchen range and the hot water from bath or shower. Most people like to have their bedrooms a few degrees cooler than the rest of the house at night and this eliminates the bedrooms as ideal locations for the thermostat.

Due to the construction of a radiant-heating system, the use of a thermostat to turn the furnace off and on is not completely satisfactory. The reason is that it is the temperature of the water in the coils that determines how warm the air in the rooms is and not the temperature of the water in the boiler. Therefore, the control system for radiant heating must in some way be able to regulate the flow of water through the lines so that if the water temperature in the boiler is sufficient, this water can be allowed to flow through the coils and heat the air. This can be accomplished by wiring the circulator into the general control system. With this method, when the thermostat demands additional heat, the circulator will start up to force the hot water in the boiler through the coils. If the temperature of the water is not sufficient to do the job, the furnace will be started up to increase the temperature of the water to the proper degree.

Control systems of this type are available at heating stores and can be easily installed by following the directions provided with them. As some of these units demand special fittings installed in the lines, selection of the control system should be undertaken before the entire system is hooked up. If this is done, you can install the special fittings while the rest of the job of the heating system is under way.

Domestic Hot Water from Boiler

The domestic hot-water supply can be heated by the boiler used for the house heating system. If a storage tank is used, a system such as the one shown in the section of this book on plumbing can be used. If a tankless system is used, an automatic tempering valve must be installed on the boiler to reduce the temperature of the hot water used for the domestic supply to a safe point. The water inside the boiler used for the house heating system is far above the temperature that is required for domestic use. If no water is used for some time, the domestic supply becomes overheated. The tempering valve is connected to the boiler, to the cold fresh-water line and to the domestic hot-water supply. The openings in the valve for the various pipes are clearly marked.

The valve can be adjusted to furnish hot water at any desired temperature. Once the valve has been set, the mechanism inside the valve will feed enough cold water into the line to reduce the temperature to the desired degree.

MATERIALS LIST FOR HEATING

1   Steel boiler rated at 96,000 BTU with extended jacket with 200 gallons per hour tankless coil.
1   Fill Box
1   Vent Cap
1   Ventalarm
1   12 by 30 Compression tank
1   Airtrol tank fitting
1   Autovent with overflow
1   1¼-inch angle flow control
1   No. 8 dual valve
1   ⅜" stop and waste valve
1   Circulator
1000 feet of ⅜" type L copper tubing.

Chapter 16

INTERIOR WALLS AND CEILINGS; BUILT-IN FURNITURE

WHEN it comes to covering the studding and joists to make the inside walls and ceilings, there is a wide selection of materials to choose from.

Types of Material

First of all, there is plaster. In the building trades, a plaster wall or ceiling is often referred to as "wet wall" construction because of the fact that plaster must be mixed with water before it can be applied to the wall and ceiling surfaces. Plaster provides a smooth and unbroken surface that is ideal for paint, paper or any other type of wall covering. The finish or top coat of plaster can be smooth or have a rough-texture effect. The main disadvantage to plaster is its high cost. Plastering is not a skill that can be quickly or easily acquired, and for this reason, if you select plaster for the inside wall material, you should figure on calling in a professional to do the job for you. Of course, you can cut down the cost considerably by doing your own lath work, installing the grounds and beads and acting as a helper to the plasterer, but the job is still going to run your total costs up. Another very definite drawback to plaster is that the job must be done perfectly from the lathing to the final coat. If the plaster is not properly mixed, applied and cured, it will crack, blister and cause no end of trouble. And still another disadvantage is that because of the large amount of water used in mixing, the wet plaster can be a source of damage to woodwork, which absorbs moisture from the plaster and expands. This moisture in the plaster also holds back decorating jobs such as painting or papering.

The other method of making interior walls and ceilings is called "dry wall" construction. The materials used in this method are plywood, plaster board, composition board, insulating board, etc., often all lumped under the general heading of "wallboard." These boards come in all sizes, ranging from the large building boards that measure 4' by 12' to the ceiling tiles that are only 1 foot square. With a few exceptions, building boards are nailed right to the wall studding. See Fig. 1. The exceptions are the ceiling tile and wall planks, which require additional furring nailed to the studding to serve as a nailing base. Walls and ceilings built out of wallboard can be papered and painted. These materials are, as a rule, very easy to work with. The only tools required are a hammer and saw. For someone who wants to do the entire job of building a house himself, wallboard is the best material.

PLASTER BASES

Those who prefer to stick with plaster should certainly have no great difficulty in installing the laths or plaster base. There are several materials used for the base. First of all, there are wood laths, which have been used for years but are now gradually being replaced by materials that can be installed in less time, are more resistant to fire and contain certain insulating properties. Wood laths come in bundles of 100 laths each. The lath is 48″ long, so it will fit on studding that is either 16″, 18″ or 24″ on center. The laths are about 1½″ wide.

Plasterboard, gypsum lath or rock lath is made with a core of plaster encased in paper. The size of a sheet varies from 16″ x 32″ up. The surface of the boards may be smooth, rough or perforated with holes that serve as keys to hold the plaster. Plasterboard is fire resistant.

Another plaster base is metal lath. There are expanded metal laths, expanded corrugated laths and wire laths. See Fig. 2. Metal lath comes in sheets 27″ x 96″ or thereabouts. In addition to the metal laths, there are also metal reinforcements for inside and outside corners, door arches and other points where extra strength is needed.

Installing Wood Laths

Wood laths should be soaked in water for a day before they are nailed

Fig. 1. Installing wallboard. Dry wall construction of this type offers many advantages over a plaster wall. The most important factor is the ease with which such a wall can be covered.

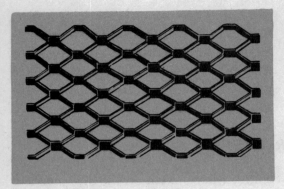

Fig. 2. Expanded metal lath.

to the studding and joists. This allows them to dry out with the plaster. If the plaster is applied to dry laths, the laths may twist or warp and crack the plaster. The laths are nailed to the studding in groups of 7 or 8, and a space of ⅜″ should be left between them. This allows the plaster to be

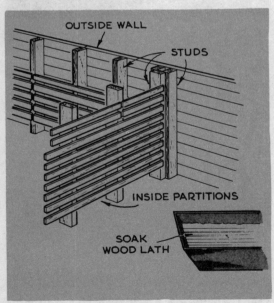

Fig. 3. Installing wood laths. Note that the vertical joint is broken every seventh course. Special partition studding enables the ends of the laths to be nailed securely.

forced in back of the laths, where it forms "keys" that hold all the plaster to the laths. Each lath should be nailed with a 3*d* nail whenever it crosses a piece of studding. Leave a space of ¼″ where the ends of laths meet, and leave a similar space when a lath reaches a corner. If, for some reason, the laths do not extend far enough for the ends to be nailed to a solid base, nail odd pieces of 2″ x 4″ to the base to bring it out until it reaches them. Do not allow the ends of the laths to go unsupported. After a group of 7 or 8 laths has been nailed on, stagger the next group so that the vertical joints do not overlap. Avoid using short lengths of laths around openings such as window or door frames, or where there are going to be openings for heating, plumbing lines or electrical fixtures. See Fig. 3.

Installing Plasterboard or Insulating Board Laths

Each of these two types of lath is installed in exactly the same manner. The laths are nailed directly to the studding and ceiling joists. As a general rule, 3*d* nails are the proper size. They should be spaced 6″ apart at the studding and 3″ where two sections of board meet. All joints between sections must come over studding or joists, and vertical joints should be staggered so that one does not come directly over the one below. Each sheet should be butted tightly against the next. Sheets should not be dampened before they are installed or before the plaster is applied. Gypsum plaster-board can be cut by scoring it on one side with a sharp tool and then pressing down along this line, first on one side and then on the other. This will produce a clean break. Insulating lath can be cut with a handsaw.

Metal Lath

Metal lath of all types is nailed to the studding or joists. It goes on horizontally and should be staggered so as to avoid long vertical joints. Do not allow a joint to occur at a corner. Bring the sheet of lath around so that it extends for at least one stud past the corner. If you allow joints to form at the corners, you are going to be troubled with cracking plaster. See Fig. 4.

Corner Beads and Reinforcements

Regardless of how well a wall or ceiling has been lathed, there are bound to be certain weak areas where the plaster is easily damaged or is likely to crack unless some additional reinforcement is used.

First of all, there are all the outside wall corners. To protect the plaster at these points from being chipped or cracked, a metal corner bead is used. These beads are made with a rounded corner and they serve as a ground or guide for the plasterer as well as protecting the plaster itself. See Fig. 5. Corner beads must be perfectly plumb, and care must be taken not to damage the thin metal bead when it is being nailed to the corner.

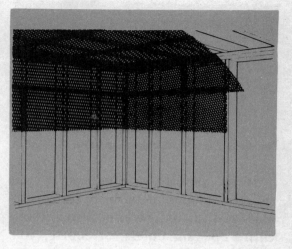

Fig. 4. Method of applying metal plaster lath. Note the overlap at joints and where ceiling and wall meet.

Inside corners, such as those formed by adjacent walls or by the walls and ceilings, must be reinforced too, because this is a spot where the plaster is especially likely to crack. Metal corner without any bead is used in these areas. See Fig. 6.

Additional reinforcement is also required on the face of the lath at the corners of any window, door or other openings in walls or ceilings. Small strips of metal lath will do for these spots. See Fig. 7.

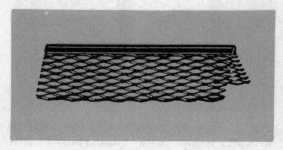

Fig. 5. Corner bead used for exterior corners.

Fig. 6. Metal lath without beading should be used for all interior corners.

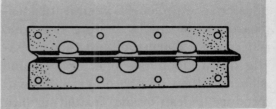

Fig. 8. Picture molding.

If you plan to have an archway or similar opening, metal forms are available that should be used around the entire opening unless, of course, you plan to use wood trim.

Picture molding, which comes in long sheets, not only serves as a means to hang pictures on the wall without having to drive in nails, but it also provides a guide for the plasterer. See Figs. 8 and 9. Be sure that this molding is level and see that joints at corners are carefully mitered.

Plaster Grounds

Plaster grounds are strips of wood that are attached along the base of the walls and around door, window and other openings where wood trim is to fit over the edges of the plaster. The reason for using them is that the plaster at these points must be perfectly true and level; if it is not, the wood trim, when installed, will hit the high spots in the plaster, causing unsightly cracks between plaster and trim. In other words, the grounds serve

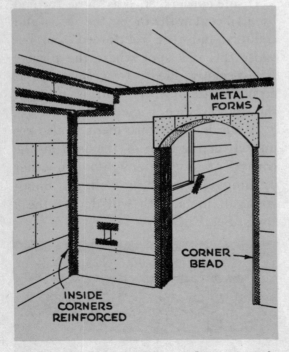

Fig. 7. How the corners and openings in a wall lathed with plasterboard lath should be reinforced with metal lath and metal beading.

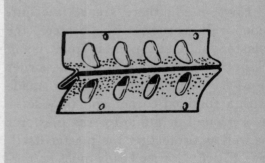

Fig. 9. A type of picture molding that makes an excellent base from which to hang articles.

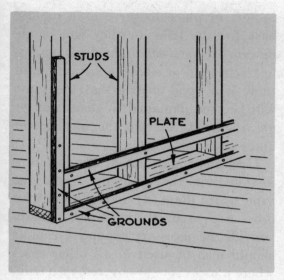

Fig. 10. Another method of applying grounds around door and window openings. As the grounds are the same thickness as the plaster and lath, they can be left in place and will serve as a nailing base for the door and window trim.

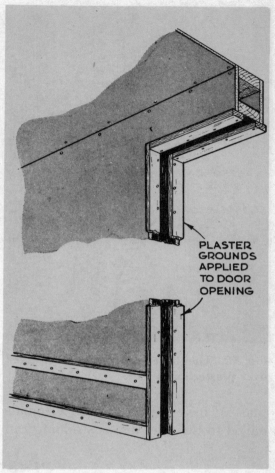

PLASTER GROUNDS APPLIED TO DOOR OPENING

Fig. 11. Plaster grounds at baseboard and around door opening. The grounds at the baseboard are left in place and serve as a nailing base for the baseboard. Grounds around the door opening are removed before the door frame is installed.

as a guide to the plasterer and help him to put the plaster on correctly.

Grounds are usually made out of 1″ x 2″ dressed lumber. This brings their actual thickness down to $^{25}/_{32}$″, which is the thickness of the finished plaster surface, including the laths. Grounds for the base of the wall should be tacked to wall plate. Usually two grounds are used in this location so that the plaster, running the entire width of the baseboard, will be of uniform thickness. These grounds can be left in place to be covered up by the baseboard. See Fig. 10. It is a good idea to mark on the sub-floor, either with chalk or nails, the location of the studding so that after the plaster is applied, the position of the studding

will still be clear. When it comes to the grounds for doorways, they can be tacked to the sides of the studding that frame the opening. See Fig. 11. Another method is to tack the grounds to the inside of the studding and make them extend out the required distance. They are removed later, after the

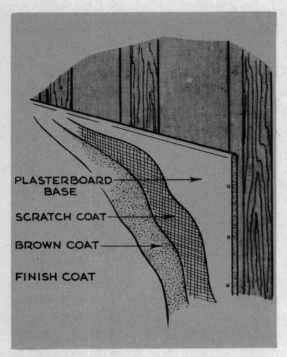

PLASTERBOARD BASE

SCRATCH COAT

BROWN COAT

FINISH COAT

Fig. 12. The three coats of plaster applied over plasterboard lath.

plaster has been applied. Grounds nailed to the sides of the studding can

be left in place to serve as a nailing base for the trim, or they can be removed. In some cases, the door jamb is installed and used as a ground, but there is a good chance that the jamb will become damaged in some way or absorb moisture from the wet plaster and expand.

Grounds for casement windows are installed on the studding frame the same as for doors. If double-hung windows are used, their frames usually provide the necessary ground. Grounds should also be used in all other cases where plaster is to be covered with trim.

In view of the fact that the grounds serve to establish the thickness of both plaster and plaster base, it may be simpler to install them before the plaster base. This will eliminate the necessity of cutting back on the base at certain points in order to provide the necessary nailing base for the grounds.

PLASTERING

Plaster is applied to the lath in three coats—scratch coat, brown coat and finish. See Fig. 12.

The Scratch Coat

The *scratch coat* can be made with 2 parts sharp sand and 1 part gypsum plaster. These should be mixed thoroughly together in a clean mixing box with sufficient water added to give the plaster the proper consistency. The water should be clean and perfectly free from oil or grease. In fact, it is

especially important to avoid getting dirt or any odd bits of hardened plaster into the fresh plaster. Have a separate container on hand so that your tools can be washed clean after each batch of plaster has been applied.

Ready-mixed plaster is also available. It comes in 100-lb. bags and requires only the addition of water before it can be applied.

Before the first coat of plaster is applied to wood laths, the laths should be dampened. If the plaster is going to be applied over metal or gypsum-board lath, this is not necessary. The scratch coat should be applied to the lath with sufficient force to push the fresh plaster through the openings between laths. The plaster that gets in back of the lath will harden and form a key, which will bond the plaster to the lath. One of the causes for sagging plaster walls and ceilings is that a sufficient amount of plaster did not get in back of the lath to make this bond. With some types of gypsum lath there are no holes for the plaster to go through because of the fact that the plaster can make a mechanical bond with the lath itself. The first coat of plaster should cover the lath by about ¼" and it should be level and true.

Before the first coat has had a chance to set, score it horizontally and vertically. This is done so that the brown coat will make a good bond with the scratch coat.

The Brown Coat

The *brown coat* is applied after the scratch coat has hardened. This coat must be applied with enough force to work the fresh plaster into the scored lines made in the scratch coat. It should be thick enough to bring the surface of the plastered wall out even with the plaster grounds. The finish coat of plaster is so thin that it will have very little effect on the over-all thickness of the plaster. You will need a straight-edge at this point to insure your getting the total area of the brown coat level with the grounds.

The Finish Coat

The *finish coat* can be made out of plaster and sand to produce a textured surface, or it can be trowel-finished, which is suitable for painting or papering. Plaster for the finish coat can be obtained ready-mixed and this is the best bet for the amateur since, if mixing directions are followed, there is little chance of failure.

The finish coat is applied in several very thin layers. The first application is ground in to make a suitable bond with the brown coat. Additional coats are applied over this to fill in any small depressions and take out irregularities. If a textured sand finish is desired, it can be obtained by working over the final coat with a piece of carpet attached to a float. A trowel finish is achieved by smoothing out the final coat perfectly evenly with a trowel.

Proper Conditions

Plaster requires very exacting conditions if it is to harden into a suitable wall surface. If the plastering is done during the hot summer months, there is the possibility that it will dry out before it has had time to set. This will cause chalky spots to appear, very often around the edges of the plaster, and the plaster in these areas can be rubbed off easily. This condition is known as "dry-outs;" you can prevent it from occuring by making sure that there are no hot drafts of air blowing over the fresh plaster. Another way of preventing it is to keep the plaster damp until it has time to set.

If you are working in cold weather, the exact opposite of dry-outs may appear. These are called "sweat-outs" and they are caused by the plaster having set before all the water in it has evaporated. This will cause the wall to have a dark appearance, and the plaster will be soft. The wall will have a damp musty odor. Sweat-outs can be avoided by being sure that there is ample ventilation in the rooms to carry off the moisture in the plaster. If the weather is cold or if it is damp, heat in the building will be necessary to remove the water content from the plaster.

DRY-WALL CONSTRUCTION

As was stated earlier in this chapter, dry-wall construction refers to any interior wall or ceiling material that does not require mixing with water for application. Grouped under this general heading are any number of composition building boards made out of a variety of materials, such as gypsum plaster, wood and vegetable fibers, plywood, asbestos and cement. In fact, there are so many materials in this field to choose from that it is quite possible to use a different one for each room in the house. As you will see, some are

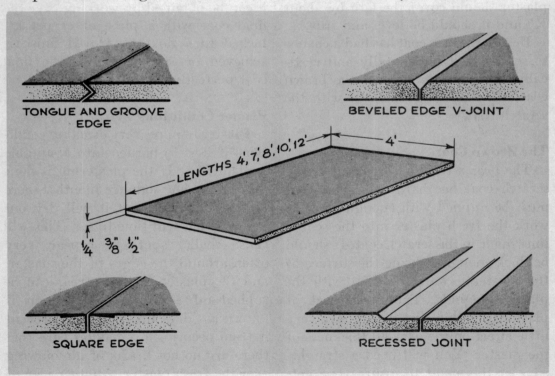

Fig. 13. The joints between sections of plasterboard can be handled in several different ways, as depicted in the various illustrations above.

definitely more suitable for certain rooms than others.

Dry walls are unquestionably the best for the amateur home-builder. They can be installed with success by anyone who possesses the normal amount of skill with hammer, saw, level and plumb line. When large sections are used over unbroken surfaces, it takes very little time to cover a large amount of wall area.

Many persons dislike the idea of anything other than plaster for walls and ceilings because they have seen dry walls with large seams between sections of board, cases where the boards have buckled or bulged out, or walls so flimsy that they seem little stronger than if they had been made out of cardboard. These conditions are the result of inferior-grade materials and poor workmanship. High-quality materials installed according to specifications will produce a surface that is free from joints or seams, and that is extremely rugged and will neither buckle nor sag.

Plasterboard

This type of building board is made out of a gypsum-plaster filler encased in heavy paper. It is sold under a great many different trade names. The standard-size sheet of plasterboard is 4' wide and will run from 6' to 12' in length. This particular type of building board does not absorb moisture readily and, therefore, unlike some of the other building boards that are more absorbent, can be used in rooms

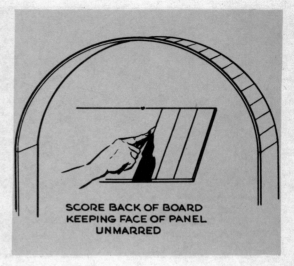

SCORE BACK OF BOARD
KEEPING FACE OF PANEL
UNMARRED

Fig. 14. Plasterboard can be bent to form rounded corners by scoring the back of the board with a knife.

such as the kitchen or bath where there is bound to be some moisture present. The surface of these boards can be papered or painted. The edges of plasterboard are treated in various ways, depending on how the finished surface is to appear. See Fig. 13. If a smooth, unbroken surface is desired, sheets with a recessed edge should be used. After these sheets are in place, Swedish putty is forced into the recess. This, in turn, is covered with a strip of perforated metal or cloth tape. The tape is forced into the putty so that the putty comes through the perforations. This putty is smoothed out and additional coats of putty are applied until the surface has been built up flush with the surface of the rest of the board. When the putty is dry, a sanding with rather light sandpaper will produce a smooth joint. Another

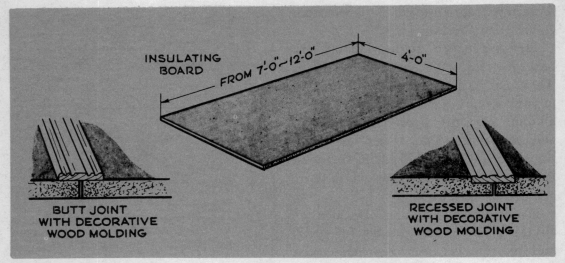

INSULATING BOARD

FROM 7'-0"—12'-0"

4'-0"

BUTT JOINT
WITH DECORATIVE
WOOD MOLDING

RECESSED JOINT
WITH DECORATIVE
WOOD MOLDING

Fig. 15. The joints between the large sheets of insulating board can be covered with a strip of molding as indicated in the above illustrations.

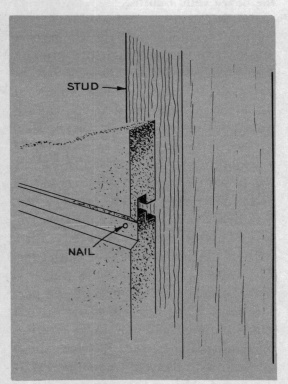

STUD

NAIL

Fig. 16. Joints of this type make it possible to install insulating board so that the nails are concealed.

way to treat the joints is to select boards with a beveled edge. When these are butted together, a v-joint is formed that is quite attractive. In fact, by arranging any type of building board in a pleasant pattern, the joints between sections can be put to good use as a decorative factor and not be a liability. Some brands of plasterboard have a factory-applied finish that resembles wood paneling. These sheets can be butted close together and the joints will appear as part of the wood grain.

Insulating Board

These boards, often referred to as wallboard, are made out of wood or vegetable fibers pressed into sheets of varying sizes. The large sheets measure 4' x 12'. These boards do have considerable value as insulation, but in cold climates they should not be counted on to provide all the wall and ceiling insulation that is necessary. (See the section on insulation.) This type of board is also somewhat more absorbent than plasterboard and, therefore, should not be used as a base for metal or plastic tile in the kitchen or bath. Because of its absorbing qualities, the large sheets should never be butted close together; if they are and if they should absorb moisture to any great degree, they will expand and bulge out. Joints between sections of

Fig. 18. Composition wood or hardboard is flexible to a considerable degree and therefore can be used on curved surfaces.

insulating board can be treated in the same fashion as those in plasterboard, that is, edges are recessed and the joint filled with putty and perforated reinforcing tape. Other types of board come with beveled, chamfered or ship-lap joints or with butt joints that can be covered with strips of molding. See Figs. 15 and 16. The molding can also be recessed into the board.

Insulating Tile and Planks

These materials are made out of the same substances as the large insulating boards. They come in many sizes, from the small tile that measures 8" x 8", to the wall plank that comes in random widths of from 6" up and in

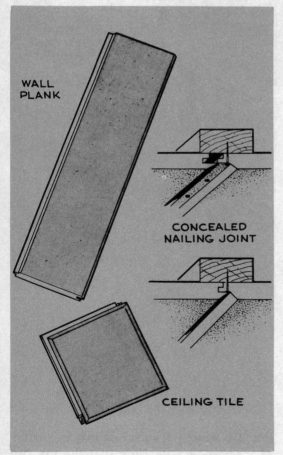

WALL PLANK

CONCEALED NAILING JOINT

CEILING TILE

Fig. 17. Wall plank and ceiling tile showing joint for concealed nailing.

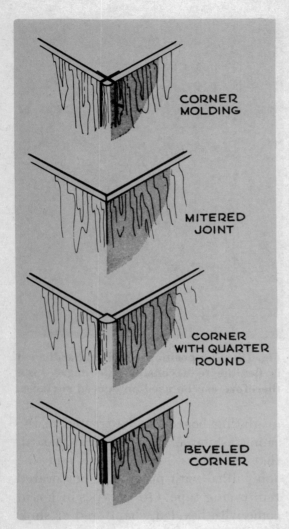

made out of wood fibers pressed into sheets that are somewhat thinner than the other types of building board so far mentioned, but that are also much more flexible. See Fig. 18. The standard size of a sheet is 4' x 12', but larger sheets are available or can be

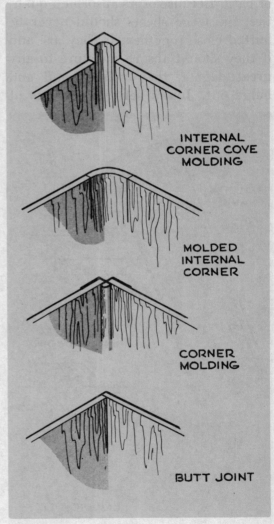

Fig. 19. Four ways to treat outside corners of plywood.

lengths of 12'. By means of overlapping joints, these tiles and planks can be nailed in such a way that the nail head is concealed, leaving a v-joint between the two sections. See Fig. 17.

Composition Board

Composition board is also called pressed-wood or hard-board. It is

Fig. 20. Four ways to treat inside corners of a plywood wall. Note that the top two methods require special corner-cover molding.

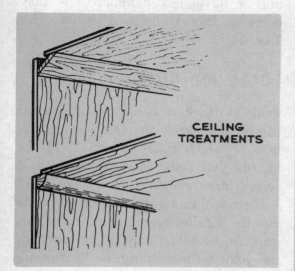

Fig. 21. Two simple methods of treating the ceiling joint for plywood walls and ceilings. Note that in the top picture, a strip of regular wall plywood is used rather than special stock molding.

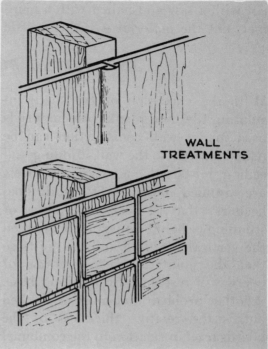

Fig. 22. Top figure shows a very simple method of covering the vertical joint between sections of plywood on walls. The lower figure shows a method that is more complicated but produces very attractive results.

ordered. This type of board, like plasterboard, does not absorb moisture readily and is ideal for the bath or kitchen. Some brands are given a finish so that they resemble a section of wall tile (see Wall and Ceiling Finishes.) The seams between sheets are covered with wood or metal strips.

Plywood

Plywood makes a very satisfactory interior wall material. There are inexpensive grades that should be used if you are going to paper or paint. The more expensive grades have a surface veneer made out of the more attractive woods, or their outer surface is grained to make a very attractive wall finish in itself. The standard size of sheets of plywood is 4' by 8'. The joints between sections can be butted together or the two edges can be beveled to give a v-joint. Plywood is usually secured to the studding by nails, but if a glue is used as well as the nails, it makes for a much stronger wall. See Figs. 19, 20, 21, 22 and 23.

Asbestos Board

Sheets of asbestos board are made out of asbestos fibers and cement. They are moisture-resistant as well as fire-resistant, and can be used for either interior or exterior work. They can be cut with a saw and nailed with a hammer, but the material is rather brittle and a misplaced hammer-blow may crack it. Sheets come 4' by 8'. See Fig. 24.

INSTALLING BUILDING BOARDS

With the exception of the small insulating tiles and planks, the materials used in dry-wall construction can be nailed directly to the wall studding and ceiling joists. Of course, if the sheets are applied horizontally, additional headers (that is, horizontal pieces of studding) should be installed between the vertical studding and the joists so that the joints between sections of board will rest on a firm nailing base. Another problem that must be worked out is the relative thickness of the boards used in relation to the combined thickness of plaster and laths. Standardized window and door jambs are made to fit where you use conventional plaster and laths, the combined thickness of which is around $^{25}\!/_{32}''$. If the boards you select for the walls and ceiling are very thin—less than $^{25}\!/_{32}''$—there will be a gap between the walls and the window and door casings. This gap can be taken care of by covering the joint with molding, or by furring out the studding so that the surface of the wall material is the same as if plaster and laths had been used.

In the case of the small ceiling tiles or wall planks, it is necessary to install additional nailing bases over the studding, for in most instances these tiles and planks will not be the right size to fit between either the studding or the joists. 1" x 3" stock can be used for

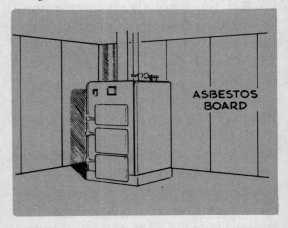

Fig. 23. Two methods of treating the base of a plywood interior wall.

Fig. 24. Asbestos board, being fire-resistant, is ideal to use around the furnace or at any other location where there is a potential fire hazard.

this job and it should be spaced according to the size of the materials you are working with.

Because of the wide assortment of types, brands and sizes of materials used for dry walls, it is virtually impossible to give exact information on how all of them should be put up. The manufacturers, however, do provide very complete specifications as to how

WOOD CLEAT

1"x4" T

Fig. 25. A simple method of getting large sheets of wallboard up to the ceiling and holding them in place until they can be nailed.

their own products should be installed, and these should be procured and carefully followed. Specifications can be obtained from your local dealer.

There are, however, a few general points that can be discussed that will apply regardless of which material is used.

First of all, be sure that everything inside the wall is in order before you start putting on the wall material. This means that the insulation should be in place, the various electrical fixtures securely fixed to the studding or joists, plumbing lines looked over to be sure that all joints are tight, and other matters of this sort checked carefully. Where openings are to be made in the wallboard for plumbing, lighting and heating fixtures, measure off the distance of the fixture from the floor or ceiling and to the nearest stud. Transfer these measurements to the wall board so that the hole can be made in the proper place and to the exact size.

When the building boards are delivered from the lumber yard, be sure you have a clean level surface where they can be placed. Some of the insulating boards or boards of the fiberous type will break off at the corners if treated too harshly, so handle them with care.

Ceilings should be covered first. If you are working alone, it will be a lot easier if you stick to the small tile or smaller size of boards. Handling the large 4' x 8' sheets alone is rather difficult. One thing you can do to facilitate getting such large boards up to the ceiling and holding them there while you nail them in place is to build a large T of 1" x 4" or similar stock. The crossarm of this T should be as long as the width of the boards, and the stem of the T should be an inch more than the distance from floor to ceiling. After the T has been made, tack a wood cleat to one of the walls near the ceiling. The cleat should be the thickness of the wallboard from the ceiling. Now slip one end of the building board into the notch formed by the cleat and the ceiling, and then hoist the board up to the ceiling by means of the T. You can tack a small cleat to the ceiling by means of the T. You can tack a small cleat to the sub-floor to hold the T in place. Once the board is in its approximate position, it is a relatively simple matter to center it exactly and nail it securely. See Fig. 25.

The walls are done after the ceiling, and the joints between wall and ceiling are then covered with strips of molding. Take care to get each section on level and watch out when cutting for doors and window openings that you do not take off too much material.

STAIRS

If you wish to install stairs at this time, you can either purchase ready-made stock stairs, or have your local lumber yard or mill make you a set to meet your individual requirements, or you can build a flight yourself. There is nothing very difficult about it, and the type of stairs shown in Fig. 26 will prove perfectly adequate.

Stairs to the attic and stairs to the basement can be constructed in the same fashion. The floor joists around the stair opening are double and, at one side of the opening for the basement stairs, there is a bearing post or steel column under the girder.

The first thing to build is the landing at the bottom, which runs at right angles to the stairs. The base of this landing is made from two 2" x 8¼"s. In the case of the stairs to the attic, the 2" x 8¼"s are notched out at the bottom edge so that they will fit over the partition sole plate. Each end must be notched, since there will be a sole plate on both sides of the stairs. At the back of the landing, the 2" x 8¼"s should be flush with the far edge of the partition studding and sole plate. At the front of the landing, they should extend 9¾" beyond the inside edge of the studding and sole plate to provide a step with a tread approximately 9" wide.

The next job is to cut a piece of 1" x 12" to the measure of the width of the landing and nail it in place to the partition studding at the back of the landing, as shown in Fig. 26. Another 1" x 12" is installed with the stair stringers, and both will serve as a base molding between the finished wall of the stair well and the stringers, treads and risers.

Now set four pieces of 2" x 8¼" over the landing to make both a second step and the top of the landing. The front piece is set so that it will be 9¾" back of the ends of the 2" x 8¼"s. An additional piece of 2" x 8¼" is set at the midpoint to provide additional support for the top of the landing.

With the rough landing completed, cut two pieces of 1" x 12" to fit on each side of the stair stringers. These will extend beyond the top ends of the stringers, as indicated in Fig. 26. The piece of 1" x 12" on the inside will make a joint with the short strip put down in the back of the landing. The outside piece will come flush with the lower end of the outside stringer.

After these two pieces have been cut to size, set them aside and go to work measuring and cutting the stringers. The stringers are made out of 2" x 12"s. At the bottom of the stairs, both stringers are notched so that they fit over the top of the 2" x 8¼" making the top of the landing. At the top, the stringers should be cut off flush to fit snugly under the bottom edge of the ceiling joists. The lower edge on this end-cut must be made vertical in order to form a suitable nailing surface for the 2" x 4" horizontal brace that is set at the top of the opening.

The next step is to cut the sawtooth pattern in the stringers so that the treads and risers can eventually be put in place. As you will note in the illustration, the risers are 8¼" deep, the treads are 9¾" wide. Use a steel framing square to mark out the dimensions of the treads and risers on the stringers.

As it is most important that both stringers be exactly the same, the best way to do the job is to cut one to fit and use it as a pattern for the second. Be sure that both stringers fit perfectly before you proceed to the next step. When the stringers are finished, the 1″ x 12″s are nailed to them. These boards must be nailed to come between the stringers and the wall studding. They should extend 2″ above the top edge of the stringer. Nail the 1″ x 12″s to the stringers with 8d nails.

Now the stringers are ready to go up, but they should not be secured in

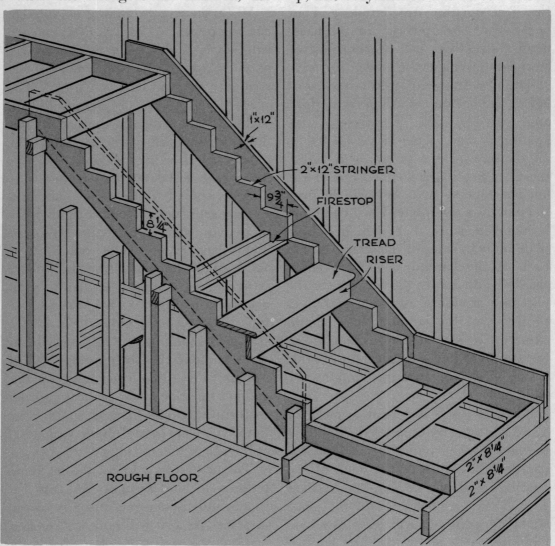

Fig. 26. Flight of stairs from first floor to attic. The same type of construction can be used for the basement stairs as well, with minor changes noted in the text.

any permanent fashion until the horizontal braces are in place and you have checked to be sure that each stringer is absolutely even with the other.

The horizontal braces at the top and middle of the stringers are supported by a vertical piece of 2" x 4", which is set directly under them and that is spiked to the sole plate and to the piece of studding next to the sole plate. The horizontal braces—2" x 4"s—are placed on edge and recessed into the stringers. Notches will have to be cut at the lower edge of the stringers to accommodate them. Nail them to the studding on each side but do not nail them to the stringers until you have checked them to be sure that they are level with each other. If there is a slight error either way, you can probably get the stringers level with wedges driven in at the notch between the edge of the stringer and

the horizontal brace. As soon as you are sure that you have the stringers level, you can go to work and nail them in place. One 20d nail should be driven through the stringer and into each piece of wall studding that it intersects. Eight-penny nails are driven through the top portion of the 1" x 12" into the studding. At the top, the stringers can be secured with nails toe-nailed into the ceiling joists and into the horizontal support. At the bottom, the stringers can be toe-nailed into the base of the landing.

A firestop at the middle of the stringers (for stairs to the attic) should also be installed at this time. It should run the entire width of the stringers, as shown in the illustration.

The last job as far as the stairs are concerned is installing the treads and risers and the finish for the landing.

BUILT-IN FURNITURE

There are many advantages in using as much built-in furniture as you possibly can. In the first place, the cost of built-in furniture is just a fraction of what you would have to pay for the ready-made article. Another important feature of built-in furniture is that you can get exactly what you want and not have to put up with something that is not quite right. Built-in furniture is ideal for the small homes because it requires less space than ordinary furniture and, as it is built in with fewer surfaces exposed, it requires less attention in the way of maintenance.

Cabinet and Worktable

Modern ready-made kitchen equipment, such as ranges, worktables and cabinets, is made to certain standards. These standards are well worth observing when it comes to completing your kitchen, even if you use your own built-in equipment. The standards were arrived at after considerable research and they will, in spite of a few possible minor inconveniences, afford the maximum efficiency and comfort for the average person.

Fig. 27 shows the standard dimensions for a kitchen range and worktable

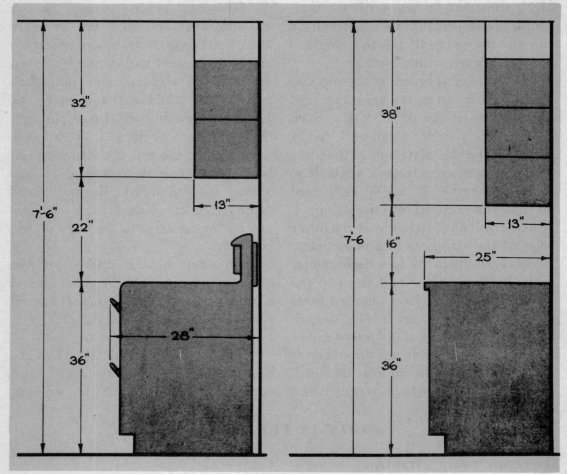

Fig. 27. Arrangement for cabinets over kitchen range and worktable.

with cabinets above. You will note that both the range and the worktable stand 36″ above the floor. This is the standard height for kitchen-sink cabinets as well. The over-all width of the kitchen range including the oven doors is 28″, and the width of the worktable is 25″. The kitchen cabinets are installed 16″ above the top of the table. Some types of mechanical kitchen aids are higher than this, and if you expect to set them up on the worktable, you should install

the cabinets a little higher up. It is not very practical to make the worktable any wider than 25″.

Cabinets above the kitchen range should have a 22″ clearance. The extra height is necessary to prevent heat and water vapor from damaging or staining the cabinets and their contents.

Fig. 28 shows a suggested layout for kitchen cabinets above a worktable with a built-in sink. The cabinets can be made out of several different materials. A frame can be built out of 1″ x 2″s and covered on the sides, top and bottom with ¼″ plywood. Batten strips nailed on the inner faces of the two sides will support the shelves. The cabinets can also be made out of ¾″

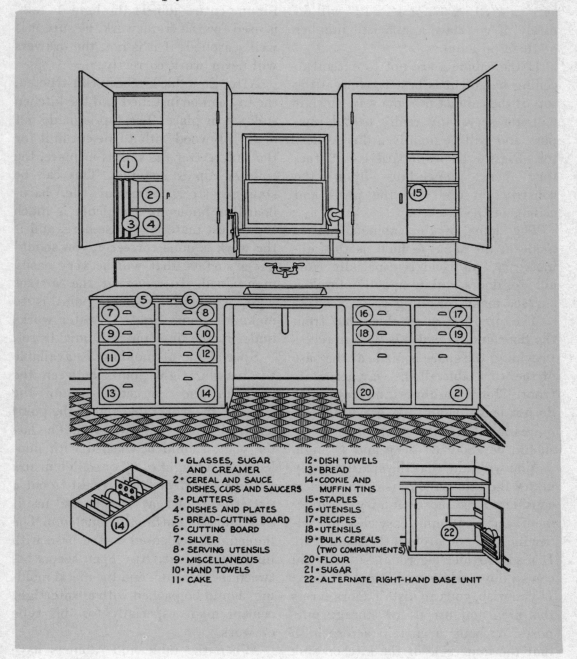

1 • GLASSES, SUGAR AND CREAMER
2 • CEREAL AND SAUCE DISHES, CUPS AND SAUCERS
3 • PLATTERS
4 • DISHES AND PLATES
5 • BREAD-CUTTING BOARD
6 • CUTTING BOARD
7 • SILVER
8 • SERVING UTENSILS
9 • MISCELLANEOUS
10 • HAND TOWELS
11 • CAKE
12 • DISH TOWELS
13 • BREAD
14 • COOKIE AND MUFFIN TINS
15 • STAPLES
16 • UTENSILS
17 • RECIPES
18 • UTENSILS
19 • BULK CEREALS (TWO COMPARTMENTS)
20 • FLOUR
21 • SUGAR
22 • ALTERNATE RIGHT-HAND BASE UNIT

Fig. 28. Layout for kitchen cabinet over worktable with built-in sink.

plywood. If this material is used, no additional framework will be required. Boards of standard dimensions, such as 1″ x 4″, 1″ x 6″, or 1″ x 12″ will do nicely, if you have a sufficient number of them on hand.

If the cabinets are not to extend to ceiling height, it is best to conceal the top of the cabinet in some way, since it will not serve any really useful purpose and will be mainly a dust-collector. Plaster or wallboard is satisfactory here, depending upon the construction used for the walls and ceiling of the kitchen.

The doors of the cabinets can be made in the same fashion as the cabinets; ¾″ plywood is especially suitable for doors, and its smooth unbroken surface makes cleaning easy.

The top of the worktable is 30″ from the floor and its width is 25″. A recess providing toe space is made at the base of the worktable all the way across its front. This is an important feature, so do not leave it out just because it requires a little extra work. The recess should be about 3″ deep and 4″ high.

You will note that the space directly under the kitchen sink is open. This is considered the most sanitary arrangement, since it permits easy cleaning under the sink and around the drain trap. It also provides leg room, so that you can sit down while working at the sink. If you wish, you can install doors across this area and use it for storage purposes, or hang a curtain across it so that the underside of the kitchen sink and the drain pipe and trap will not be exposed to view in an unsightly way.

The table frame can be made out of 1″ x 2″s, or you can use ¾″ plywood for the entire job. If the light 1″ x 2″ is used for the framework, be sure it is well seasoned; if it is not, the drawers will never work correctly.

After the table has been constructed, the top can be installed and the kitchen sink set in place. The top is made out of ¾″ plywood with a hole cut in it for the sink. After the sink is in place, the counter top is installed. This can be stainless steel, porcelain tile, hardboard or linoleum. Linoleum is much the easiest material to use here, and if the work is done correctly, you should get a surface that will be very easily maintained. In covering the surface with linoleum, the main point is to make all joints tight. If water works under it, the linoleum will quickly rot.

Special metal molding is available for making tight joints between the linoleum and the sink, around the edges of the worktable and at the point where the table joins the wall. The latter point should be flashed with linoleum for a height of 8″ or so. To insure getting a perfect fit, it is best to cut a pattern out of heavy paper and use it as a guide for cutting the linoleum. The linoleum is cemented to the base with linoleum cement. Any open seams between the linoleum and the metal molding should be packed with a watertight cement made especially for this type of work.

When the table and cabinets have been completed, they should be painted

Fig. 29. Bedroom closet arrangement.

or given some other sort of protective finish. Enamel makes a very satisfactory finish for any woodwork in the kitchen because its smooth surface does not readily collect dirt and grease and can be easily cleaned with a cloth.

If plywood is used for the cabinets, you may prefer to stain the wood and then give it a protective coating of varnish.

If the kitchen is to be equipped with ready-made cabinets, care should be taken in selecting them. These cabinets are made of either wood or metal; both are suitable provided that the construction is of high quality. Watch out for cabinets made of wood that is obviously too light to stand up for very long under normal day-to-day use. A good, solid, well built cabinet will last

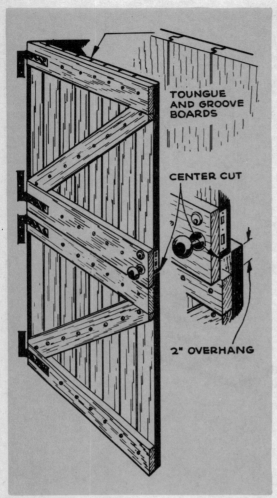

TOUNGUE
AND GROOVE
BOARDS

CENTER CUT

2" OVERHANG

Fig. 30. An easily constructed Dutch door.

front of each tray has been hollowed out at the top so that no handle is necessary.

Bookcases are a very personal matter. Some families will require a good deal of storage space for books while others will need only enough for a few volumes. Record lovers will require space to store their large and small record volumes, as well as individual records.

A bookcase that is to be used for general purposes, such as fiction and other literature, should have shelves 8" deep and 8" high. It should have a base between the first shelf and the floor 6" or so in height to protect the lowest row of books from dirt and the like. For average purposes, a bookcase should not be more than 7' high; anything over this will be inconvenient to reach.

Shelves for oversize books must be considerably wider and higher than those required for ordinary books. Rather than increasing the height of shelves, these books are laid flat.

Shelves for records and record albums must be especially constructed so that the albums can stand upright. The measurements required here are 15" by 13" for the large-size albums, and 13" by 11" for the standard size. Sections of plywood can be installed in this type of shelf to provide each album with a compartment of its own. This eliminates the possibility of having to move a lot of the albums out of the way in order to take out one. The same type of arrangement can be used if you have

a lifetime, but a shoddy product will last only a season or two before the doors stick and the joints open up.

Closets and Bookcases

Fig. 29 shows the construction of the closet in the large bedroom. Shelves are made out of ¾" stock and the doors out of ¾" plywood. The construction of the trays is the same as that for the kitchen cabinet. The a lot of loose records. Individual compartments made out of plywood will protect the records from damage and make selection easy. The top of the record should come flush with or under the top of the plywood, and a small recess can be cut in the plywood to allow the record to be taken out easily.

BUILDING A DUTCH DOOR

Fig. 30 shows a dutch door that can be made very easily. It is of batten construction and is made out of 1⅜″ thick, tongue-and-groove boards. The width of the boards pictured in the illustration is roughly 4″, but any size of board you have on hand or wish to use can be employed with equally good results.

Make the door up in one section at first. Put on the bottom and top ledge strips and run screws through these to hold the individual boards in place. Check your work with a square as you go along so that you are sure that the door is going to be level at both ends. When this much of the work has been completed, place the door in the frame to see if it fits properly. If any trimming has to be done, it should be done now. When the door fits the frame perfectly, take it out and draw a line across it 2″ above the mid-point. Be sure this line is level. Saw across this line. Now you can complete the work on the two halves of the door. Start with the bottom half and draw a line 2″ below the point that was sawed. Place the upper ledge strip for the bottom section so that its upper edge comes flush with this line. Screw the ledge strip into place. After this, cut a brace to run between the top and bottom ledge strips on the lower half of the door. Now draw a line across the upper section of the door. The distance of this line from the bottom edge of the upper section should be 2″ less than the width of the ledge piece to be installed. This is done so that the ledge piece on the top section of the door will overhang, and the seam between sections will be covered on the inside and not allow air to enter the house. Install the final ledge piece and put a brace between the two ledge strips on the upper half of the door.

The door is now ready to be hung. You should use two hinges on each location. They can be attached to the ledge strips.

BATHROOM AND KITCHEN WALLS

Because of the special requirements of the bathroom and kitchen, their walls are usually finished off in a somewhat different manner than those in the rest of the house.

The best type of wall surface for either of these two rooms is one that will not catch and hold dirt, can be easily cleaned without danger of dulling the finish, will resist staining, will

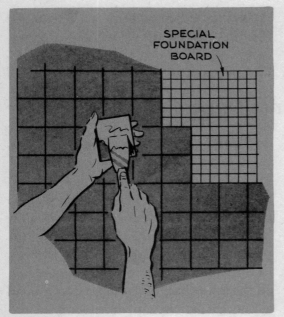

Fig. 31. Applying wall tile over a special foundation board.

not be damaged by moisture and yet will be attractive. There are several materials that you can select to fill this particular bill. Of course, if the walls are plaster, they can be painted with a good wall enamel and this will do nicely.

Metal Wall Tile

These are individual metal tiles. The standard size is 4½″ by 4½″. They are made out of stainless steel or aluminum with a finish of baked enamel or porcelain. As the finish is fused to the metal, there is no danger of its cracking and chipping. These tiles are extremely light in weight. A square foot of tile will only weigh around three pounds. This means that the tile can be placed directly over a solid wall of plaster, plasterboard or composition board without the need of any extra reinforcement.

The tiles are cemented to the wall base with a special liquid adhesive that is waterproof. The tile can be installed before or after the fixtures are in place. Of course, putting the tile on before the fixtures go up will save a good deal of cutting and fitting.

The first step in installing the tile is to check the base to which they are going to be attached. Only plaster, plasterboard, composition wood or a

Fig. 32. Draw a level line across the wall before you start to apply either tile or tileboard so that you will be sure that the material is perfectly level at the top. A plumb line dropped from this level line will insure that the vertical joints between tile are straight.

special metal-tile foundation board is suitable. The more porous types of building board should not be used because they tend to expand too much when they absorb moisture.

If you are going to lay the tile up against plaster, plasterboard or composition board, you should check over the wall to be sure that it is perfectly level and true. If you find that it is not perfect, you can cover it with a grooved foundation board. This will supply the proper base for the tile. This type of board is marked off in 1½″ squares, and the rounded corners of the tiles fit into the grooves between the squares. See Fig. 31. The foundation board is nailed and cemented to the wall. Be sure that it is put on perfectly level, because if the foundation board is not right, you will not be able to get the tile on in a straight line. See Fig. 32. The usual treatment is to tile the lower half of the wall and then use some other type of covering for the upper half. Of course, you *can* tile the entire wall.

The back of each tile is given a coat of waterproof cement and then is placed up against the foundation board. Holes can be cut in the tile with special equipment made for this purpose, which you can probably rent from your dealer, but the tile can also be cut with ordinary tin snips.

Special tiles are used where the wall meets the floor. They form a cove base and eliminate a crack at this point. Special tiles are also available for inside and outside corners.

Fig. 33. Metal or plastic tile can be installed before or after the fixtures have been installed.

As you can get metal in many different colors, you can work out some very interesting wall patterns.

Once the wall has been tiled, a special waterproof grout is applied over the surface. Press this into the joints and then wipe off the excess with a squeegee. Additional pointing of the joints can be done with the fingers.

Other types of metal tile are attached directly to the plaster or plasterboard wall. They can be butted close together, or have a small gap between each tile that is later filled with a special waterproof cement. Filling the joint between the tile with cement requires more time than if the joints are

Fig. 34. Placing the tile on the wall.

line is perfectly level. Do not try to lay the tile up from the floor without this line because you will probably find that, in spite of all your efforts, the floor line is not quite level and therefore the tile will not be level. It is best to strike this line across the wall and then work down from it. If you are going to tile the entire wall, make a line midway up on the wall and then work up and down from it. See Fig. 34.

Plastic Tile

Plastic tiles are almost the same as metal ones, but are made of plastic instead of having a metal base. They are cemented to the wall with a special cement and can be fastened directly over either plaster or plasterboard. See Fig. 35.

The same general directions for application apply to this type of tile as to the metal type. Plastic tile can be cut with special cutters, but a fine-tooth saw will do the trick perfectly well. The color on the tile runs right through the plastic, so there is no danger of the finish chipping, cracking or becoming dull from cleaning.

Tileboard

This type of covering is a little different from the individual tile. It is made out of composition wood or pressed wood that is scored off so that it resembles a section of tile wall. It has a finish of baked enamel. In one kind, the grooves between the squares are painted white. Another kind of tileboard has only horizontal lines, while

butted close together, but it also produces a more watertight surface. See Fig. 33.

One point you have to be careful about is the seams where the tiles meet plumbing fixtures. As there is a possibility of moisture getting in back of the tile at these points, special metal molding is used to form a waterproof joint.

If you are using tile without a foundation board, your first step is to make a line across the wall to indicate the top of the tilework. Make sure that this

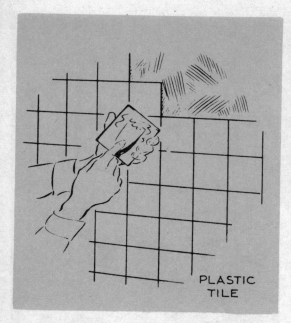

PLASTIC TILE

Fig. 35. Fastening plastic tile to a base of plasterboard.

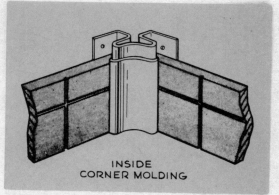

INSIDE CORNER MOLDING

Fig. 36. Metal molding used for the inside corners around the kitchen sink and worktable.

a third is perfectly plain. A section of tileboard measures 4' wide and up to 8' in length. It can be cemented directly to a plaster or plasterboard base. Special metal trim is used for inside and outside corners, and for joints between sections and around plumbing fixtures. The base molding is made of pressed wood.

The best time to install tileboard is before the plumbing fixtures go into place; this will eliminate a good deal of cutting. Cutting and fitting tileboard accurately is a little more complicated than with individual tiles because you are working with a large sheet of material.

The first step in installing tileboard is to draw a line around the walls of the room to use as a guide in getting each section of tileboard on level and even with the sections on the adjoining walls.

Now the sections of tileboard can be fitted and cut to size. A good, sharp, fine-tooth handsaw will do for cutting the material. Any holes required for fixtures can be made by first drilling a hole with a brace and bit and then cutting out the required amount with a keyhole saw.

The molding should now be installed, and be sure that it is absolutely plumb. Test each section of tileboard before you apply the adhesive to the back in order to be sure that it fits correctly. See Figs. 36, 37 and 38.

The tileboard is attached in place with a special liquid adhesive that is applied over the entire back of each section. Use a special, notched spreader for this purpose and get the adhesive on evenly. Some brands of adhesive must be applied to the wall as well as to the tileboard. As soon as the ad-

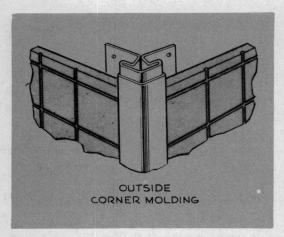

Fig. 37. Metal outside molding for linoleum kitchen sink and counter tops.

Fig. 38. Installing a sheet of tileboard in the kitchen. Note the special base molding that is put in place before the tileboard goes on.

hesive is on, put the section of tileboard into position and press it firmly against the wall so that the cement makes contact at all points. If you get any of the adhesive on the outside face of the tileboard or on the molding, wipe it off before it has a chance to harden.

The adhesives used for all types of tile and linoleum are very difficult to get off your hands. Coating your hands with soap before you start to work will make it easy to wash off any cement that you might pick up along the way.

Linoleum

A special light-weight linoleum is used for wall coverings. Ordinary floor linoleum is too heavy. This type of covering makes a very satisfactory finish for either the bathroom or kitchen, but it should not be used inside shower stalls or around built-in tubs because of the danger of moisture getting in back of it.

Wall linoleum can be installed over walls made of plaster or plasterboard (after several additions have been made in the framing). It cannot be installed over any other wall material.

If the wall is made of plaster, it must be smooth and dry and, of course, perfectly plumb. There should be no metal beading on outside corners and, in fact, there should be no square corners at all. All outside corners should be rounded to a radius of ⅝". The reason for this is to allow the linoleum to be bent around corners without cracking.

If the corners were square, this would be impossible, and you would have to have a joint.

When it comes to hanging linoleum on a plasterboard wall, you have quite a little work to do. In the first place, you need header studs at the top and bottom of the wall as well as every 24″ between the top and bottom. The plasterboard should be joined with butt joints and these should be reinforced with perforated tape. All nails should be countersunk and the holes filled with a plastic filler, which, when dry, should be sanded down smooth.

Fixtures should not be installed until the linoleum is in place.

The walls should be coated with a special size to prevent their absorbing the adhesive used to hang the linoleum. A metal strip of cap-molding should be nailed in place on the wall before the linoleum is hung.

The adhesive is now applied and the linoleum is hung in vertical sections from the cap strip down to the floor. All seams must be vertical, and you should not have any seams closer to the corners than 6″.

Of course, you are by no means limited to just one type of wall material for the entire bathrooom or kitchen. You can use several together to very good advantage, such as tile for the lower half of the wall and linoleum for the upper portion.

You will need 2,200 sq. ft. of plasterboard for the interior walls and ceilings of the basic house. You should also get 20 lbs. of finishing nails. This amount will be enough not only for the walls and ceilings, but also for other jobs.

Chapter 17

BUILDING WITH GLASS

GLASS is coming into its own as a building material for private homes, and if you want to build some interesting and decorative ideas into your home, you should consider glass as a medium. Structural glass, for example, can be used for many purposes, and it can be useful as well as ornamental. A piece of structural glass in back of the kitchen range makes a surface that can be cleaned of grease and dirt in a matter of seconds with a damp cloth. Glass for

Fig. 1. When glass blocks are to be used for exterior walls, they must always be set up in mortar.

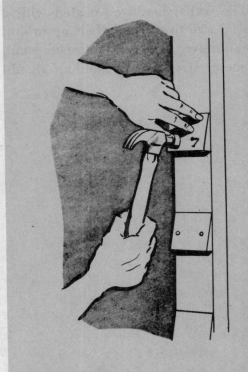

Fig. 2. Nailing the wood wedges to the frame.

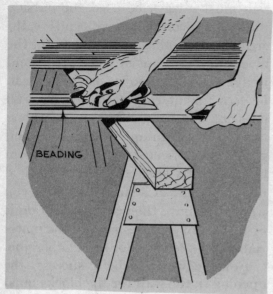

Fig. 3. Planing off the beading on one side of the starter strip.

this purpose comes mounted on plasterboard. The plasterboard sticks out beyond the glass for an inch or more, so the glass can be easily put in place by nailing the edges of the plasterboard to the wall studding. A full-length structural-glass mirror in the bedroom is well worth having. Structural glass comes either flat or corrugated and

Fig. 4. The side of the starter strip with the beading removed should be placed face down on the sill of the opening and then nailed.

can be fastened by the method just mentioned, or by means of special wood-molding.

GLASS BLOCKS

Glass blocks can be used to very good effect for either inside or outside walls. They will not only bring additional light to dark rooms, but further, a glass wall or section of wall can have a very pleasing appearance.

These blocks are translucent but not transparent. In other words, while light will pass through them, it is not possible to see through them.

Glass blocks are hollow inside and are tightly sealed around the edges, so that they have considerable value as insulation and can be used on outside walls without fear of excessive heat loss.

The standard sizes of glass block are 5¾", 7¾" and 11¾" square. The edges of each block are corrugated and sanded so that they will bond to mortar or can be set up with wood strips and wedges.

You must remember when working with glass blocks, however, that they are no more than a curtain. In other words, while a wall of glass blocks can support its own weight, it cannot be counted on to provide any additional support. For this reason, when an opening for glass blocks is cut in either an inside or outside wall, it must be reinforced, just as if a window or door were going to be installed.

There are two methods used for setting up a section of wall with glass blocks. One is to set them up in cement mortar, just as if they were bricks or masonry blocks. This type of construc-

tion must always be used for outside walls as it is completely air- and weather-tight. The other method is to set the blocks up by means of wood strips and wedges. This type of construction can be used for interior work where a wall does not have to be either air- or watertight. The advantage of the wood and wedge type of construction, aside from the ease with which the blocks are laid up, is that if, at some later date, you want to remove the wall, you can do it in just a few minutes and all the materials can be re-used for some other job.

For the work to be a success, the opening in the wall for the blocks must be cut to the correct measurement. If you want a wall of glass blocks, your

Fig. 5. Placing the wood strips in the vertical joints between the blocks.

Fig. 6. Tapping down the strips of wood at the vertical joints.

Fig. 7. Horizontal beading strips are used between courses of blocks.

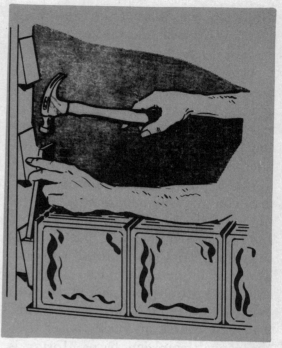

Fig. 8. As each course is completed, the wood wedges are driven down to hold the blocks in place.

first job is to get a table from your dealer showing the exact size that the rough framing of the opening must be for a section of glass blocks of the size you have chosen as the most desirable for your purpose.

SETTING THE BLOCKS IN MORTAR

After the opening has been made to the correct size, the next step in laying up the blocks with mortar is to make a chase in the top and sides of the opening. This can be easily done by nailing an exterior wood casing around the opening so that it will overlap the blocks at the sides and top by at least ¾". No chase is required along the sill. In fact, to make a chase at this point would be to invite trouble from moisture that might well seep in between the blocks and the edge of the wood trim.

The next step is to line the sides and top of the opening with expansion strips. These strips are made of fiberglass and can be purchased from your local dealer. They are needed to take up the difference in expansion and contraction between the glass blocks and the wood framework around the opening. An expansion strip is not required along the sill. The sill should, however, be coated with asphalt emulsion. This will keep the wood from absorbing moisture from the mortar and will also prevent decay.

After the opening has been prepared, the blocks are laid up with the mortar. The correct mix for the mortar is 1 part cement, 4 parts clean fine sand and 10 per cent by volume of hydrated lime. Add enough clean water to get a workable plastic, and do not mix more than you can use in 30 minutes. As the edges of the blocks are both sanded and corrugated, you will find no difficulty in getting the mortar to stick. The mortar joints should be ¼″ thick, and the entire joint should be well packed so that there will be no voids. The first course of blocks is set over the asphalt-emulsion base. Mortar is applied over the asphalt and the blocks

set into it. When the first course is completed, spread a layer of mortar over the tops of the blocks and lay the next course into this horizontal mortar bed. See Fig. 1. To provide additional strength, wire reinforcing is used along the horizontal joints every three or four courses. Your dealer can supply you with it.

Be careful to wipe off any mortar that gets on the face of the blocks before it has a chance to harden.

After the entire wall has been completed, the edges must be finished off so that they are air- and water-tight. First of all, take some oakum and drive it in between the edges of the blocks and the inside face of the chase. Finally, put caulking compound over the oakum.

INSTALLING THE BLOCKS WITH WOOD STRIPS AND WEDGES

As was mentioned before, this method of construction should never be used for exterior walls.

The size of the opening should be determined by checking over the manufacturer's table. Along with the glass blocks, you will also need a number of beaded wood strips and wedges. After the frame has been made, make sure that it is plumb and level. Next, nail wood wedges to the 2″ x 4″'s that make the sides and top of the frame. The point of each wedge should face up. The location of the wedges will depend on the size of block used. If 5¾″

blocks are used, the wedges should be spaced 6″ on center; if 7¾″ blocks are used, put the wedges 8″ apart, and so on. See Fig. 2.

Now you have to prepare a base strip for the first row of blocks. This is done by taking one of the beaded wood strips and planing the beading off of one side. See Fig. 3. Put the strip on the sill of the opening with the beaded side facing up. This first strip should be nailed into place. See Fig. 4. Lay the first course of blocks along this strip. Be sure that the beading fits into the depressions made for it in the sides of the blocks. Strips of wood, also with beading on them, are put between the blocks. See Fig. 5.

Tap these gently down into place. See Fig. 6.

When one course has been finished, lay a strip of wood beading across the top (Fig. 7) and then tap in the grooved wedges at the sides to hold the blocks securely in place. See Fig. 8. Continue up the wall in this fashion until the last course has been put in.

When the last course is in place, the header wedges are driven in. The wall is now complete except for the trim. The trim is nailed around the edges of the opening to cover up the wedges. Some 1″ x 3″ stock will be sufficiently wide for this job. If you wish, the wood trim between the blocks can be painted to give additional decorative effect.

Glass blocks set up in wood can be used to make the ends of coffee tables, bookcases and similar items.

Chapter 18

INTERIOR TRIM; HANGING DOORS

Now that most of the heavy work is out of the way, you can get started on putting up the interior trim. If you like to do cabinet work or jobs where fine measuring and cutting are required, you will enjoy this sort of work. If you prefer the rough sort of building where a slight error here and there is not important because it will soon be covered up, you will not be very happy with trim. Here, unfortunately, is something that cannot be very well covered up but stands out like the proverbial sore thumb for all eyes to see. Anyway, try to do your best work on the trim and do not try to rush it. Another point—make it as simple as possible, unless you happen to have special skills.

You will need a fine-tooth back- or miter-saw for this job as well as a good miter box. This is minimum equipment. If you have special power tools, so much the better.

INTERIOR TRIM

Do not try to install trim until you are sure that the plaster (if plaster has been used for the interior walls) is pretty dry. Trim should be put together with tight joints and if the wood is going to do a lot of swelling and shrinking, you will never get a really tight seam anywhere. If the weather is damp, it might be best to hold off on this job until there is a dry spell or until you can get some sort of heating system going to keep the air dry.

Door Jambs

Door jambs come in three sections— two side pieces and a header. The side jambs are usually grooved so that the header can be fitted between them.

There are two types of jambs that are in common use. One is made out of stock about 1⅜" thick with a rabbet that acts as the door stop. The other type is made out of thinner stock and has no rabbet. Instead, a stop bead made of wood is either nailed to the face of the jamb or nailed into a recess cut into the jamb. There is not a great deal to choose between these two jambs except, perhaps, that the heavier one is more solid and there is no chance that the stop bead can come loose. See Fig. 1.

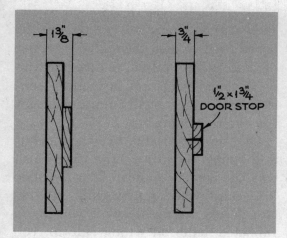

Fig. 1. Two door jambs. The heavy 1⅜″ is usually preferred.

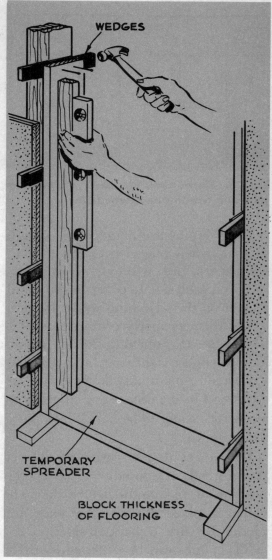

Fig. 2. Getting door jambs perfectly level by means of wood wedges and a level and straight edge.

As soon as you get the door jambs, give them a priming coat of paint. If the interior wood is to be stained, then just prime the back of the trim.

The trick in getting a door jamb in place is to have it absolutely plumb. If it is not, you will have a hard time getting the door to hang properly. The first step is to assemble the three pieces of the jamb and nail the header to the side jambs. After this has been done, cut a piece of wood to fit the exact distance between the side jambs at the header and use it along the bottom of the opening to keep the side jambs an equal distance apart.

If the rough framing was done accurately, the door jamb will fit with a little clearance on each side. Put wood wedges into this space between the rough frame and the side jambs so that you will be able to get the jambs absolutely plumb and will have something to hold them that way until they are nailed in place. Be careful not to drive the wedges in too far as this will cause the sides of the jamb to buckle out and make it impossible to get the door to fit. See Fig. 2.

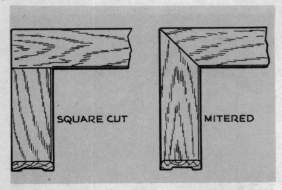

Fig. 3. Two methods used in making joints on window and door trim.

Door jambs are made wide enough so that, when placed over the 2″ x 4″ framework, they will extend sufficiently far on each side to cover the lath and plaster on the adjoining walls. Be sure to get them properly centered in relation to the door opening because if you let one edge extend too far over, you will have to plane this down as well as add wood to the other edge in order to allow the casing to be nailed into place properly.

Use a regulation carpenter's level and a good straightedge to check the position of the jambs before they are nailed in place. Be sure that they are plumb. Be sure to check all sides.

The jambs can be fastened by driving the nails right through their sides, through the shingles and into the rough framing of studding. Unless the opening is much too wide for the jambs, 16d casing nails will do the trick. Do not worry about the wood wedges. They can stay put and their ends can be cut off later with a saw. (Just be careful not to damage the sides of the

jambs with the saw.) As soon as the jambs are in place, you can remove the board used to hold them at the proper distance at the bottom. A threshold can be installed here, but in modern construction this is usually omitted except for exterior doors.

One thing to watch for when installing jambs—be sure to remember which way the door is to open. This is not so important when jambs with separate stop beads are used, but if you put a rabbeted jamb on wrong side to, you either have to take it down or else put up with a door that swings in when it should swing out. This is one of those little things that you can very easily forget.

The next project is to put the casing around the doorway. There are two ways to make the joints between the top pieces of casing and the side pieces. One way is with square-cut joints and the other is with mitered joints. Fig. 3 shows these two types. A square-cut joint is perfectly adequate and, if the joint is tight, will look perfectly all right. It is simple to make and should not cause any trouble. The mitered joint is a little more involved and requires very careful cutting and measuring if it is going to be tight.

The width of the trim used is more or less a matter of choice. The general emphasis these days is on narrow trim, but that does not mean a great deal. Of course, the trim must be wide enough so that it covers up the joint where the plaster or wallboard ends. If you use a square-cut joint, you can use any the wider a piece of stock is, the more it will shrink as it dries out. If you use wide stock with a mitered joint and it does any shrinking, the joint will open out and will not look very nice.

The casing, as was the case with the jambs, should be given a priming coat of paint or at least be back-primed before it goes up. The casing should not completely overlap the edges of the jamb. Leave a space of about ¼". Casing nails are used to fasten the casing in place, and you will want to finish off

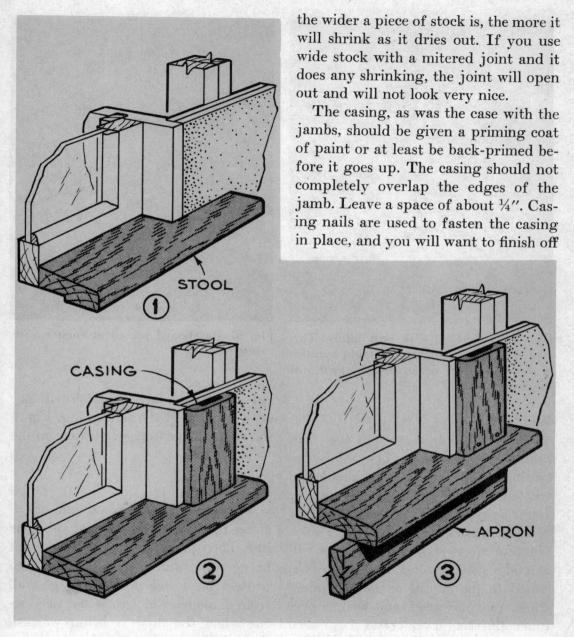

Fig. 4. Three steps in applying trim around window frames.

width trim you want. If you use a mitered joint, it is best not to use stock over 3" in width unless it is very well seasoned. The reason for this is that

each nail with a nail-set so as not to damage the casing with your hammer.

The two types of trim pictured in Fig. 3 are very simple to handle.

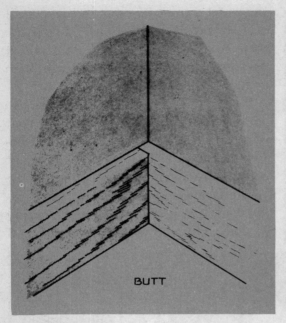

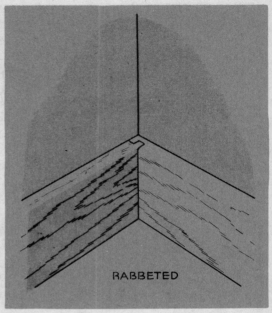

Fig. 5. Baseboard with butt joints. This type of joint is not very suitable because if the wood does much shrinking, it will open up.

Fig. 6. Baseboard joined at corner with rabbeted joint.

Windows

The next job is to put the trim around the windows. The joints between pieces of this trim should be treated in the same manner as the joints around the door casing. The first piece that goes on is the stool. This is notched out at each end so that it will extend a little beyond the casing. It is nailed to the subsill or rough framework. You may need some wedges here to get the stool level. After it is nailed in place, the side casings go on. These two pieces should be cut to size, plumbed and then nailed into place. Check the head casing before you nail it on to be sure that it is level. The apron goes on next, and it should be cut so that it comes out flush with the outside edges of the side casing. Fig. 4 shows the main steps in putting on the window trim.

Baseboards

These are pieces of wood trim nailed along the base of the wall at the floor line. Their purpose is to cover the joint between the wall and floor and also to protect the lower portion of the wall from damage or moisture that may occur when the floor is being washed. Sometimes the baseboard is called a mopboard.

The height of the baseboard is more or less a matter of personal choice. The best height is probably 6″ or so, but it can be more or less if you prefer.

Because of the size of the rooms, it should be possible to get lumber for the baseboards that is sufficiently long so that the only joints you will have are those that occur at the corners.

There are three methods of making *inside* corner joints. Fig. 5 shows a butted joint, Fig. 6 shows a rabbeted joint, and Fig. 7 shows a mitered joint. Of the three, the rabbeted joint is the best. The other two are not so satisfactory because as the boards shrink, the joints will open up.

The only type of joint that is suitable for *outside* corners is the mitered joint; if the other two were used, you could not avoid having the end grain of one board exposed.

Baseboards are nailed directly to the wall studding with 8d casing nails. Two of these are used at each stud.

Before nailing the baseboard into position, examine Fig. 8 to see the relationship of the baseboard with the finished floor and the shoe mold.

Back-prime the baseboard before it is installed.

The base shoe, or shoe mold, is a strip of ½″ or larger quarter-round trim nailed across the joint between the floor and the baseboard. Fig. 8 shows the correct method of nailing this strip of wood so that if either the baseboard or flooring shrink, there will be no open seam. The base shoe should never be nailed to the baseboard.

The base mold fits on the top of the baseboard. Sometimes the top of the baseboard is rounded off or milled out so that the base mold can be

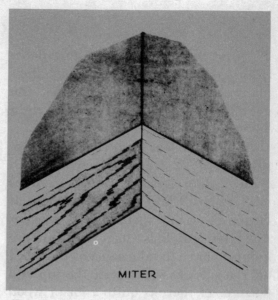

Fig. 7. **Baseboards with mitered joints.**

omitted. If present, it should be nailed to the studs. The nails should go in at an angle to draw it down tight against the baseboard.

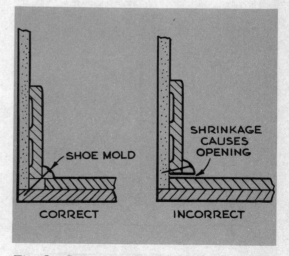

Fig. 8. **Correct and incorrect way to nail shoe mold in place. When the correct method of nailing is used, shrinkage at the baseboard or flooring will not expose any unsightly and dust-collecting cracks.**

HANGING DOORS

The first thing to do in hanging doors is to go back and check your floor plans so that you will be sure that you get the doors to open in the right direction.

After that has been done, you are ready to go to work. When you purchase a door from a lumber yard or mill, you will find that it is somewhat larger than the opening for which it was intended. This means that you are going to have to take some of the wood off the sides as well as off the top and bottom. If there is quite a lot of wood to be removed, you can use a saw. If you only have to take it down a little, use a plane. A jack plane 18 inches long is very good for this job. A short plane will not produce such an even

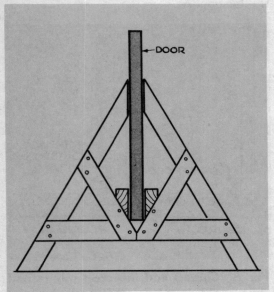

Fig. 9. A simple jig of this type will make it easy to hold a door on edge for fitting and planing.

job. Fig. 9 shows a simple jig that you can make to hold the door secure while you plane down the sides or ends.

Square off the bottom of the door and saw off the lugs or the end of the stiles that stick out beyond the bottom rail. Now hold the door in the opening and check to see how much must be removed. Next, plane down one edge of the door until it fits the frame. Then plane or saw down the top edge until it fits the head of the jamb. Now you can hold the door in the opening and scribe the other edge from the inside. There should be between $\frac{1}{16}''$ and $\frac{1}{8}''$ clearance between the door and the jamb on all sides. A 5¢ coin or a piece of cardboard will give you the approximate clearance necessary. If the finished flooring is already in place, $\frac{1}{8}''$ clearance at the bottom will be sufficient. If you have not put down the finished flooring as yet, it would be best to postpone taking any more wood off the door until you are sure of the exact measurements.

After the door has been fitted, the hinges are attached. You will need two loose-pin butt hinges for interior doors and three for the heavier exterior doors. The top hinge is usually set about 7″ or so from the top of the door and the bottom hinge comes about 11″ from the floor. If a third hinge is used, set it midway between the bottom and top hinges.

Take the lower hinge, place it on the edge of the door and mark the gain that is to be cut out. The gain should be cut to a depth equal to the thickness of the hinge leaf. Do the same for the top hinge and then screw the leaves in place. Now put the door into the opening, wedge it into correct position and mark the jambs. To prevent the door from binding on the jamb, keep the ends of the hinge leaves about ⅟₁₆″ away from the rabbet or stop. Cut in the gain on the jambs for the top and bottom hinge and then attach the leaves. Place the door back into place, drop the pins into place so that the two leaves are held together, and then check the door to see that it opens and closes freely without any binding.

The next step is to install the latch. You can use one of many types of latch. The most common types are mortised into the stile of the door. See Fig. 10.

After the door hinges and the latch have been installed, give the top and

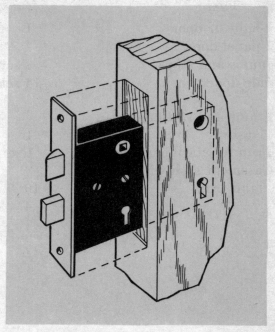

Fig. 10. **Method of installing mortice lock in door.**

bottom of the door a coat of aluminum paint to keep moisture out of the seams.

MATERIALS LIST FOR INTERIOR TRIM, DOORS AND WINDOWS FOR THE BASIC HOUSE

Material	Quantity	Dimensions
Colonial pine base	300 feet	1″ x 4″
Base molding and quarter-round	300 feet	
Flush door with frame and trim	1	3′ x 6′ 8″ x 1¾″
4-light fir door with jamb, sill and trim	1	2′ 8″ x 6′ 8″ x 1¾″
2-light fir door with jamb, sill and trim	1	2′ 10″ x 6′ 8″ x 1¾″
Brass hinges	9	

Material	Quantity	Dimensions
2-light fir door	1	2′ 8″ x 6′ 8″ x 1¾″
2-panel door	7	1⅜″
Jambs and stops	7 sets	
Side door trim	14 sets	
Frame and stationary sash	1	7′ x 4′ 2″
Trim for stationary sash	1 set	
Casement sash with frame and trim	10	3′ 2³⁄₁₆″ x 3′ 1¾″
	4	4′ 2⅜″ x 3′ 1¾″
	1	4′ 2⅜″ x 1′ 6″

Chapter 19

THE FINISH FLOORING

You have a wide selection of materials to choose from when it comes to the finish floor. There are hardwoods like oak, maple or birch, or softwoods like southern pine, Douglas fir or redwood. If you prefer, you can use linoleum, or linoleum or asphalt tile. Of course, all the floors in the house need not be finished with the same material by any means. You can use a hardwood or softwood flooring in the living room and bedrooms and a composition type of flooring in the kitchen, bathroom and utility room.

For years, only hardwood flooring was considered suitable for first-class work, but we are getting away from that school of thought more and more, and today it is not at all unusual to find all the floors in a house covered with linoleum or asphalt tile. Composition flooring of good quality will give many years of service, plus a decorative and colorful effect.

HARDWOOD FLOORING

Hardwood flooring must not be put down until all the other work inside the house has been completed. It should be the last item on the program. If the walls have been plastered, be sure not to lay the flooring, or even store it in the house until the plaster is absolutely dry. If hardwood flooring is left near wet plaster, it will absorb some of the moisture and expand. Later on, after it is in place, it will shrink and there will be cracks. Do not have the flooring delivered until the day it is to be laid down, and do not have delivery made on damp or wet days. To safeguard the flooring against moisture,

it is best to work with it either during very dry weather or after the heating plant is in operation so that the air in the house is dry.

Hardwood flooring is usually tongued and grooved on both sides as well as at the ends. It comes in different widths, and it is best to use the narrower boards as there is less chance that cracks will appear in the finished floor and also less chance of the boards' cupping. Some brands of hardwood flooring come with a factory-applied finish. These are more expensive than the unfinished flooring, but they are ready for use just as soon as they have been nailed down. Unfinished flooring must be given some sort of a finish as soon as it is down and before it has been put into use.

Laying a Hardwood Floor

The first step in laying a hardwood floor is to prepare the sub-floor. This should be done before the flooring is delivered. Sweep the sub-floor clean and then go over it carefully and drive down any nail heads that are sticking up. Check to be sure that the sub-floor is adequately nailed down, because if it is not, you may be troubled with squeaks after the finish flooring is in place. Any high spots on the sub-flooring should be taken down. Be sure that it is absolutely dry. As soon as you are satisfied with the condition of the sub-floor, cover it with a layer of 15-pound asphalt felt. Lay the paper from wall to wall and allow the strips to overlap about 4".

Flooring is usually laid along the longest dimension of the room. The first step, then, is to lay one board up against the wall with the tongue edge facing out. The groove edge should not quite come to the outside surface of the baseboard. See Fig. 1. If the sub-flooring was laid straight instead of diagonally, the finish flooring must be laid at right angles to it. The first strip is nailed with 10d floor nails driven right straight down through the board at the groove edge. The nails should be spaced about 10" apart and should be near enough to the edge so that they will be covered by the shoe

molding. The first strip of flooring can also be nailed through the tongue. You will see from Fig. 1 that the nail is driven in where the tongue leaves the shoulder, and at an angle of between 45° and 50°. Do not try to drive the nail all the way down with a hammer as you may easily strike the wood and damage it. Use a nail-set or another nail to finish off the driving in and to countersink the head.

The correct type and size of nail to use will depend on the wood and the thickness of the flooring. This information can be obtained from the lumber yard.

Each board should fit snugly against the next, but do not drive them up against each other with too much force for this may damage the wood and cause cracks later on. The best way to get one board tightly up to the next is to use a scrap piece of flooring. Slip the groove edge of the scrap piece over the tongue of the board that is being installed and then tap the edge of the scrap board with the hammer. This will push the floor board up tight.

It is the practice these days not to have thresholds on interior doors and, therefore, it is not necessary to break the flooring when you come to a door. It can be carried right on through into the next room. Use the long runs of boards where appearance counts the most and save the short lengths for halls, closets, etc.

You want to be sure that the two strips of flooring near the baseboards are parallel to the wall. The first strip can be made parallel before it is nailed down. When you have come to within a few feet of the opposite wall, check and see if the flooring is parallel with it. If not, you can take off a little of the groove edges and so bring the last board parallel with the baseboard.

Baseboards can be installed either before or after the flooring is in place. Fig. 8 in Chapter 18 shows how the shoe molding is nailed in place. Note that the nail does not go through either the flooring or the baseboard but goes right past each into the sub-flooring. The reason for this is to make sure that there will be no cracks between the baseboard and shoe or the finish floor and shoe, even though there may be some shrinkage. As soon as the finish floor is down, apply a finish. This is

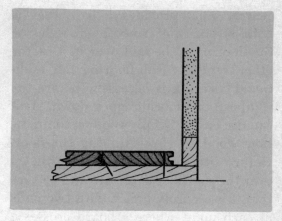

Fig. 1. How the first strip of flooring should be nailed down. Note that this strip does not come up against the wall but is kept a fraction of an inch away. This is to prevent the floor from buckling should the wood expand.

covered in the chapter on Painting and Finishing.

SOFTWOOD FLOORS

This type of flooring is installed in exactly the same manner as hardwood flooring except for the size of nail, which will depend on the thickness of the wood. If $^{25}/_{32}''$ softwood flooring is used, 8d wood flooring nails are used and they are spaced at least every 10 inches.

COMPOSITION FLOORING

Rather than using wood floors throughout the house, you may prefer one of the many types of composition floor coverings, such as linoleum or asphalt, or linoleum, rubber or plastic tile. These can be used along with some floors of hardwood or softwood, or the entire house can be floored with them. All these materials come in numerous designs and colors and are suitable for every room throughout the house. As a general rule, no type of composition floor covering should be laid over a single sub-floor. It is done, of course, but it is not wise because it reduces the wearing ability of the flooring and so there is nothing really saved. About the only exception is when the sub-floor is made out of $^5/_8''$ plywood securely nailed to joists spaced 16" on center. This provides a base that is both strong and smooth enough for the flooring to be laid over it. But for other types of sub-flooring, an additional covering is necessary before the composition flooring goes down. You can use either ⅜" plywood or composition wood to cover up the sub-floor. Before either of them is put down, go over the sub-floor carefully and be sure that it is securely nailed with two nails at each point where a board crosses a joist. Drive in any nail heads that may be sticking up and be sure that there are no squeaks. If there are, you can usually take care of them by driving an extra nail into the joist at the point of the squeak. If you do not take the squeaks out now, you may find it impossible to remove them after the floor covering is in place. Any boards that are cupped should be planed or sanded down. Only after all these precautions have been taken can the plywood or composition wood be nailed down. Both should be nailed with rosin-coated nails spaced about 6" apart. Remove any grease or oily marks and, if necessary, coat the surface with a size to seal the wood pores so that the adhesive used for the final floor covering will make a strong bond.

Laying Linoleum

Linoleum should always be laid over a felt base. The felt is cemented to the flooring with a linoleum cement, and the linoleum is in turn cemented to the felt. The seams between the sections of felt should run at right angles to the seams between sections of linoleum, so decide in advance where you want the seams in the linoleum to run and then lay the felt in the other direction. Be sure that the felt is on smoothly and that there are no bulges in it.

Linoleum becomes rather brittle in cold weather and, therefore, it is wise to let it lie loose in a heated room overnight or longer before you work with it, if the outside weather is cold.

When you are ready to start work, cut the felt and cement it in place. Seams between strips of felt should be butt joints but do not let any of the strips overlap. Once the felt has been cut and fitted, apply the cement to the floor. The best tool to use for this job is a linoleum-paste spreader. Now the felt goes into position. It should be rolled down—a kitchen roller will do nicely for this—so that it is absolutely flat. Next the linoleum itself can be put down.

Roll the linoleum out and start to fit and cut it. The best tool for cutting is a linoleum knife. The linoleum should not come up directly against the plaster or sole plate. Leave a small gap at these points to take care of expansion of the linoleum. The gap can be covered later on with wood trim. Fitting around doors and other places where accurate cutting is necessary can be easily done by making a pattern out of heavy paper. Cut this pattern so that it fits perfectly and put it into place. Coat it with glue and then roll the linoleum down over it as far as the linoleum will go. The paper will stick to the linoleum so that, when the linoleum is rolled back up, the pattern will be in place and you can easily mark the linoleum for cutting.

Once the linoleum has been cut, it is ready to be cemented in place. It is a good idea to use waterproof cement around all seams as this is the point where water usually gets in to soften up ordinary cement. After the linoleum is down, go over it with a 150-pound roller so that it will be flat and tightly joined to the felt.

You can either rent or borrow this roller quite readily from your linoleum dealer.

Linoleum and Asphalt Tile

These tiles come in different sizes and can be purchased in either squares or rectangles. As for getting the floor ready and putting down the felt, the procedure is the same for either type of tile as for regular linoleum.

Few rooms are absolutely square, and it would be a mistake to start laying the tile at one side and work over to the other. The chances are that before you got very far you would see that the tiles were not coming out straight, but at that point it would be too late to do much of anything about it. The best way to lay the tile is to find the exact center of the room after the felt is down and lay the tile from this point out towards the edges of the room.

Measure the width of the room at each end and then find the midpoint between each of these measurements. Run a chalk line between these two midpoints. Measure this chalk line and find its midpoint. Use a large square to run lines from this point to the two opposite walls. Now you have located the exact center of the room and, in addition, you have divided the room into four quarters.

Next, starting at the exact center, lay a few feet of the tile dry in whatever pattern you have selected. If you are satisfied with the pattern and also that the tiles are coming straight, take them up and apply the cement to the felt. Do not apply the cement over the entire floor or even to an entire quarter. Just cover as much as you can reach from one spot. Working from the center point, press each tile into the cement, getting the joints between them as snug as possible. Do not try to push too hard because you may move one of the tiles out of alignment. If you kneel on the tile it will help to hold it in place. Continue to lay the tile until one entire section has been finished.

Tile for the border will have to be fitted and then cut to size.

As soon as one quarter of the floor has been completed, go back over it carefully and, using a mallet, press down all the seams. Wipe off any excess cement that may be on the tile or around the seams.

You can now move on and do the other three quarters in the same manner, always starting from the exact center-point of the room.

PARQUET HARDWOOD FLOORING

Instead of using a conventional type of hardwood floor, you may prefer a parquet floor. This is made out of squares of hardwood flooring that are themselves made out of strips of flooring glued together. The square is mounted on a felt base and each square is cemented in place with a mastic.

This type of flooring is installed in much the same fashion as asphalt or linoleum tile. Again the best place to start work is the exact center of the room, for this will insure that the sections of flooring are straight regardless of the fact that the room may not be quite square.

After the center of the room has been determined, apply the mastic to a few square feet of the sub-floor in one quarter and set the sections of flooring into place. The sections are butted tightly against each other.

FINISHING HARDWOOD FLOORS

Floors should be given a protective finish just as soon after they are put down as possible. If you delay doing this job for very long, the flooring is almost sure to become rough and worn and dirty and, when you finally get around to putting on a finish, you will find that you have made a great deal of extra work for yourself.

The first step in finishing the floor is to make it smooth. You can do this by hand with a scraper and sandpaper, but you will find that doing it this way will take forever. It is much more practical to rent an electric floor-sander from your lumber dealer or hardware store. Along with the large floor-sander, you will need an edger, which is a small sanding machine that enables you to sand to within about ½" of the wall and in the corners where the large sander cannot reach. There will be a few spots that even the edger cannot touch; these you must do by hand.

The first sanding should be done with No. 2 grade sandpaper. Go across the grain first and then finish up by sanding with the grain. This first sanding with a coarse grade of paper will take out most of the high spots in the flooring. Now put a No. ½ grade sandpaper on the machine and work the floor over with this. Go down through successive grades of sandpaper until you end up with a No. 00 sandpaper.

Be sure to keep the sander moving at all times when the paper is touching the floor. If you do not, you may scar up the flooring a little. Another point to watch out for is the condition of the sander. If it is worn and not absolutely level, it will do more harm than good.

After you have finished with the power sander, go back and do by hand any areas that are left over. Use the same grades of sandpaper on these that were used with the sander.

Once the floor has been sanded down, do not walk on it until the finish is on. If you do, you will leave footprints that will have to be sanded out.

Now dust the floor and it is ready for the finish. You have a choice of several materials for this.

Varnish

This finish can be used on any type of flooring. The usual method of applying it is to use three coats. Special floor varnishes should be used. Varnish intended for interior trim or furniture does not have the wearing quality of floor varnish. The drawback to varnish as a finish is that it must be waxed to prevent wear and, unless the wax is applied in thin coats, the floor will be slippery. Another drawback is that it takes a good while to complete the finish as each coat must be given ample time in which to dry hard before the next coat is applied.

If you wish, the floor can be stained before the varnish is applied. Stains are applied with either a cloth or brush. After the wood has had time to absorb some of the stain, the excess is wiped off with clean cheesecloth. After the stain has been applied, a filler of one sort or another is required. You can use a paste or liquid filler or shellac. When the filler is hard, it should be given a sanding with No. 00 sandpaper.

Now the varnish can be applied. Exercise the same precautions in applying floor varnish as are outlined for varnishing trim in the Chapter on Painting and Finishing. Be sure that the floor is clean and that there are no pockets of dust in the corners.

Shellac

Probably more floors are finished with shellac than with any other type of finish. It provides a very high luster and, because it dries so rapidly, an entire finish can be applied to a floor and the floor can be ready to be walked on in twenty-four hours or so. The disadvantage of shellac is that, like varnish, it must be protected by wax to prevent wear and scratching. Another disadvantage is that when shellac becomes wet it turns white.

If you are going to use shellac for a finish, be sure that it is pure shellac and not some sort of substitute. It should not be over six months old and should be in a glass container because, if it has been in contact with metal for very long, it may discolor certain woods. Shellac is sold as either a 5-pound cut or a 4-pound cut. For floor finishes, use the 4-pound cut and add 1 part denatured alcohol to 2 parts shellac as it comes from the can. Be sure that you use denatured alcohol and not anti-freeze.

Shellac can be applied over a stain or right over the natural wood. You will need 3 thin coats. Give the first coat at least three hours in which to dry. After this, give the finish a sanding with No. 00 sandpaper. Dust the floor clean and apply the second coat. This should be given a longer drying period than the first coat; twelve hours is about right. Sand this coat down with

No. 00 sandpaper after it is hard, and then apply the third coat.

For best results with shellac, it should be applied when the temperature is between 70° and 75°. The atmosphere should be dry because if it is damp, the shellac will dry with a cloudy appearance. The floor should be waxed after the final coat of shellac has had at least eight hours in which to dry. A paste wax should be used for this purpose. And you will save a good deal of time by using an electric waxer to do the job—it not only speeds up the work, but you will be able to get the wax on in thin coats that will not make the floor slippery.

Floor Seals

Floor seals are somewhat different from either varnish or shellac. While varnish and shellac remain on the sur-

face of the wood to form a protective coating, a floor seal goes into the wood's pores. These penetrating seals make an excellent finish. Although they do not have quite the same luster as either shellac or varnish, they are easily patched when worn spots appear and they take wax without becoming too slippery. Usually two applications of a seal are necessary, but in some work only one is required. Seals are applied to the floor with a wide brush or mop. The floor must first be sanded smooth.

There are a great many different brands of floor seals on the market. As the directions for application will vary according to the brand, it is not practical to give detailed instructions. The important thing to do is to read over the manufacturer's directions carefully and then apply the seal in the prescribed manner.

CONCRETE FLOORS

Floors of this type can be covered with wood flooring, with a resilient type of flooring such as linoleum, with paint or merely with carpets. If radiant-floor-panel heating is used, wood flooring should not be put down because the space between the wood flooring and the concrete would act as insulation and prevent the heating system from working adequately. Even if the wood flooring is cemented directly to the concrete, the insulation value of the wood itself is enough to prevent the heating system from working properly. Other types of floor covering can

be used with success with radiant-floor-panel heating.

Wood Floors on Concrete

There are two ways that flooring of wood can be placed over a concrete sub-floor. One method is to put down wood sleepers and nail the floor boards to these. The other method is to use parquet flooring that is specially prepared at the factory and can be cemented directly to the concrete with a special mastic.

The sleepers for regulation hard-wood flooring can be embedded in the concrete when it is poured or anchored to it with metal clips. If the concrete is already in place and hard and no provision for anchoring the sleepers was made, they can be attached with masonry anchors. The sleepers should be spaced every 16″ on center and should run at right angles to the finished flooring.

After the sleepers are in place, they should be covered with waterproof building paper. This is necessary to keep any moisture away from the flooring. After the paper is down, the floor boards are nailed to the sleepers in exactly the same fashion as if you were nailing them to a wood sub-floor.

Resilient Flooring

Before you attempt to lay any of the resilient floor coverings such as linoleum, asphalt tile, rubber, etc., you should make sure that the concrete slab is absolutely dry. This can be done by placing a piece of tar paper over a section of the floor and allowing it to remain down for twenty-four hours or so. At the end of this period, pick it up and see if there is any moisture on the underside.

There are some types of floor covering that can be used over a damp base, but most require a base that is dry throughout the entire year.

After you have made the test with the tar paper, you can go to work and install the covering that you have selected. First of all, get a copy of the manufacturer's specifications for laying that type of covering on concrete floors. The reason for this is that some types of covering require a felt lining, while others require that the floor first be coated with a special primer and the flooring cemented directly over this rather than to a felt.

As for the actual application of either linoleum or one of the types of tile, the same methods of cutting and fitting are used for concrete sub-floors as were described for use on wood sub-floors.

Ceramic and Clay-Tile Covering

You can, if you wish, cover the concrete-slab floor with ceramic, clay or concrete tile or even with flagstone. Any of these coverings will, of course, give you a long-wearing floor that is easily cleaned and very hard to damage.

The first step is to apply a coat of cement grout over the concrete slab. Before this has a chance to harden, it is covered with a ¾″ thick mortar bed. This is made with 1 part Portland cement, and from 3 to 4 parts clean fine sand. Add just enough water to get a plastic that has a workable consistency. Do not mix up more mortar than you can cover with flooring in 30 minutes.

The tiles are set into this mortar bed and tapped into place. Be sure that they are level and even. A small joint is left between each tile and this can be filled later with a thin mortar made with 1 part cement and 1 part sand. Force it into the joint and then wipe off any surplus on the tile before it has a chance to harden.

Painting Concrete Floors

Concrete floors can be painted with ordinary oil paints intended for floors or with special concrete-floor paints that will not be damaged by dampness or the active lime that is present in fresh concrete. If an ordinary oil paint is used, it is important to know that the floor is perfectly dry. You can use the tar-paper method previously described to make sure that there is no dampness present. You will have to neutralize the lime in any event. Make a solution of 3 pounds of zinc sulphate to a gallon of water. Brush this on the concrete and use plenty of it so that it will soak in. Allow several days for the concrete to dry and then brush off the crystals that have formed on the surface. After this, the floor is ready for paint.

Special synthetic oil paints do not require this treatment. They can be applied directly to the concrete.

Floors in unfinished basements are often given no finish at all. If the concrete tends to be dusty, it can be coated with a concrete hardener, which will keep it from sanding and can be painted over at some later date.

Chapter 20

PAINTING AND FINISHING

EVERY step in building a house is important, and painting and finishing is no exception. Woodwork exposed to the weather should be painted just as soon as possible to prevent it from absorbing moisture. There is not quite as much rush with interior painting except for floors, which should be given a protective coating of some sort before they are put into use.

EXTERIOR PAINTING

A good paint job will not only protect the outside of your house, but it will also make it more attractive, so take pains with the selection of your color scheme, the paint you use and the manner in which it is put on.

The exterior of the house—that is, any portion that will be exposed to the weather—should be painted with a good grade of exterior paint. Do not take the time and trouble to mix your own paints because, in the first place, this is rather tricky work and you may not get a good quality of paint and, second, there are many fine ready-mixed paints on the market that are better than anything you could mix yourself. Be sure that you have good paint brushes; they are as important for the job as is a good paint.

As a general rule, painting should start at the highest point of the house and work down. If the roof wood shingles are to be stained, this should be done first of all. Stain is easily applied by brush, and the main point is to get it on evenly and to keep it off other woodwork that is to be painted. After the shingles have been done, do the cornice trim, the siding, and then the window and door trim.

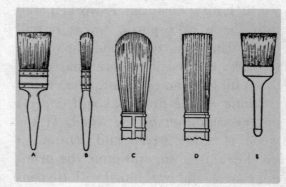

Fig. 1. Flat wall brush for exteriors and other large surfaces and a varnish brush. *A, B* and *C* show the wall brush. *D* shows the bristle contour of an inferior wall brush. *E* is a seamless ferrule varnish brush.

The first rule to follow for good results in painting is to be sure that the wood is both dry and clean. Do not paint right after rain or during damp weather. Allow the wood to become bone dry before you begin to apply paint. Another point is not to try to paint when the temperature of the air is below 50° F. Below this temperature, paint will not flow properly and the job will not turn out well. The best way to insure that the wood is clean is to wipe it down with turpentine. Rough spots in the wood should be sanded smooth. Knots and sappy spots should be coated with either orange shellac or aluminum paint before the first coat of paint is applied. Unless this is done, the rosin will bleed through the paint after it is dry.

The First Coat

The first coat of paint, the *priming coat,* is the most important of the three coats that are required for exterior work. Unless this coat is worked well into the wood's pores, where it will dry and make a strong bond, the weight of subsequent coats of paint may cause it to pull loose and peel off. The proper thinning of the first coat will depend on the condition of the wood. If the wood is rather green and contains a good deal of rosin and gum, the priming coat should be thinned with turpentine. The turpentine will act on these gums as a solvent and allow the paint to penetrate the pores of the wood. If the wood is very gummy, it might be wise to wipe it down thoroughly with turpentine before painting. On the other hand, if the wood is very dry, the first coat should be thinned with linseed oil to replace the oils in the paint that will be absorbed.

The first coat of paint should be worked into the pores of the wood. Do not just flow the paint onto the wood; slap it on and work it in. Many experts feel that the only way to get a priming coat applied properly is by brush. A paint sprayer does not force the paint into the pores as well as can be done by a brush. For the second and third coats, a sprayer can be used if one is available.

The Second and Third Coats

As soon as the first coat of paint is dry, go over the surface and fill in any holes or nail heads with putty. The putty should not be applied before the first coat goes on because the wood will absorb the oils out of the putty and cause it to dry out and crack or fall out. After the putty is hard, give it a light sanding and then apply the second and third coats. Be sure to allow ample time between coats for the paint to dry. The exact time required will depend on the weather conditions, but be sure that the paint is good and hard before you go ahead with another coat.

The general practice is to paint the siding first and then do the trim around doors and windows. This trim was given a priming coat when it was installed, so only the second and third coats are required for it. In spite of the common practice of painting the trim a different color than the siding, it is not essential by any means. You can paint it the same color as the siding or you may select any other color that appeals to you.

Wood Siding Shingles

Shingles used for siding can be stained or painted. The reason that these shingles can be painted while roof shingles cannot, is that siding shingles are not so apt to absorb moisture as roof shingles.

Because of the rough texture of shingles, it is easier to apply paint by a sprayer. If you use a brush, use an old one since the rough surface may damage a good new brush. (Shingle stain is applied by brush.)

Asbestos-Cement Shingles

Asbestos-cement shingles can be painted with an oil paint, but you will be better off if you use an asbestos-cement-shingle paint. The reason for this is that it is difficult to be sure that the shingles do not contain moisture and, if they do, using an oil paint on them will turn out badly. The special paints designed for these shingles will not be damaged by moisture either inside the shingles or on the outside surface of the paint itself.

Stucco

Stucco is best painted with special Portland-cement paints that will not be damaged by moisture and will provide a certain amount of waterproofing for the stucco.

INTERIOR WALL FINISHES

If the walls in the house have been plastered, they should be given some sort of a finish just as soon as possible. Fresh plaster without any protective paint over it, while looking perfectly all right, will absorb dirt and dust and you will find it almost impossible to get it clean. It is best, therefore, to put some sort of a finish over the plaster as soon as possible.

Types

As far as paints for plaster go, you can use either an oil paint, a water-thinned paint or calcimine. An oil paint will provide a good durable surface that can be washed and cleaned repeatedly, and that will serve later

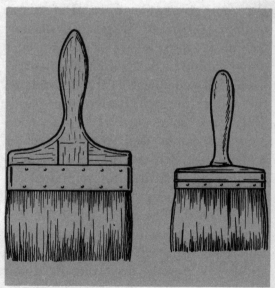

Fig. 2. A flat calcimine brush, left, and a Dutch calcimine brush, right. Both come in widths up to 8 inches.

Fig. 3. Proper way to hold a brush in order to work into corners.

as a base for paper or for any type of paint you may wish to apply. Oil paint is probably the most satisfactory finish of all, but it costs the most and requires the most time to apply. Before an ordinary oil paint can go over plaster, the plaster must either be about a year old or should have the lime in it neutralized with a chemical. If this is not done, the active lime will destroy the paint. There are some special types of oil paint that can be used over fresh plaster without fear because they contain synthetic oils that are not damaged by lime, but ordinary flat wall paints cannot be used. The lime in the plaster can be neutralized by making a solution consisting of 2 pounds of zinc sulphate crystals dissolved in about one-half a gallon of water. This solution should be applied liberally over the entire wall surface. Allow it to dry on the plaster and then brush off any crystals that remain on the surface. A coat of varnish size should be applied to prevent an uneven absorption of the paint by the porous plaster. A coat of paint the same color as the finish paint can be used in place of the varnish size. After this is on, the three coats of paint can be thinned according to directions and then applied. If the ceiling is to be painted, it should be done first and be followed by the walls.

Rather than go to the time and trouble of neutralizing the lime and applying three coats of oil paint, you may prefer to use a good grade of water-thinned paint. The better brands of this type of paint can be applied directly to fresh plaster, and they will serve later on as a base for oil paint or for additional coats of water-thinned paint. They can be washed and they dry very quickly and have no odor, as an oil paint does. Of course, some of these paints do not quite deliver all that they promise, so before you select one, do a little asking around and find a brand that has given good results right along.

Application

The main trick in applying one of these quick-drying paints is to get the sections joined up before the paint begins to dry. A great help in doing this is to close all windows and doors in the room that you are working in. This will prevent drafts of air from passing over the painted surface and evaporating the water out of the paint too rapidly.

As far as the actual application of the paint goes, brush it on in 1-foot squares, working from the top of the wall down. By covering a small area at a time and working quickly, you will have ample time to join up the sections before the paint around the edges has set.

Fig. 3 shows the proper way to hold the brush when you come to painting in the corners.

Calcimine is the least expensive finish you can use on a wall, and it can be put on fresh plaster directly after a size has been applied.

As far as painting the various wallboards goes, you do not, of course, have to worry about neutralizing the lime. These products can be painted with an oil paint, water-thinned paint or calcimine just as soon as they are in place. The better types of board do not require any size for calcimine or water-thinned paint but do need one for an oil paint. This size is usually a varnish size. Directions for decorating wallboard are available from your local dealer and should be consulted.

When you come to the door casings and the doors, consult Fig. 4, which shows the parts of the casing that should be painted the same color as the door itself. Needless to say, it is not

Fig. 4. The shaded parts of the casing, as shown above, are the parts that are painted the same color as the door.

necessary to finish all the walls in a house with the same type of paint. For example, it is always best to use an oil paint, such as enamel, in the bathroom and kitchen because here you want a surface that is waterproof and that can be washed easily. In living rooms and bedrooms, calcimine is perfectly satisfactory for the ceiling with a water-thinned paint for the walls or, if you wish something a little more expensive and durable, a water-thinned paint on the ceiling and an oil paint on the walls. Of course, for children's rooms you need a good, durable and washable surface that only oil paint can supply.

WALLPAPERING

You will find it a good deal easier to paper walls before fixtures are installed. If this is done, the paper can be put up with minimum amount of fitting and the holes for the fixtures can be made in the paper after it is in place.

Wallpaper should not be applied to plaster walls until the plaster is com-

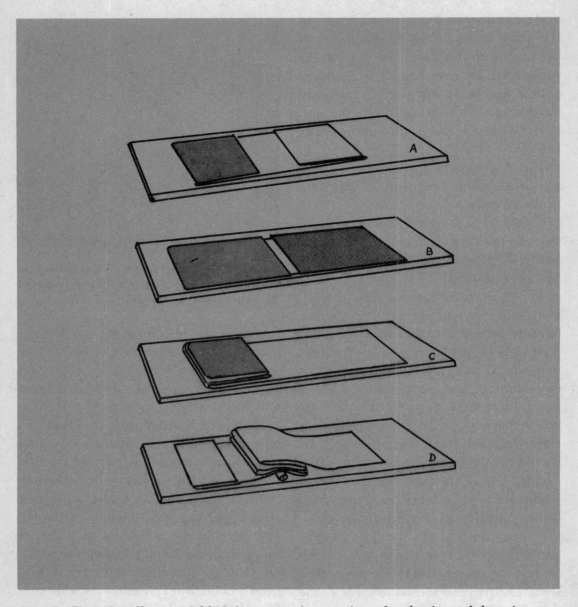

Fig. 5. Pasted wallpaper folded for convenient handling. Top to bottom: for vertical hanging, top edge at right; for cutting into strips; for horizontal hanging, top edge at bottom; for ceiling hanging, matching edge at bottom.

pletely dry. If the paper is going to be applied to some type of wallboard, the board must first be covered with a lightweight felt. Strips of felt are joined at the seams with tight butt joints. Plaster walls must be covered with a glue size before the paper is hung. Size for this purpose comes in powder

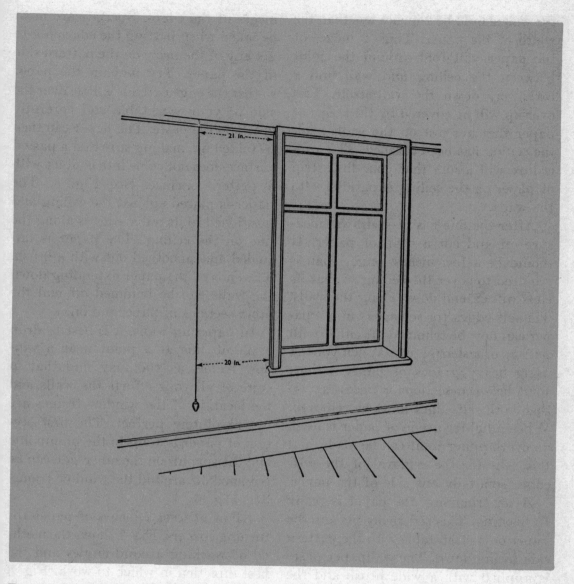

Fig. 6. Checking the alignment of a window by means of a plumb line. This window is not vertical and the wallpaper will have to be cut to fit.

form; it needs only to be mixed with water for use.

As a rule, ceilings are painted rather than papered, but if you wish to paper the ceilings, they should be done before the walls. You will need some good scaf-folding for this job so that you will be able to get the paper up into place with a minimum amount of effort.

The best method of getting the paper on straight is to draw a line across the ceiling. The distance of this line from the wall should be 2 inches less than the width of the paper. Thus, 2 inches of the paper will fold around the joint between the ceiling and wall and a little way down the wall itself. This overlap will be covered by the strips of paper that are put on the walls after the ceiling has been finished. This procedure will insure that your first strip of paper on the ceiling is parallel with the walls.

After the line has been drawn, measure off and cut a strip of paper. It should be a few inches longer than is required to cover the ceiling so that its ends will extend down along the walls. The self-edges (or selvages) of the paper can now be trimmed off either with scissors or a sharp knife. When you are using heavy grades of paper, a butt joint between sections is necessary, so then both self-edges must be removed. When a lighter grade of paper is used, an overlapping joint can be made, and this calls for the removal of the self-edge from only one side of the paper.

After trimming, the paper is ready for pasting. This is done by placing the paper on a clean table with the pattern side facing down. The wallpaper paste is applied with a wide brush and the pasting should begin at the center of the paper and work out to within a few inches of the edges. Special care must be taken when pasting the edges not to get any of the paste on the pattern side of the paper. Try moving the paper so that the edge extends a little over the side of your worktable and carefully brush on the paste. The paper can then be folded up, making sure that a pasted surface does not come into contact with a pattern surface. See Fig. 5. The paper is placed against the ceiling and positioned so its outer edge is along the line on the ceiling. The paper is unfolded and smoothed out with a brush. The ends of the paper extending down the walls can be trimmed off and the other sections of paper put on.

In papering walls, it is best to drop a plumb line at a point near a window frame, as you may find that in spite of all your efforts the walls and the location of the window frames are not absolutely perfect. The first section of paper is hung to the plumb line and the surplus on the other side can be trimmed off around the window frame. See Fig. 6.

Allow at least 2 inches of paper for turning corners. Fig. 7 shows the method of working around angles and the best direction in which to work. Fig. 8 shows how to get the paper to fit around door frames and similar openings.

FINISHING THE WOODWORK

As far as the interior woodwork goes, the finish used here will depend on the quality of the wood and the general decorative scheme of each particular room. The woodwork can be painted with trim enamel or given a natural finish with varnish, shellac or wax. Attractive wood with a natural finish is

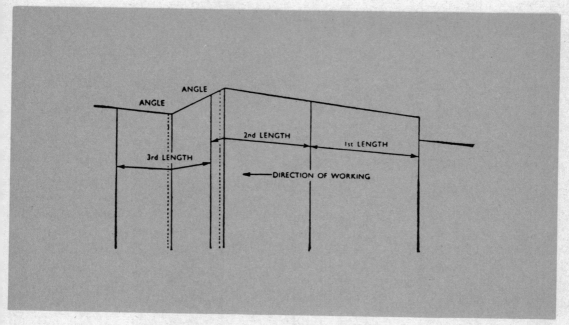

ANGLE

ANGLE

2nd LENGTH

1st LENGTH

3rd LENGTH

DIRECTION OF WORKING

Fig. 7. How to paper around corners and the direction in which to work.

very popular today. If you wish, the wood can be stained with a wood stain to bring out the grain and change the color somewhat.

Painting Wood Trim

The first step, if you wish to paint the wood trim with an interior trim paint or enamel, is to give all the woodwork a good sanding down with No. 1 sandpaper or steel wool. Dust off the woodwork and then coat the knots and sappy spots with orange shellac or aluminum paint. Now you can apply the first coat of paint. This should be thinned in accordance with the manufacturer's instructions. Start working at the highest point in the room and work down. After the first coat of paint is dry, fill in any nail holes or flaws in the wood with putty or plastic wood. Give the filler

time to dry and then rub the surface down with sandpaper. The second and third coats can then go on.

Staining Woodwork

If the woodwork is to be stained and given a natural finish, it must first be sanded down smooth with No. 0 sandpaper. Dust the surface clean and then apply a stain. There are many different types of stain that you can use for this purpose, but most amateurs prefer an oil stain. This can be applied to the wood with either a brush or a clean cloth. The edge grain of wood will tend to absorb more stain than the other surfaces and this will make the edges darker. To prevent this from happening, apply a mixture of half-and-half turpentine and linseed oil to the edge grain before you apply the stain.

Fig. 8. How to fit wallpaper around a door. The shaded areas have already been covered with paper. In hanging the rest, cut and fit the narrow strip first.

Remember when staining that the longer the stain is allowed to remain on the surface the deeper it will penetrate and the darker will be the wood. Also keep in mind that when stain dries it will be just a little lighter in color than when wet. It is best to stay on the safe side and have the stain too light than too dark. If it is too light, you can always apply another coat.

The stain should be applied to the wood and after time has been given for it to sink in, the surplus is wiped off with a clean cloth. Allow twenty-four hours for the stain to dry and then go on to the next step. If you are working with wood that has an open grain, such as oak, elm, chestnut or walnut, a filler is next on the list. Fillers come in paste form and are thinned with turpentine before application. A filler is necessary to plug the pores of the wood so that when the varnish is applied, it will not sink into these little depressions and dry out with a rough surface. Of course, you do not have to use a filler. You can apply the varnish directly to the wood and sand it out smooth after it is dry. But you will find that several coats of varnish will have to be applied and sanded smooth before you have a base suitable for the finish coat. If the wood has *not* been stained, you need a neutral filler. If the wood *is* stained, you need a filler of the same color as the stain or tint that was used on the wood. The filler is applied across the grain and then finished by rubbing with the grain. Allow it to set for about fifteen minutes and then wipe it off with a piece of clean burlap. Wipe across the grain and then with the grain. Give the filler a day to dry and then give the entire wood surface a light sanding.

Varnishing

Most of the trouble encountered with varnish is the result of the surface's not being properly prepared. The wood must be absolutely clean, dry and smooth. The temperature of the air

Fig. 9. A varnish brush 3 or 4 inches in width should be used for varnishing trim and floors.

where varnishing is being done should be around 70°. When the weather is cold, varnish will not flow out properly. When it is too hot, the varnish will dry too quickly. Not only must the wood be dry, but the air around it must not be damp. Do not varnish during damp weather or in the early morning or late evening when dew is falling.

The wood should be sanded down with No. 00 sandpaper before the first coat of varnish is put on. Flow the varnish onto the surface, working with a full brush at all times. You will probably find that the best way to get the varnish on is to apply it across the grain and then brush it with the grain. Do not try to cover too much area at one time, for if you do, the edges of the varnish may set before they can be joined up with the next section. And do not try to go back over a spot that has already been varnished because once the varnish has set, it will not flow out again and the brush will roughen up the surface. Catch any sags and wrinkles before they have a chance to set. Work from the highest point down and do the baseboard trim last because your brush is very likely to pick up some dirt at this point. Two or three coats of varnish should be applied and each should be sanded down with No. 00 sandpaper to produce a smooth finish.

MATERIALS LIST FOR PAINTING THE BASIC HOUSE

Exterior paint, 8 gallons
Water-thinned paint, 11 gallons

Floor enamel, 3 gallons
Interior enamel, 1½ gallons

Chapter 21

FINISHING THE ATTIC AND BASEMENT

WHEN the time comes for you to finish off the attic, you will find that if you made the necessary provisions when doing the house framing and setting in the utilities, the job will not be hard.

Dormer Windows

The first step is to install the dormer windows. As the rafters have already been framed to take dormers, you have very little extra work to do besides the actual building of the dormers themselves.

As it will be necessary to make an opening in the roof, this sort of work should be done in mild weather and you should have a large piece of canvas on hand so that the opening can be covered up in case of rain.

If you are careful in removing the roofing at the point where the dormer is to be installed, you may be able to use a lot of this material for the dormer. Do not remove any more of the roofing or roof boards than is necessary. If you take off too much, you will have to spend a lot of extra time getting it back on.

Once the opening has been made, the rafter that was set in at the dormer opening in the roof frame can be removed. As this was only nailed in place, it will not be difficult to take it out. After it is out of the way, the opening in the roof is ready for the dormer and you can go ahead with the job just as if it were being built during the original construction. See Chapter 8.

Side Walls and Partitions

Step number two in finishing off the attic is to build up the side walls and the partitions. The side walls are made by first tacking a 2" x 4" sole plate to the attic floor 5'5" from the eaves. This will give the sidewall a height of 4'6".

When the sole plate is in place, the vertical studding is put in. This will be nailed at the base to the sole plate and to the side of the roof rafters. Fig. 1 shows the manner in which the tops of these studs are cut so that they can be nailed to the roof rafters. Study the framing plans for the attic and notice that some of the sidewall studs have been omitted. This is to leave large openings into the area in back of these walls for storage purposes.

The partitions in the attic are framed just like the house partitions. A 2" x 4"

Fig. 1. How wall studding in the attic should be cut to join with the roof rafters.

sole plate is nailed to the floor and a top plate is nailed to the edges of the collar beams. Studs are spaced 16" on center.

Insulation; Wiring; Plumbing

Once the partitions have been put up, the attic space should be insulated. Of course, if you have insulated along the rafters and across the collar beams,

further insulation will not be necessary; but if the attic floor was insulated, then the attic rooms should be treated in the manner outlined in the chapter on insulation.

Electric wiring can now be installed in so far as bringing in the wiring and wiring in the outlets is concerned. Plumbing and heating lines should be brought up into their proper location and the position of the plumbing fixtures should be roughed out.

Note in the attic floor plan that to get the necessary headroom, the shower stall has been pulled out towards the center of the bathroom. Be sure that you do not use a shower stall that is any higher than the one given or, if you do, that you bring it out to a point where it will fit.

If you wish—and it is a highly desirable feature—a window can be installed at each end of the attic. They will provide a good deal more light and air.

From here on out, finishing off the attic is just the same as for the other rooms in the house. Interior wall and ceiling materials go up, and these can be the same as used elsewhere. Interior trim and flooring go on and the attic is ready for living purposes.

FINISHING OFF THE BASEMENT

This is the sort of job you can do after the rest of the house and grounds have been completed, or you can wait even longer and do it whenever you have the energy.

For the most part, it is not a good idea to try to do anything with the basement for several months after the house has been completed because, in the first place, the poured-concrete masonry may not as yet be completely dry and the dampness will be difficult to get rid of no matter how hard you try. Second, by not covering up water and heating lines, you will make it a lot easier on yourself in case there are a few little errors here and there that show up after you have lived in the house for awhile.

The first thing to do before you make any plans for the future use of the basement is to make certain that the floors and walls are dry. You are very apt to find that they are damp, but this is more likely the result of condensation than of a leak in the concrete. In most cases, after the concrete has had time to become dry throughout, the dampness can be taken care of by providing the basement with plenty of fresh air.

If you do not plan to use the basement for anything more than a workshop, storage area and so forth, you can finish it by merely giving the walls a coat of cement paint. This will make the place a good deal lighter and the walls will be easy to clean when necessary. If the floor appears to be sanding or dusting, a coat of concrete hardener will take care of this condition.

If a portion of the basement is going to be used as a play or game room, you should partition this part off from the space containing the furnace, hot-water heater and other utilities. The same sort of construction is used here as required for interior partitions discussed earlier in the book. The side of the partition facing the furnace should be covered with asbestos board, and the ceiling too. This will provide a certain amount of protection against the possibility of fire in this area.

The ceiling in the game room should be covered with either wallboard or plywood, and it is a good idea to insulate between the ceiling joists as this will reduce the amount of sound coming up through the floor. You may find that it is necessary either to recess some of the pipes running across the ceiling into the joists or to make a false ceiling under the pipes. Be sure that you will have sufficient headroom after the false ceiling is in position.

The walls of the basement should be lined with some type of wall material and it should be furred out from the masonry. Sometimes plaster is applied directly to the masonry, but this often becomes damp and musty through condensation. It is better to keep the interior wall material away from the masonry.

Be sure to leave openings in the wall so that you can get at plumbing valves and the like without having to remove an entire section of the wall. Small openings for this purpose can be fitted with doors.

As for the basement game-room floor, it can be painted with special floor enamels suited for this purpose or covered with clay tile. If you are absolutely sure that the floor will not become damp, it can be covered with wood or some type of composition flooring that is recommended for this purpose.

Steps

Basement steps should have treads about 9″ wide and risers 8″ high. You can make the stairs out of pre-cast concrete stair units, but for rough work of this type a poured staircase is suitable.

The first thing to do is to make a form. This can be done with lengths of 8″ wide stock set on edge to act as forms for the risers. No form on top for the treads will be necessary as the concrete can be mixed thickly enough so that it will not flow over. The forms can be held in place by driving wood wedges between their ends and the foundation wall. Additional bracing can be made from lengths of any odd stock you have on hand. Place it from the middle of the form to the rear wall of the stair well.

When all the forms are in place, the concrete can be poured. The surface should be troweled to a rough texture to provide a firm footing.

Chapter 22

DITCHES AND DRY WELLS; DRIVEWAYS AND WALKS

Rainfall Disposal

If you are building in a location where there are storm sewers, the discharge from the roof gutters can be connected into them with drain tile and your problem is over. For those without this convenience, there are several alternate plans.

It is a bad idea to allow the water from gutters to flow from the openings of the downspouts onto the earth. In the first place, there is a good possibility that this water will eventually find its way into the basement. Another drawback is that the water will wash away the topsoil in this area and make it impossible to grow a lawn or have a garden in the immediate area. Sometimes a concrete slab is put down right under the downspout and this deflects the water somewhat, but it is not too efficient. A better method is to have a concrete strip around the entire foundation wall at grade level. This should be 3′ wide and there should be a slight joint between it and the foundation wall. The joint can be packed with asphalt felt, tar or caulking compound.

Dry Wells and Ditches

The most effective way to take care of rain water is to bring it from the downspouts to a dry well or blind ditch. A dry well can be built exactly like a cesspool. The opening of the downspout is connected to it by means of drain tile laid underground. Joints should be packed tight with mortar and the top of the downspout should be covered with a wire cage to prevent leaves and other debris from flowing into the dry well and eventually filling it up. A very simple type of dry well can be made by taking the bottom out of a barrel and sinking it in the ground. Fill the barrel up with small rocks and then bring in a line from the downspout. Wire netting is placed over the top of the barrel and this in turn is covered with topsoil. A blind ditch is nothing more than a long ditch filled with rocks. The line from the downspout is brought into the ditch and then the ditch is covered with topsoil. The ditch should have a slight pitch so that the water will drain through it and be absorbed by the surrounding soil.

DRIVEWAYS

Concrete Driveways

A good solid driveway from the main road up to your house is essential, not only for the convenience of the family, but so that deliveries of fuel, groceries, etc., can be made with a minimum of effort. In planning a safe driveway there are two main points to consider. First of all, it should not slope too steeply to the road. Try to grade your driveway so that it is as level as possible. Another safety factor is to provide enough room at the end of the drive or at some other point so that a car or small truck can be turned around. Backing down a steep drive into a busy thoroughfare can be a very risky business.

There are two types of concrete drive that you can use. One is the ribbon type of drive, which is made of two ribbons of concrete 2' wide with a space between them of 2'10''. This is the least expensive type of drive to build, but even with curbs on the outer edges of the ribbon, there is a chance that a careless driver will run off the ribbons and damage the adjoining lawn or gar-

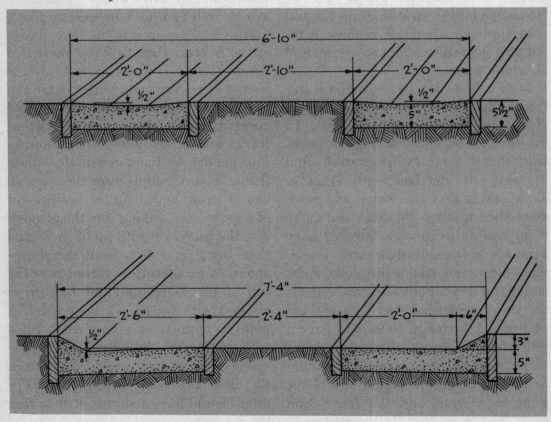

Fig. 1. Ribbon type of driveway, with and without curbs.

den. The slab type of concrete drive with curbs on the edges is much better, for there is less possibility of driving off it.

Building a Ribbon-Type Drive

It is very important when building this type of drive that the sub-base be compact and solid. If it is not, your drive is going to crack very easily. If the subsoil is well drained, you do not need any special base, but if it is clayey, you should use a base of gravel or cinders 6" thick under the slab. The slab itself should be 5" thick unless heavy trucks are going to go over it, in which case it should be 6" thick. See Fig. 1.

The first step in making the driveway is to lay out the forms. Either 2" x 6" or 2" x 8" lumber can be used for this job. The pieces are set on edge and stakes driven in along the outside to hold them in place. You will need spacers the width of the ribbon placed between the two side forms to hold them the right distance apart. They should be placed every 6 feet. A ribbon without curbs should be 2' wide, but if you plan on a curb, increase this to 2'6" for each ribbon. Fig. 1 shows a simple method of forming the curb. If there are curves in the driveway, the forms for these can be made out of plywood.

Expansion Joints

You will need an expansion joint in the driveway every 40 feet or so. You should also have one where the drive-

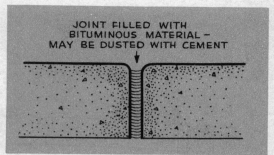

Fig. 2. An expansion joint between two concrete surfaces filled with a bituminous material.

way joins the apron of the garage or any other concrete or masonry work. If expansion joints are not used, there is danger of the concrete's cracking. Expansion joints can be made by placing a strip of asphalt felt between two sections before the fresh concrete is poured, or by leaving a space and filling it later with a bituminous compound. See Fig. 2.

Pouring the Concrete

Refer to the table given in Chapter 5 for the correct mixture to use for this job. The entire ribbon is not poured in one operation. Alternate 6-foot sections

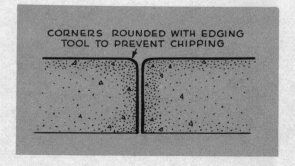

Fig. 3. The edges of adjoining sections of concrete should be rounded off to prevent their chipping.

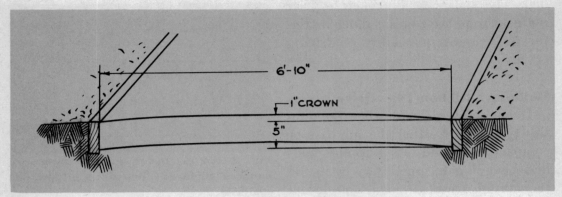

Fig. 4. A simple type of concrete slab driveway.

are poured and then, when the concrete is sufficiently hard, the spacers are removed and the remaining sections are poured. This allows for a slight expansion joint between each 6-foot section. The corners of the sections should be rounded with an edging tool to prevent chipping. See Fig. 3.

A Slab-Type Drive

Drives of this sort without curbs should be 6'10" wide. See Fig. 4. If curbs are to be installed, the over-all width of the drive is increased to 7'4",

which allows for two curbs 6" thick on each side. See Fig. 5. The same precautions in preparing the sub-base and using a fill in clayey soils apply to this type of drive as to the ribbon drive. The slab type of drive should be 6" deep if it is to handle heavy trucks. To allow for proper drainage, it is best to have the top of the concrete slab about 2" above the finished grade. The driveway should also be given a slight crown so that water will drain off. Fig. 6 shows a driveway with such a crown. A board with a hollowed-out edge is used to

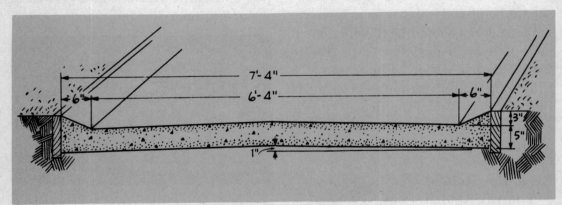

Fig. 5. Curbs on the edges of the driveway will prevent vehicles from running off the concrete strip and damaging the lawn or garden.

make the crown. This board is placed with its ends on the top of the form boards and is then worked down along a section of the fresh concrete, molding it to the slight crown desired. The forms for a slab driveway, along with the expansion joints, the mixture, and the method of pouring are just the same as those used for the ribbon type.

When you are working over the surface with a wood float, make certain not to remove the crown.

WALKS

Concrete Walks

You can have either concrete-slab walks or concrete-flagstone walks. A slab walk should be 4′ wide and 4″ thick. For small, back entrance walks, you can reduce the width to 3′ but the thickness should remain the same as for the wider walks.

The subsoil should be graded and tamped down so that it is solid. If the soil is not well drained, you will need a 6″ cinder base under the concrete, just as you do for a driveway. If you find that the walk must go around a tree, be sure to make allowance for the growth of the tree. If you do not, you will find that the tree will break up your walk as it grows.

Forms for the walk can be made out of 2″ x 4″s on edge with stakes on the outside to hold them in place and separater pieces running between the two sides. The location of these pieces will depend on how long you want each square of concrete to be. As a rule, they are placed every 4′ or 6′ apart. You will need expansion joints for this type of walk every 40 feet or so and at all the points where the walk joins other masonry. The walk should be given a slight crown so that water will drain

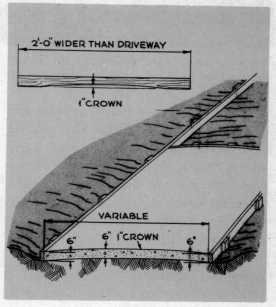

Fig. 6. A concrete walk or drive should be given a slight crown so that water will drain off easily. Detail at top of picture shows the board used to make the crown.

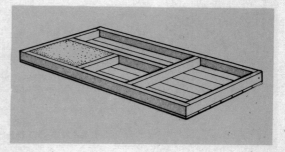

Fig. 7. Forms for making concrete flagstones can be made out of 2″x4″s.

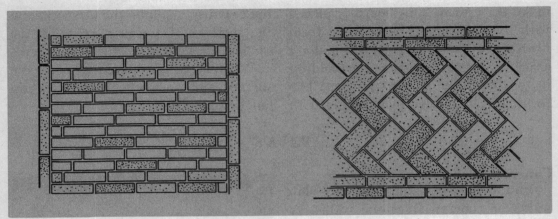

Fig. 8. Two attractive designs for brick walks. The bricks can be laid either in sand or on a concrete slab with a mortar bed.

off it easily. Be sure that the forms are level. Alternate sections are poured first. After each section has been poured, work it over with the strike board to give it the proper crown. After each section has had time to set for a few hours, the surface can be finished off with a wood float.

Concrete Flagstones

There are several ways to make a concrete-flagstone walk. One method is to construct a form to make the flag-stones with and, when they are hard, to set them in place. Fig. 7 shows a simple type of form for this purpose made out of 2″ x 4″s. This form will produce flagstones for a walk 18″ wide, but of course, you can use any arrangement of the stones to produce any width of walk you want. The bottom of the form is made of sheathing boards.

The form should be put together on a level piece of ground and the nails

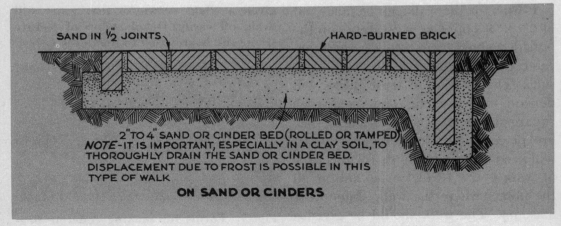

Fig. 9. How a brick walk or terrace can be laid on cinders or sand.

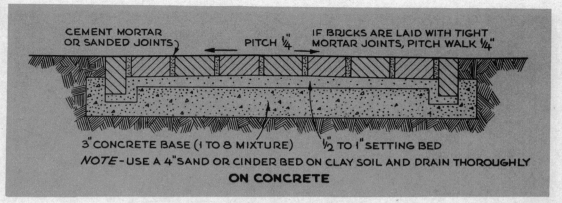

CEMENT MORTAR OR SANDED JOINTS

PITCH ¼"

IF BRICKS ARE LAID WITH TIGHT MORTAR JOINTS, PITCH WALK ¼"

3" CONCRETE BASE (1 TO 8 MIXTURE)   ½ TO 1" SETTING BED

NOTE - USE A 4" SAND OR CINDER BED ON CLAY SOIL AND DRAIN THOROUGHLY

ON CONCRETE

Fig. 10. Brick walk or terrace with concrete base.

should not be driven in all the way because this will make it difficult to remove them after the concrete is hard. Let the heads stick out about ¼″ or so. Oil the inside of the forms to prevent the concrete from cracking. Pour the concrete into the forms and after it has had a while to set, finish off the surface with a wood float. At the end of two days, the forms can be stripped off, but be careful not to damage any still soft concrete. Put the blocks someplace where they will not be damaged and keep them covered with damp burlap or straw for at least ten days before they are put into use.

Another method of making a concrete-flagstone walk is to pour the concrete into holes made in the lawn. The first step here is to mark out the walk with strings. After this, dig out about 4″ of sod and soil in whatever shape you want the flagstones to be. Make sure that the edges of these holes are upright. When this has been done, the concrete can be poured into the holes.

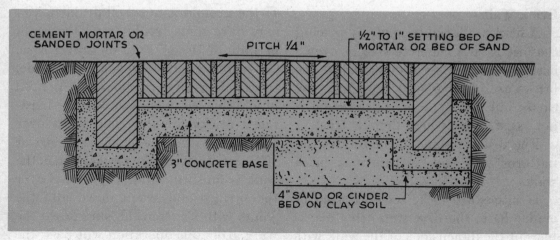

CEMENT MORTAR OR SANDED JOINTS

PITCH ¼"

½" TO 1" SETTING BED OF MORTAR OR BED OF SAND

3" CONCRETE BASE

4" SAND OR CINDER BED ON CLAY SOIL

Fig. 11. Brick walk on concrete base with bricks set up on end.

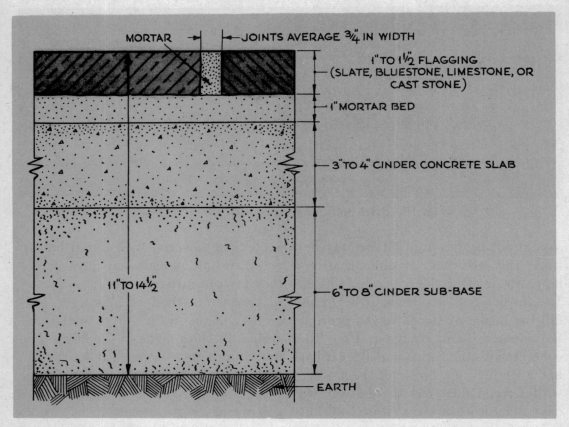

Fig. 12. Slate laid over a concrete base with the joints between slabs of slate filled with mortar. This is the best type of construction to use on outdoor terraces.

Brick Walks

A brick walk can be made by placing the bricks on a concrete slab or over a base of sand. In warm climates, the bricks are often placed right over the earth, but this type of construction is not satisfactory where there is frost.

Fig. 8 shows some of the interesting patterns that you can use in a brick walk.

If bricks are to be set on a sand or cinder base, the first step after marking out the dimensions of the walk with parallel lines, is to dig for the sub-base.

If the ground is not well drained, you may have some trouble with this walk in spite of the 4″ sand or gravel base. After the excavation has been made, the sand or cinders should be poured in and packed down solidly. The hard-faced bricks are then laid right over this base without mortar. A space of ½″ is left between the bricks. When the walk is finished, sand is sprinkled over the surface and swept down into the joints with a broom. Hosing down the walk after this operation will pack the sand into the joints. Apply any additional sand necessary to fill the joints to the top of the bricks. See Fig. 9.

A brick walk on a concrete base is much more durable than one put over a sand base but, of course, it requires much more work. You will need a 4" bed of cinders or sand under the concrete if the soil is not well drained. The concrete base should be 3" thick. This base should be poured in the same manner as a concrete walk, that is, it should be poured in alternate sections with expansion joints where necessary. Over the concrete base, a ½" or thicker setting-bed of mortar is applied. This is given a slight crown so that water will drain off the finished walk. The bricks are dampened and then set into this base. The joints between the bricks can be packed with mortar or they can be

left open and filled with sand. See Figs. 10 and 11.

Natural Flagstones

Natural flagstones of slate, limestone or bluestone make an excellent material for the terrace or the walks. They can be laid on either a concrete slab or on a base of cinders. For the most part, when the stones are used for a terrace or some other spot where furniture is going to be placed, they should be set in concrete. This will eliminate that common hazard of sitting down in a chair and having it suddenly list over to one side as one of the legs sinks down into the earth between two stones. See Fig. 12.

When the stones are going to be set in concrete, you want a 6" cinder base

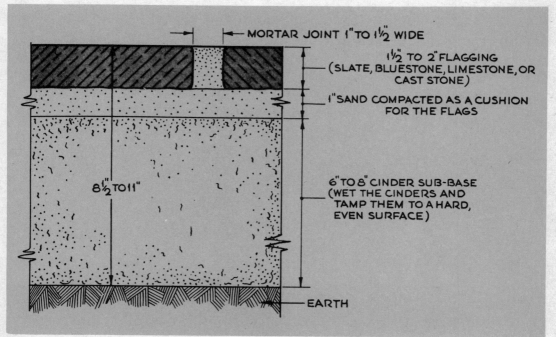

Fig. 13. Slate laid over a cinder base with mortar between the sections of slate.

under a 4″ slab. The stones are set in a 1″ mortar bed with ¾″ joints between the stones. The joints should be filled with mortar. When the stones are laid without a concrete base, you want about 8″ of cinders that are packed down until they are a solid mass. Over this base, a layer of sand 1″ thick should be applied. The stones are then put in place and the joints between them filled with either earth or mortar. See Fig. 13.

Chapter 23

LANDSCAPING THE PLOT

IT IS assumed that when the location of the house on the plot was under discussion, some thought was given at that time to the location of lawns, gardens and recreation areas. Now that the house is finished, you can go ahead and work out the detailed plans for this sort of work and complete the projects.

PLANNING LAWNS, GARDENS, PLAY AREAS

The first step in landscaping your plot is to take a sheet of paper ruled off into squares and draw your plot on it to scale. After this, draw in your house in its proper location and also walks, driveways, trees and other important features such as rock formations, etc. Now you will be able to see at a glance exactly what you have and how much of the plot is left for landscaping purposes.

The average family will be interested in having a lawn, a flower garden, perhaps a vegetable garden, and sufficient space left over for play and recreation purposes.

What you will have to do is divide up what is left of your plot so that you will get the maximum number of items that you want and at the same time not have the lawn or garden so small that it detracts from rather than adds to your home.

The first point to bring up is the front lawn because this is a very important feature in making your house attractive. The front lawn should be large enough to provide a well balanced setting for the house, but it should not be so large that keeping it up is going to be a headache. Do not make your lawn too big, because if you do, you

Fig. 1. Adequate landscaping is important if your house is to look its best.

may find that most of your weekends in the summer are going to be taken up in cutting grass. This does not mean that you should not have a decent-size lawn—a house without some lawn is hardly a house at all—but it does mean that you should limit the size of the lawn so that it will be a pleasure to look at and take care of rather than merely a horrible chore.

The best rule to follow in planning a front lawn is to have it as broad and open as possible. Do not cut the lawn up with walks and drives, if it is possi-

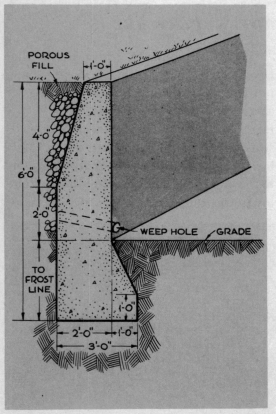

Fig. 2. Concrete retaining wall. Note the weep holes to prevent water pressure in back of the wall from cracking the masonry.

ble to avoid them. A small but unbroken expanse of lawn in front of your house will be much more effective than one twice the size that is divided into several small sections.

Small lawns around in back of the house are also very desirable and can be made extremely pleasant if they are protected by a screening of shrubs or trees.

The size and location of the flower gardens will have to be decided on too. Vegetable gardens for the most part are located in back of the house and they should not be too large unless you do not mind the work attached to keeping up a large vegetable garden.

Flower gardens can be either formal or informal. Formal gardens are usually placed in more or less secluded spots, but informal gardens can be blended right in with the general landscaping picture. If there is an outcropping of rocks on your site, this area can be made to serve very nicely as a rock garden.

The size of the recreation area is more or less a matter of taste, but if you are looking forward to a lot of outdoor recreation, you should make the plot big enough for games, badminton courts, outdoor suppers, etc. For example, if you plan to have a badminton court, you will need a space 30′ by 60′. The same area is required for croquet. If you plan on other features of outdoor living, such as an outdoor fireplace, terrace, and so on, keep these in mind when you plan the size of your recreation area.

The first step in landscaping is to grade the subsoil. Fill in all depressions as well as any holes made during the contruction work. Trenches for the sewer line and water pipes should be carefully filled with subsoil and not with any of the debris left over from the construction work. If these trenches are not well filled with soil, the topsoil over them will settle and cause you a good deal of trouble later on. The subsoil should slope gently away from the house so that water will drain away rather than flow down along the foundation wall and possibly into the basement. If any retaining walls are required, they should be installed at this time. Fig. 2 shows a type of wall constructed out of poured concrete. Note the weep holes along the base that allow the water in back of the wall to drain on through rather than building up back pressure, which in time would crack the wall. Remove all roots and debris from the subsoil, as buried wood will attract termites.

MAKING A LAWN

The first step in making a good lawn is to prepare the subsoil, which should not be done while it is wet. It should be graded down from the house with gentle flowing lines. Do not make the lawn absolutely flat if there are natural slopes to the site. If you run into any deep depressions and they cannot very well be filled in, drain tile should be put down so that water accumulating at these points can be carried off. Avoid steep slopes, however; these will make cutting the grass extremely difficult. Be sure that the subsoil is packed solidly. After this, the topsoil can be put on. If you kept the topsoil separate from the subsoil when the excavation work was done for the basement and foundations, you can probably use it for your lawn. It should be free of weeds, roots and stones. You should have about 6 inches of topsoil for an adequate seed bed. If you do not have a sufficient amount of topsoil or if you do not have any at all, you will have to buy some. Be sure that you know what you are getting and paying for. Some home-owners have paid for topsoil and then found after it was delivered that it was not much better than the subsoil that they already had. Ask around and get the name of a dealer who will supply you with really good topsoil.

Before you go any further, you should have the soil tested so that you will know what and how much fertilizer must be added to it to make it suitable for grass. You can get small soil-testing kits and make the test yourself, or you can send a sample of your soil to the county agent or the state department of agriculture and they will make the test for you.

The topsoil should be spaded to a depth of 4 inches. After this, is should be pulverized and then raked and packed down until it forms a smooth bed. Next, a good lawn fertilizer should be applied. The time of year that the grass seed is planted will depend on what part of the country you live in. As a rule, in northern and eastern portions of the country the seed should be planted in the fall while in southern states the seed is planted in the spring. Fall-sown grass is able to compete with weeds very well because it gets an early start in the spring, but it must be sown early enough in the fall to allow it to make a good beginning before winter.

The best way to plant the seeds so that you will be sure of getting a uniform coverage over the entire seed bed is to sow one-half the amount of seed to be used in parallel strips and then sow the remaining seeds at right angles to the first half.

After the seeds have been sown, rake lightly and then go over the lawn with a roller. Finally, the lawn should be watered lightly and kept damp until the seeds have become rooted into the soil. The grass should not be cut until it is three or four inches tall.

If there are any bare spots in the lawn when the grass begins to grow, loosen up the soil and reseed. Weeds should be removed as they appear.

TREES

The chances are that your plot will either have no trees at all, in which case your problem will be where and how many trees to plant, or it will contain too many trees, in which case your problem will be to pick out the trees that are to remain and those that must come down. It is, of course, a lot cheaper to take a tree out than to put a big one in.

You should give a good deal of thought to the location of the trees around your house and the type of trees to use because they can make a vast amount of difference in the over-all picture that your home presents.

Trees are used to provide a background or frame to the house, to provide shade for various sections of the house, and also as screens and windbreaks. Naturally, some types of trees are better for these jobs than others.

For the purpose of landscaping, trees are divided into two groups, evergreens and deciduous. Evergreen trees keep their leaves or needles on all year around, while deciduous trees shed their leaves in the fall.

One of the great mistakes many people make in using trees around their home for one purpose or another, is that they forget that trees are going to grow. In many cases, trees intended for shade purposes have been put too close to the house so that by the time they reach their full growth, it becomes necessary to take them down. Another common mistake is to plant too many trees close together because at the early stage of their growth, one tree did not appear to be capable of doing the job by itself. Before you select a tree for any purpose, find out what its width and height will be at maturity.

Some types of trees grow faster than others and this may be an important point in selecting one particular tree when you are in a hurry to get shade or a screen. Among the fast-growing trees are poplars and box elders. These trees will grow much more rapidly than hardwoods such as oak, maple and hickory, but on the other hand, they do not live as long and you might find that in thirty years or so all your shade and screening trees were dying off. Some trees are not satisfactory in certain areas because of the prevalence of certain insects and diseases.

When trees are used around the house to provide shade during the summer months, deciduous trees should be chosen. Their leaves will provide shade in the summer and when they drop off in the fall, it will allow the winter sun's warmth to reach the house. Shade trees are not required on the south side of the house. Evergreens should not be used for shade trees and they should not be placed less than 100 feet from the house. Of course, this applies only to the large evergreens and not to the smaller varieties used for shrubs. Except when used for the purpose of shade, trees around the house should be grouped so that the tallest ones are farthest away. When the job of landscaping has been finished, this will produce a gentle slope through the trees and shrubs, across the lawn and a slight rise at the shrubs around the foundation walls.

Trees used for screens or windbreaks can be either evergreens or deciduous.

When you are deciding on what sort of trees to plant around your house, do not forget about fruit trees such as apple, peach and pear.

Planting Trees

When trees are delivered from a nursery, they come prepared for planting. Your first job will be to dig a hole sufficiently large so that the roots can be spread out in their natural position. Three or four inches of pulverized topsoil should be placed at the bottom of the hole. Trim off any broken or dead roots and then place the tree in the hole. Fill topsoil in under the roots and bring it up to the proper height. The soil around the roots should be lightly packed into place. When the hole is about two-thirds full of soil, pour in slowly as much water as the soil will absorb. Now put in the remaining soil.

It is very important to provide the newly planted tree with adequate support until the roots have taken a good hold in the ground. This is especially important with evergreens because unless they are securely fastened down, they may be blown over by winter winds. Guy wires are the most effective means of supporting the young trees, but the wires should not come in contact with the bark of the tree. Sections of old garden hose can be used around the wires to insulate them from the tree. During dry weather, the newly planted tree should be watered at frequent intervals. Be sure that the ground around the tree is thoroughly soaked and not just dampened on the surface.

SHRUBS

Shrubs of varying sizes can be used for foundation planting, for screening and for many other landscaping purposes. They can be either evergreen or deciduous and very often the two types can be mixed together favorably.

Foundation Planting

The shrubs that are set around the base of the house serve two very useful purposes. First of all, they hide the foundation wall and, second, they help to tie the house to the lawn. The shrubs used in this location should be dwarf stock as these will not grow so high that they will have to be cut back to keep them from covering up windows. Do not place shrubs around the basement windows; they will cut out the circulation of air to the basement as well as blocking the light. Shrubs should not be placed too close to the foundation wall; if they are, they will provide an entrance for termites in spite of the termite shield between the foundation wall and the house sill. A good rule to follow is to keep the shrubs at least one foot away from the foundation. Do not make the mistake of completely covering the entire foundation wall with shrubs as this will create the unreal appearance that the house is supported by shrubbery instead of by a solid masonry foundation. Place the shrubs so that sections of the foundation wall can be seen.

Another point you should keep in mind is that shrubs, like trees, will grow and, therefore, their position and spacing should be made on the basis of how large they will be when they have reached maturity rather than how large they are at planting.

Around the foundations, a few deciduous shrubs mixed in with the evergreens produce a highly pleasing effect.

Groups; Screening; Hedges

This type of planting is used to soften the straight lines in walks or drives or at the junction of walks and drives.

Screen planting can be used either to insure privacy or to hide an unpleasant view. If you want all-year-round screening, evergreens should be used and they should be high enough to do the job.

These can be used as screens or to divide sections of the plot into separate pieces. For example, if you have a portion of your plot set aside for recreation, you might use a hedge between this and the lawn or backyard.

Selecting Shrubs

The first point to consider in selecting a particular shrub for a job is the height of the shrub at maturity. With the exception of hedges, shrubs with the proper natural height are more desirable than those that must be cut back at frequent intervals. If you use shrubs of different natural heights for the same job, the smaller ones should be placed in front of the higher ones.

Another point to watch out for is to be sure to use a sufficient number of evergreens—especially in foundation planting. Deciduous trees are fine in the spring, summer and early fall, but after that they lose their leaves and will not do much in the way of concealing the foundation wall. Also, bright evergreens around the house are a very cheerful sight during the winter months.

Planting Shrubs

You can purchase the shrubs you will require from a local nursery, but many home-owners prefer to go out into the countryside and dig up their own. Native shrubs usually do very well if transplanted properly, and as they are natural to the locality, they give the house the appearance of belonging on the site.

Before the shrub is planted, all broken and dead roots should be cut off. The hole should be large enough so that the roots can spread out in their natural state and the bottom of the hole should be covered with rich topsoil. Place the plant in the hole and then work topsoil around the roots in the same fashion as was done for trees. Keep packing the soil down as it is added and then, when the hole is filled, pour a bucket of water slowly around the roots. Now add enough topsoil to complete the filling.

GARDEN WALLS AND FENCES

A definite part of landscaping is the construction of walls and fences. Walls can be made out of either natural stone, concrete masonry-blocks or bricks. The wall can serve as decorative effect alone or it can be used for screening purposes and to insure privacy.

All three types of wall will require a solid concrete footing poured below the frost line. This footing should be half again as wide as the wall and the same depth as the wall is wide. A brick or concrete block wall has to be only 8″ thick, but one made of natural stone should be at least 16″ thick if it is to be solid. The stone can be laid up dry or with mortar, but building a dry stone wall requires a good deal of skill and time if it is to be firm.

If there is going to be a gate in the wall, provision should be made for hanging this from the masonry rather

Fig. 3. An attractive and easily constructed wood fence.

than from a wood frame. A wood frame in contact with the masonry may rot out quickly and be a constant source of annoyance.

Bolts for the gate hinges can be set in the mortar joints during the construction of the wall.

Brick and concrete block walls should be capped with 3 inches or so of cement mortar at the top.

Moreover, this cap should be slightly rounded in order to allow rain water to drain off.

A white fence is an attractive item. See Fig. 3. This one is both simple and easy to make and, what is more, it will not require the same amount of time and work to paint as does a picket fence. The uprights for this fence are made with 2″ x 4″s treated with a wood preservative so that they will resist decay and insects. The cross-pieces are 1″ x 3″ or 1″ x 4″ with a cap made out of the same materials running along the top at right angles to the piece directly below.

MATERIALS LIST FOR BASIC HOUSE
ON CONCRETE SLAB

Material	Quantity	Dimensions
Ready-mixed cement	23 cu. yds.	
2″ x 8″	27	14′
	31	12′
2″ x 6″	65	16′6″
2″ x 4″	136	16′
1″ x 6″	28	16′
1″ x 4″	10	8′
1″ x 2″	10	16′
1″ x 3″ No. 2 Common grade	192′	
Sheathing	2,582 board ft.	1″ x 8″
Asphalt shingles	12 squares	
Beveled siding	1,326 board ft.	½″ x 6″
Exterior trim	220′	1″ x 3″
Building paper	5 rolls	500 sq. ft. each
Pine base	300′	1″ x 4″
Base molding	300′	
Roll insulation with vaporproof paper	1,600 sq. ft.	3″
¾″ plywood	10	4′ x 8′
Closet door trim	110′	1″ x 3″
Shelving	100′	1″ x 6″
Flush door with frame and trim	1	3′ 0″ x 6′8″ x 1¾″
4-light fir door with frame and trim	1	2′ 8″ x 6′8″ x 1¾″
2-light fir door with frame and trim	1	2′10″ x 6′8″ x 1¾″
2-panel door with trim, jambs and stops	6	2′ 6″ x 6′8″ x 1⅜″
	1	2′ 0″ x 6′8″ x 1⅜″
Stationary sash with frame and trim	1	4′2⅜″ x 6′5¼″
Casement sash with frame and trim	3	3′2³⁄₁₆″ x 3′1¾″
	4	4′2⅜″ x 3′1¾″
	1	4′2⅜″ x 1′6″
Chimney blocks	64	7¾″ x 3¾″ x 12¾″
	64	7¾″ x 3¾″ x 14¾″
Flue-tile	9 sections	8½″ x 13″ x 2′
Copper flashing	2	12″ x 12″
	1	4′ x 4′

Plasterboard, 2,200 sq. ft.

Chimney thimble

Clean-out door

Cement mortar, 2 cu. ft.

Nails: 16d, 50 lbs.; 8d, 2 kegs; finish, 20 lbs; 4d, 72 lbs; 5d, 12 lbs

30lb asphalt felt, 5 rolls

Louvers, 2

Hinges: brass, 9; interior, 21; cabinet, 33

Mortice locks, 10

Latches, 7

Medicine cabinet

Towel racks, 2

Soap dish and toothbrush holder

Paint: exterior, 24 gal.; water-thinned, 11 gal.; floor enamel, 3 gal.; interior enamel, 1½ gal.

4″ x 4″ sanitary T branch

4″ x 4″ Y branch

4″ clean-out plug

4″ x 4″ sanitary T branch with 2″ tapping

4″ sanitary T with 2″ tapping, 2

5′ sections 4″ cast-iron soil pipe, 8

Increaser

4″ closet bend

Drain traps, 4

1½″ drain T, 6

Elbows: 1½″, 5; ½″, 14

T fittings, 7

2″ galvanized pipe, 11′

1½″ galvanized pipe, 30′

¾″ galvanized pipe, 10′

½″ galvanized pipe, 50′

Kitchen sink

Bathtub with shower and fittings

Lavatory with fittings

Water closet with flush tank

30-gal. hot-water heater

Entrance cable, 16′

Service head

Sill plate

Switch box

Grounding bushing

4″ or 3¼″ outlet boxes, 30

2½″ switch boxes, 29

Cable connectors and bushings, 100

Ceiling fixtures, 7

Ceiling fixtures with pull chain, 2

Wall fixtures, 2

Outside fixture

Single switches, 6

Double switches, 2

3-way switches, 2

Convenience outlets with plates, 14

Special outlets with plates, 3

Switch plates, 12

Metal hangers, 9

Door bells and buttons, 2

No. 14 3-wire, 50′

No. 14 2-wire, 350′

No. 12 2-wire, 50′

No. 6 ground cable, 10′

Space-heater with flue pipe, rated at 80,000 BTU

PRICES FOR COMPLETE MATERIALS

East Coast $2916.31
Middle West $2919.42
Rocky Mountains $3102.91
West Coast $2554.00

MATERIALS LIST FOR ADDITIONS TO THE BASIC HOUSE

Basement: 7′ High

Material	Quantity	Dimensions
2″ x 10″	8	16′
	26	14′
	34	12′
2″ x 6″	8	16′
1″ x 6″	466 board ft.	
1″ x 3″	192′	
Hardwood flooring	935′	1″ x 3″
Linoleum	182 sq. ft.	

Flight box stairs

Mixed cement, 9 cu. yds.; or 900 concrete blocks and 1.1 cu. yds. mortar

Main bearing partition: 425 concrete blocks, .5 cu. yds. mortar; or 6 2″ x 10″ 18′ long, 2 4″ x 6″ 14′ long

Attic, Gables and Dormers

Material	Quantity	Dimensions
2″ x 6″	4	6′
	3	8′
2″ x 4″	74	16′
1″ x 6″	808 board ft.	
Base trim	152′	1″ x 3″
Interior doors with trim, jambs and stops	2	2′6″ x 6′8″
	5	2′0″ x 6′8″
Casement sash with frame and trim	4	4′2⅜″ x 3′1¾″
	1	3′6³⁄₁₆″ x 3′6¼″

Insulation, 1086 sq. ft.

Wallboard, 986 sq. ft.

Roofing materials, 50 sq. ft.

⅜″ plywood, 435 sq. ft.

Linoleum, 435 sq. ft.

Flight box stairs with open start step

Gutters, 75′

Traps, 2

Closet bend

Sanitary T; 1½″, 2; ½″, 3

Elbows: 1½″, 2; ½″, 3

1½″ galvanized pipe, 20′

1″ galvanized pipe, 30′

½″ galvanized pipe, 20′

Metal shower stall

Lavatory

Water closet

Medicine cabinet

Towel racks, 2

Toothbrush holder and soap dish

Convenience outlets with plates, 8
Ceiling fixtures, 3
Ceiling fixtures with pull chain, 3
Wall fixture
Single switches, 3
3-way switch
Octagonal outlet boxes, 6

Square outlet boxes, 12
Switch plates, 4
Metal hangers, 6
Fibre bushings, 60
No. 14 2-wire, 200′
Lbs nails: 5d, 8; 8d, 12; 8d casing, 7; 8d finish, 7; 10d, 10; 16d, 5; 20d, 4

Garage and Breezeway

Material	Quantity	Dimensions
Mixed cement	42 cu. yds.	
4″ x 4″	4	6′5″
2″ x 8″	13	20′
	26	12′
2″ x 6″	5	12′
	12	8′
	2	18′
2″ x 4″	56	6′5″
	32	16′
1″ x 6″	4	16′
1″ x 6″	1,668 board ft.	
Copper flashing	36′	12″
Fir door	1	3′0″ x 6′8″
Overhead doors	2	8′0″ x 7′0″
Casement sash with frame and trim	1	3′3″ x 3′4⅛″

Siding, 450 sq. ft.
Roofing material, 760 sq. ft.
Double switch
Octagonal outlet boxes, 2
Rectangular outlet boxes, 2

Ceiling fixture: interior, 1; exterior, 1
Fibre bushings, 6
No. 14 2-wire, 50′
Lbs nails: 8d, 22; 8d casing, 5; 8d finish, 4; 10d, 24; 16d, 6; 20d, 6

Chimney, 2-Flue (3-Flue)

Material	Quantity	Dimensions
Flue-tile	7 sections	12″ x 12″ x 2′
	7 sections	12″ x 8″ x 2′
	(32 sections)	(12″ x 8″ x 2′)

Common bricks, 1,000 (1,500)   Mortar, 14 cu. ft. (21 cu. ft.)

Fireplace

Common bricks, 1,000
Firebricks, 90
Fireclay, 30 lbs.
Hearth assembly

Mixed cement, 2 cu. ft.
Damper
Angleiron, 42"
Angleiron, 36"

Chapter 24

A CAPE COD COTTAGE

As you can see from the plans, this cottage is very similar to the basic house in appearance as well as construction.

While it is somewhat smaller than the basic house and does not have a second floor that can be used for living purposes, the first floor has been planned to provide ample space for a small family.

Eliminating the attic room and the dormer windows decreases the cost of this house considerably in comparison with the basic house.

Examine the first-floor plan of the Cape Cod Cottage and you will see that all the really important features of the basic house are there. There are two good-size bedrooms and a spacious living room with a fireplace for luxurious living. Ample space has been given to the kitchen, and the bath, while compact, is most adequate. There is plenty of closet space in each bedroom, and there is also a storage closet in the kitchen. The utility room off the kitchen contains the heating equipment and the hot-water heater.

Although the attic space is not practical for use as living quarters, it can be used very handily for storage pur-poses. The access to the attic is through an opening in the first-floor ceiling. This opening is fitted with a trap door.

The Cape Cod Cottage is an excellent house for a small family. It is by no means merely a summer home but has been planned for all-year-round living.

Foundations and Floor Slab

The first floor of the house is poured concrete, which is covered with asphalt tile after all the rest of the house has been completed. If the floor is properly constructed according to the directions given in the chapter on pouring slab floors, it will be dry and comfortable both winter and summer.

Information required for building the house foundations is given in the foundation plan. The foundation walls can be either poured concrete or masonry blocks. They are set on a footing that extends below the frost line. Running through the approximate center of the house is a footing for the main bearing partition and for the fireplace base. This footing does not have to extend more than 12" in depth as it will not be subject to frost. Heavy

The Cape Cod Cottage

unbroken lines on the foundation plan indicate the foundation itself, while the broken light lines indicate the footings.

Once the foundations have been poured, two 2″ x 4″s should be anchored to the top of the foundation wall to serve as a sill and a nailing base for the wall partition. When these are in place, the ground can be prepared to receive the concrete-slab floor. The floor, as you will note from the longitudinal section, is 4″ thick and the top comes level with the top of the sole plate. It is poured over a 6″ base of cinders or gravel, well tamped. Refer to the section in this book that deals with pouring concrete-slab floors to see exactly how the floor is insulated from the foundation walls before the concrete is poured and what methods should be used to waterproof the floor.

Framing

When the concrete is hard, the house frame can be erected. Study the four framing plans for the walls to learn the manner in which the wall studding is put up. Wall studding should be 7′1½″ high.

The four framing-elevation plans show the rough openings for the doors and windows. As is the case with the other houses covered in this book, the dimensions for the window rough openings apply to a particular brand of wood casement window. If the brands of casements available at your local lumber yard do not fit these dimensions, make the rough openings to match the available casements.

You will find it a good deal easier to frame all four walls and complete the roof and then go back and cut out the openings in the studding for the doors and windows than to try to make them before you erect the walls.

After the four walls are in place, go to work on the main bearing partition. It should be the same height as the outside walls, as it is going to support the ends of the ceiling joists.

When the bearing partition is in place, the ceiling joists can be installed. The ceiling framing plan will provide most of the necessary information you will need. The joists can be 2″ x 6″s since their span is not very great and the attic is to be used only for limited storage space.

Openings will be required in the ceiling for the fireplace and furnace chimney and also for an access panel for the attic. The ceiling framing plan shows the exact location of the opening for the chimney as well as the necessary dimensions. Note that the joists on each side of the opening are double and that double headers are used at the ends of these joists. The joists around the opening for the access panel do not have to be doubled because the ends of the tail joists will be supported a short distance back by one of the interior wall partitions.

The next step is to install the rafters on the roof. You will be able to get by with 2″ x 6″s because here also the span is not very great and additional supports will be put between the rafters and the ceiling joists.

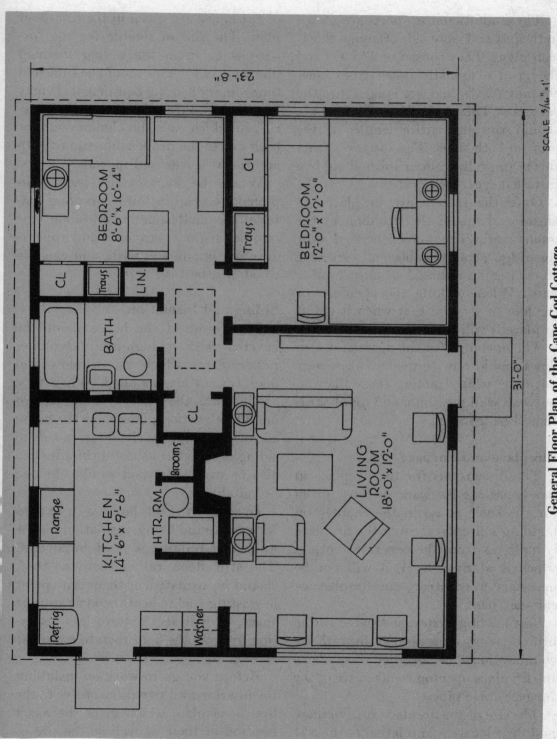

General Floor Plan of the Cape Cod Cottage

These additional supports are shown in the left and right side framing-elevation plans. They consist of 2" x 4"s and they run diagonally down from horizontal 2" x 4"s that are spiked into the rafters. These horizontal 2" x 4"s should run the entire length of the roof on both sides. The supports from this beam to the ceiling joists should be installed every three rafters.

Once the rafters are in place, go ahead and install the studding at the gable ends. The louver located near the ridge at each gable end can be a stock item purchased at any lumber yard. When making the opening for the louver, be sure that when it is put in place it will be properly centered.

The openings for the doors and windows should now be made if they were not done while framing the walls.

Next, wall sheathing and roof boards should be installed.

Fireplace and Furnace

The dimensions for the fireplace in this house are the same as those given for the basic house in the chapter on building a fireplace. Since the fireplace is built up from the concrete footing, which is at floor level, it will not be necessary to construct any fireplace or chimney base.

The heating system is located in the utility room, so a second flue in the chimney must be installed just above the fireplace opening to take care of the furnace stove pipe.

The size of the fireplace and chimney and their location in relation to the rest of the house are given in the first-floor plan. The size of fluetile for the furnace is given in the ceiling framing plan as 8" x 1". This should be sufficient for ordinary heating equipment. It may be possible to use a smaller size of fluetile, in which case the chimney can be built out to the proper dimensions with additional bricks and mortar.

When the chimney has been completed, you can install the roofing material. Asphalt shingles are about the best bet as far as economy and appearance go, but if you wish, you can use wood or asbestos shingles.

Siding and Insulation

The frame of the house should be covered with a high-grade building paper, after which the window and door frames are installed. When they are in place, the exterior siding can go on. The elevation plans show the house as covered with bevel siding, but drop siding or wood or asbestos shingles can also be used. Plywood would likewise be suitable.

In as much as this house is to be used for year-round living, insulation for the walls and ceilings is most important. The attic floor, rather than the roof, should be insulated, as there is no point in wasting fuel to heat the attic storage space. It will also require less insulation to cover the floor than to cover the rafters.

Before you go to work on installing the interior wall partitions, refer to the first-floor plan, which gives the exact location of these as well as the size of the necessary openings for doors and closets. Note that the studding for one wall of the bathroom is made out of 2″ x 6″s in order to allow a 4″ cast-iron soil pipe to pass up through it.

Utilities

Once the bathroom walls have been completed, the plumbing system should be installed. This system can be of the same type as described for the basic house.

The electrical wiring should also go in at this time. You will need three 15-ampere branch circuits and two 20-ampere appliance circuits for the kitchen and the portion of the living room that is to serve as a dining area. You may require individual circuits also for the kitchen range, hot-water heater and laundry equipment.

Plaster or a good grade of wallboard should be used for the interior walls and ceilings.

The flooring can be wood set away from the concrete base by means of wood sleepers, or you can apply asphalt tile directly to the masonry.

CAPE COD COTTAGE MATERIALS LIST

Material	Quantity	Dimensions
Mixed Cement	19 cu. yards	
2″ x 6″	55	16′
	25	14′
	25	12′
2″ x 4″	200	16′
1″ x 6″	32′	
1″ x 4″	150′	
1″ x 2″	7	16′
Fibreboard sheathing	950 sq. ft.	
Beveled siding	1,140′	1″ x 6″
Roof Sheathing	988′	1″ x 6″
Roofing material	832 sq. ft.	
Building paper	950 sq. ft.	
Insulation	1,568 sq. ft.	
Wallboard	1,572 sq. ft.	
Baseboard	110′	1″ x 3″
Shelving	100′	1″ x 6″
Entrance door with frame and trim	1	3′ 0″ x 6′8″
	1	2′ 10″ x 6′8″
Interior doors with trim, jambs and stops	4	2′ 6″ x 6′8″

Material	Quantity	Dimensions
Interior doors with trim, jambs and stops	2	1' 10" x 6'8"
	3	1' 8" x 6'8"
	2	2' 0" x 6'8"
	2	1' 5" x 6'8"
	1	1' 6" x 6'8"
	2	10" x 6'8"
	2	12" x 6'8"
Casement picture window with sash and frame	2	4'2⅜" x 6'5¼"
Casement window with sash and trim	4	4'2⅜" x 3'1¾"
	3	3'2³⁄₁₆" x 3'1¾"
Clay flue-tile	4 sections	12" x 12" x 2'
	4 sections	12" x 8" x 2'
Copper flashing	2 pieces	12" x 12"
	1 piece	4' x 4'

Louvers, 2

Gutters, 64'

Nails: 6d, 24 lbs; 8d, 30 lbs; 16d, 18 lbs; finish, 20 lbs; 4d, 48 lbs; 5d, 9 lbs

Hinges: 6 brass; 36 interior

Mortice locks, 9

Latches, 9

Common bricks, 2,000

Firebricks, 100

Fireclay, 30 lbs.

Clean-out doors, 2

Chimney thimble

Cement mortar, 1 cu. yd.

Damper

Angleirons: 1, 42"; 1, 36"

Ash-dump

Hearth assembly

Mixed cement, 2 cu. ft.

Paint: exterior, 24 gal.; water-thinned, 11 gal.; enamel, 1½ gal.; floor, 3 gal.

Steel boiler (96,000 BTU) with jacket with 200-gal. per hour coil

Fill box

Vent cap

Ventalarm

12 x 30 compression tank

Airtrol tank fitting

Autovent with overflow

1¼" angle flow control

No. 8 dual valve

⅜" stop and waste valve

Circulator

⅜" type L copper tubings, 1,000

4" x 4" sanitary T branch

4" x 4" Y branch

4" clean-out plug

4" x 4" sanitary T branch with 2" tapping

5' sections 4" cast-iron soil pipe, 8

Increaser

4" closet bend

Kitchen sink

Bathtub with shower and fittings

Lavatory with fittings

Water closet with flush tank and fittings

Medicine closet
Towel racks, 2
Toothbrush holder
Soap dish
Drain traps, 4
1½″ drain T, 6
Elbows: 1½″, 5; ½″, 14
T fittings, 7
1½″ galvanized pipe, 30′
2″ galvanized pipe, 11′
½″ galvanized pipe, 50′
¾″ galvanized pipe, 10′
Hot-water heater
Service head
Sill plate
Switch box
Grounding bushing

Convenience outlets and plates, 12
Special outlets and plates, 3
4″ outlet boxes, 5
2½″ switch boxes, 27
Cable connectors, 100
Fiber bushings, 100
Ceiling fixtures, 4
Ceiling fixture with pull chain
Wall fixtures, 2
Outside fixture
Switches: single, 4; double, 1; 3-way, 2
Metal hangers, 5
No. 14 2-wire, 350′
No. 14 3-wire, 50′
No. 12 2-wire, 50′
No. 6 wire ground cable, 10′
Doorbells and buttons, 2

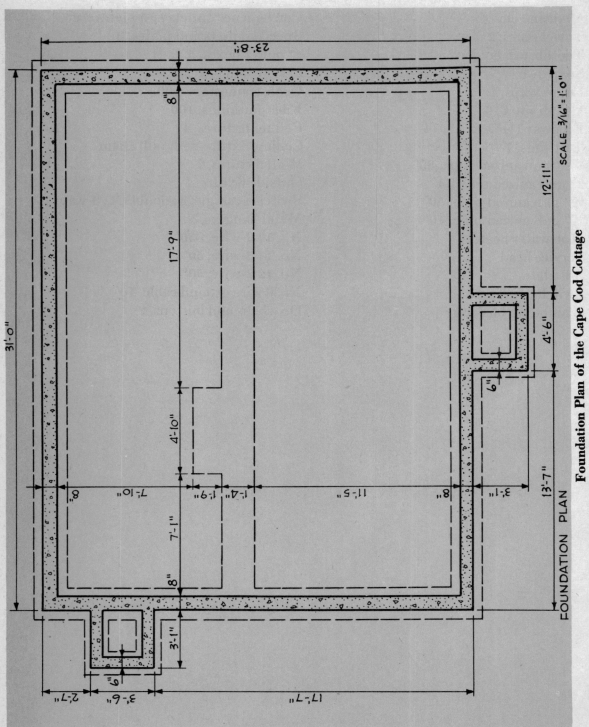

Foundation Plan of the Cape Cod Cottage

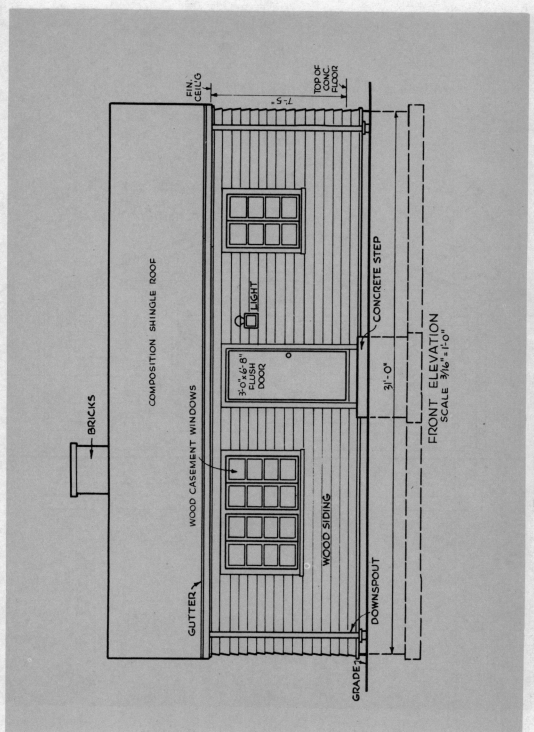

Front Elevation of the Cape Cod Cottage

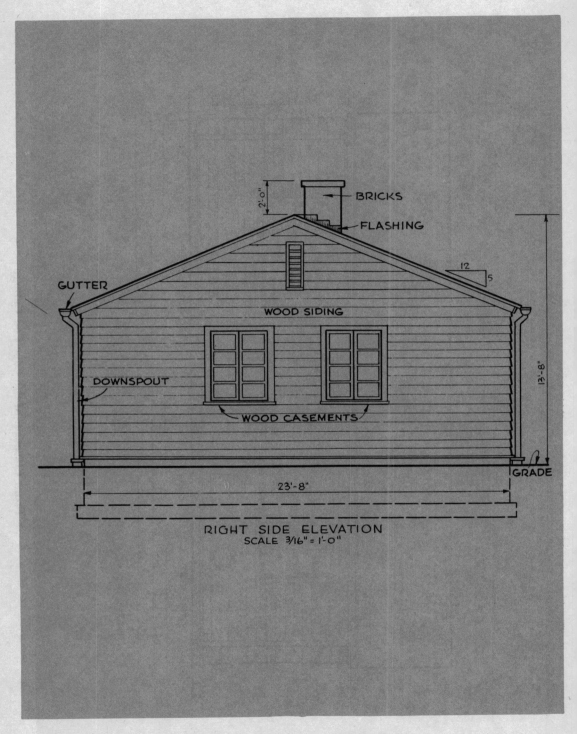

Right Side Elevation of the Cape Cod Cottage

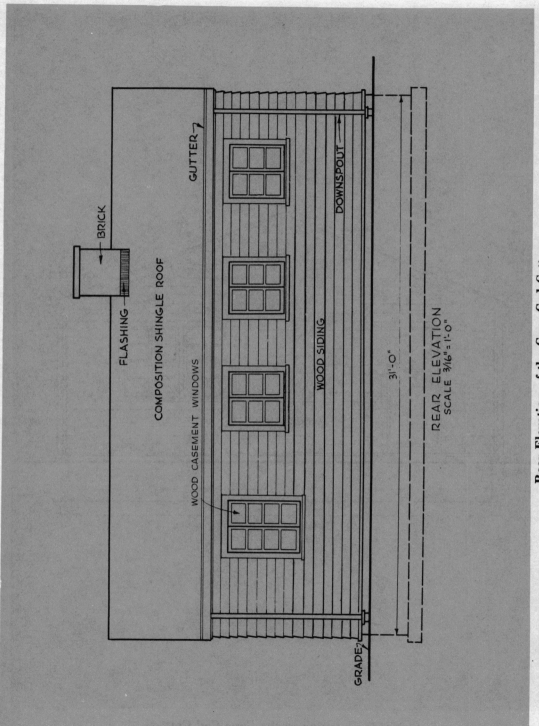

Rear Elevation of the Cape Cod Cottage

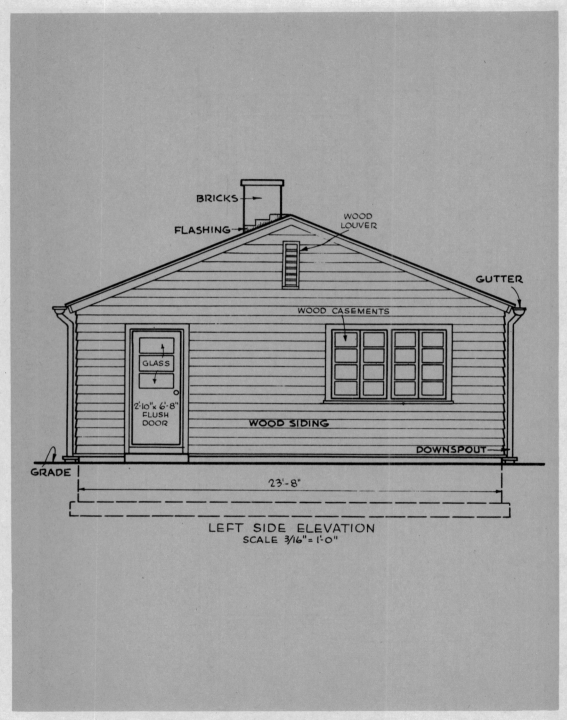

Left Side Elevation of the Cape Cod Cottage

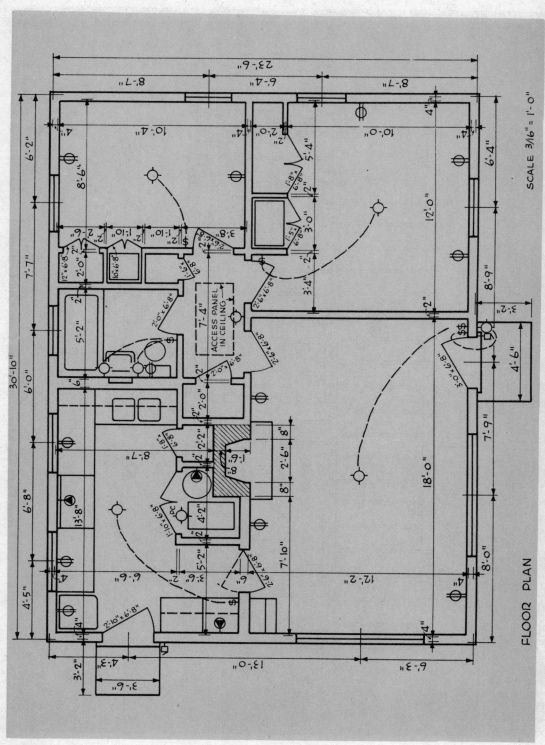

Floor Plan of the Cape Cod Cottage

FLOOR PLAN

SCALE 3/16" = 1'-0"

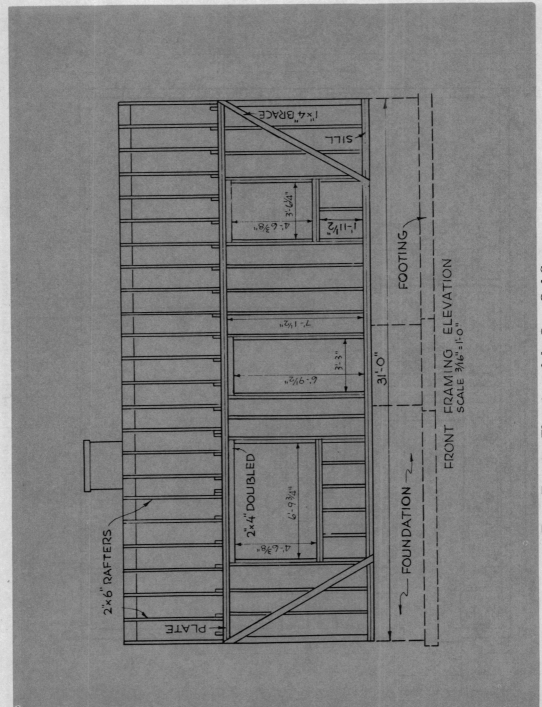

Front Framing Elevation of the Cape Cod Cottage

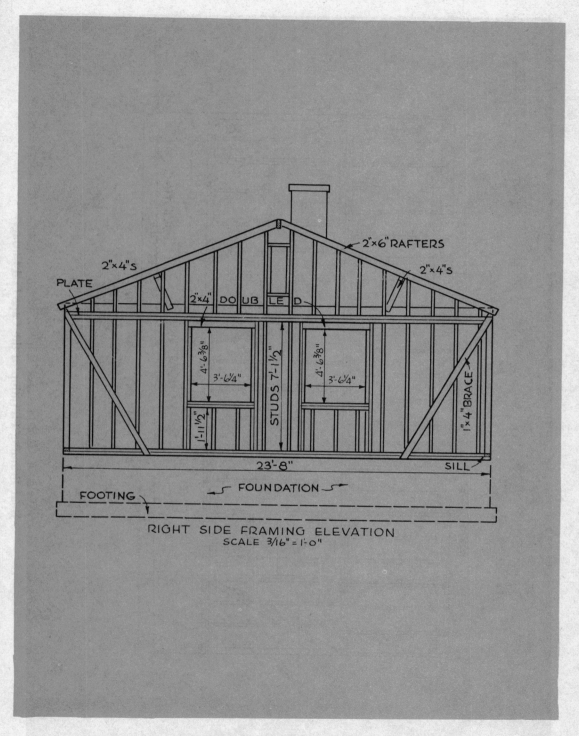

Right Side Framing Elevation of the Cape Cod Cottage

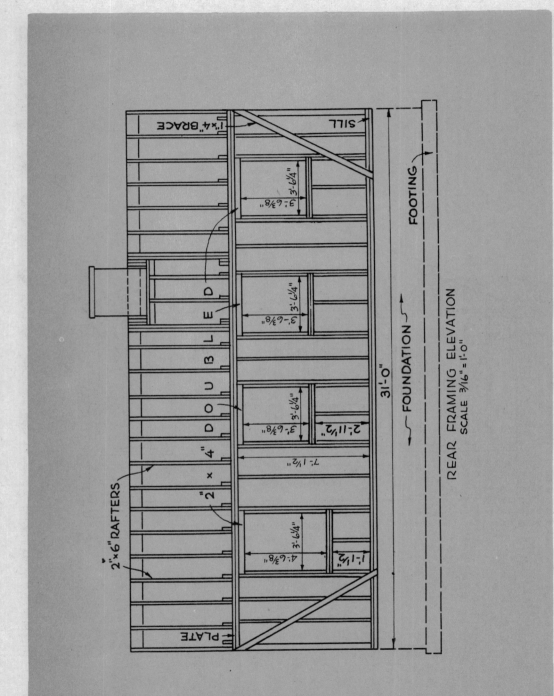

Rear Framing Elevation of the Cape Cod Cottage

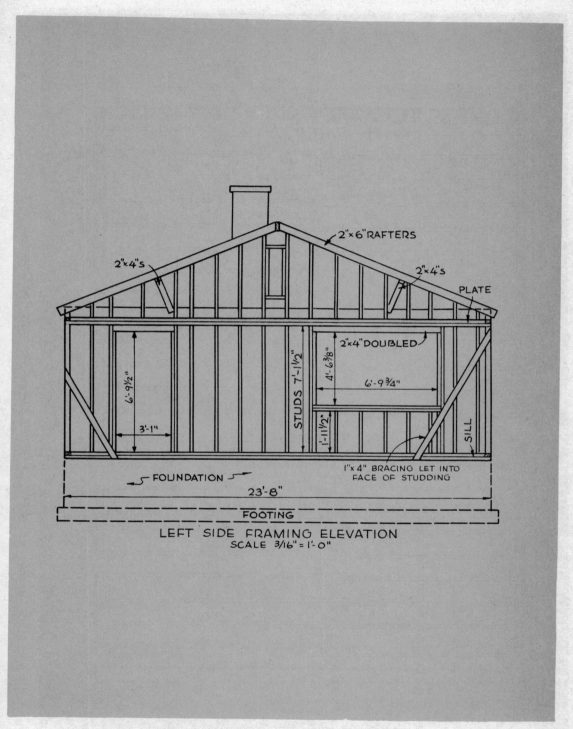

Left Side Framing Elevation of the Cape Cod Cottage

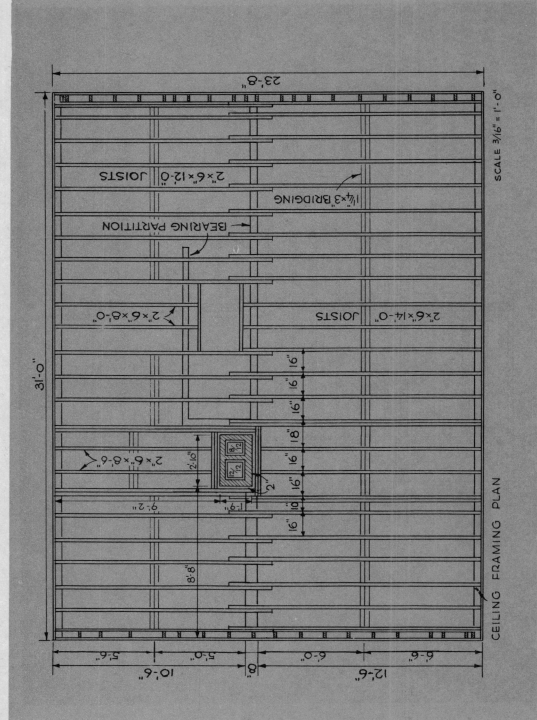

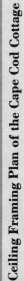

Ceiling Framing Plan of the Cape Cod Cottage

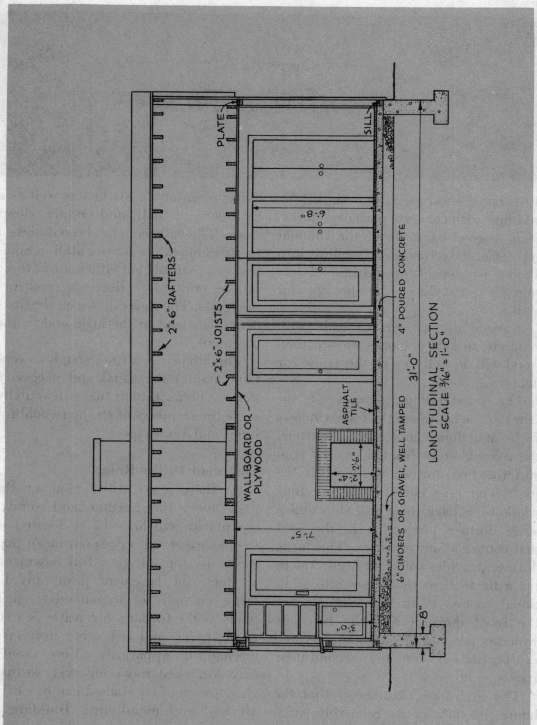

Longitudinal Section of the Cape Cod Cottage

Chapter 25

A COLONIAL HOUSE

THIS house was especially designed for building with concrete masonry blocks. It is a good example of the colonial type of architecture, and it will fit into almost any locality, regardless of terrain or the style of the surrounding homes.

Anyone who prefers to build with concrete masonry blocks rather than wood will do well to pick this house for his own.

The outstanding features of the front of the house are the four windows with small lights and batten shutters, the colonial-style front door, the trim and the two dormer windows in the roof. The rear elevation shows four windows, a back door and step and a large dormer projection in the roof that contains four windows. This large dormer provides sufficient headroom in the attic to turn this space into additional rooms. With the rear dormer, the front dormers and the two side windows provide adequate light as well as ventilation for the second-floor rooms.

The first-floor plan shows that the house, in spite of its relatively small size, contains two bedrooms, a large living room and a kitchen as well as a bathroom, a hall and ample closet space. The bathroom has been designed to accommodate a shower stall in addition to a bathtub, but either one of these can be omitted to decrease construction costs. The stairs shown on the first-floor plan lead to the attic and to the basement.

The kitchen is large enough to contain, besides the usual and necessary items, a breakfast bar that will actually serve the members of the household for lunch and dinner too.

Basement Utility Room

As there is no utility room on the first floor, the heating and similar equipment will have to be located in the basement. This does not mean that the house must have a full basement. In fact, the basement need only be large enough to accommodate such items as the furnace, hot-water heater, water pump and any other necessary mechanical apparatus. You should leave sufficient room, however, so that these pieces of equipment can be easily serviced and maintained. Building a basement utility room rather than a

The Colonial House

full basement will not only save time but will also decrease your cost of construction. If a half- or quarter-basement is used, it must be positioned so that access to it can be had by the stairs located on the first-floor plan.

Foundations

The foundations for the Colonial House should be either poured concrete or masonry blocks. Either type should be not less than 8″ thick. Footings for the foundation walls must extend below the frost line.

To eliminate the necessity of having to use a wood or steel girder through the center of the house to support the floor joists, a wall of masonry can be erected. If there is only a half- or quarter-basement in the house, the masonry wall can run unbroken from one outside wall to the other. If a full basement is desired, the masonry wall should be broken at some point to provide a doorway. The opening over the top of the doorway should be covered with a reinforced-concrete lintel. The outside foundation walls and the masonry partition should all be of the same height so that the joists will be perfectly level.

Footings for the fireplace and chimney should also be installed while the foundations are being built.

Important Items

Before you start work on the house, read over the instructions given in this book on how to work with concrete masonry blocks. You should also take the plans of the house to a masonry dealer so that he will be able to give you all the materials that you will require.

Besides the standard-size building blocks, you will need 14 window sills. One of these must be suitable for the double window shown on the right elevation. You will also need the same number of reinforced, pre-cast window lintels, two door lintels and two door sills. The type of jamb block required for framing around the window openings will depend upon what type of window you plan to use. Some of these blocks are designed for wood window frames, others for metal frames.

Another important item you will require is a suitable number of joist jamb blocks. These are used to provide spaces on which to rest the outer ends of the floor joists.

Before starting to build, you should also decide what type of heating equipment you intend to use. If a warm-air system is selected, you must decide further whether or not the ducts are to be run up through the masonry walls.

Insulation is another important factor. You can make your home a great deal more comfortable and reduce heating costs too if you insulate the walls. This is done by filling the voids in the blocks with a granular fill insulation, which is poured right in as the blocks are laid up.

The interior partition can be of wood, but you can also use interior-partition masonry blocks. If blocks are used, they should be tied into the exterior walls with metal straps.

Floor joists should be 2"x10"s, and they should be spaced 16" on center. You will need bridging between the joists on all spans that are more than 8' wide.

All joist-ends that rest on the masonry walls should be cut to a bevel 3" deep. If this is not done and the joists should fall by any chance, they will damage the walls badly.

After the joists are in place, you can cover them with sub-flooring. This will provide you with a good working platform for building up the walls.

The Finished Walls

The appearance of the finished walls can be affected considerably by the manner in which the mortar joints between the blocks are finished off. If the outside wall is to be covered with stucco, the mortar joints can be struck off flush with the wall surface and, when partially set, can be compacted with a rounded or V-shaped tool.

If you would like to give to the wall the appearance of bevel siding, the mortar joints must be treated in a special manner during construction. The vertical joints between blocks must be struck off flush and then rubbed with a piece of carpet or burlap to remove the sheen from the surface. The horizontal joints are struck flush and, when partially set, are compacted with a pointing tool. This treatment will emphasize the horizontal joints and obscure the vertical ones.

Unless you are able to get hold of a machine to cut the concrete blocks at the proper angle, it is not worth the time to try to make the gable ends of the house with blocks. Level off the four walls at the correct height and then attach top plates. After the roof rafters are in place, the gable ends can be framed with wood studding and covered with a siding that will resemble the exterior treatment of the concrete blocks.

Partition; Joists; Rafters

The next job is to construct the main bearing partition. This runs through the approximate center of the house and can be made of wood or masonry blocks. It must be brought to the same height as the four outside walls. It must also be capped with a wood plate so that the ends of the ceiling joists can be secured to it.

The ceiling joists are 2"x8"s and they are spaced 16" on center. One end of each joist will rest on the foundation wall and the other on the main bearing partition.

Roof rafters are 2"x10"s, also spaced 16" on center. They should be strengthened by collar beams and knee studs, whether or not you plan to finish off the attic. A bevel cut will let them rest on the top plate, while a heel cut will let them overhang.

After the rafters are up, frame the gable ends and then go to work on installing the dormer windows. These are framed in exactly the same manner as the dormers described for the basic house. Roofing boards can be applied after the dormers have been framed.

Chimney; Interior Walls

The chimney and fireplace should be constructed next. They can be built out of concrete masonry blocks made especially for this type of work. After the chimney has been brought through the roof, the roofing material should be applied.

Window and door frames are now installed in the spaces left for them in the exterior walls.

The construction of the interior partitions follows. Like the main bearing partition, they can be built either of wood or of masonry blocks. If blocks are used, you must plan to bring the required pipes for the bathroom and kitchen up through the center of the walls as you build them. If the partitions are to be of wood, the pipes can be run up after the walls have been framed.

The inside walls of the house must now be lined with wood furring strips. Regular 2"x2" stock will be sufficient, and it should be spaced 16" on center.

When all the strips are up, you can install the electrical system. The furring strips can be used to support the outlet and switch boxes as well as the cables.

After all these are in place, the interior-wall material can be applied. It can be either plaster or wallboard.

The plumbing fixtures and final electrical fixtures are installed at this point.

Exterior Walls

The exterior masonry walls of the house can be left plain, but this is not always satisfactory. If the joints were treated to give the effect of bevel siding, the surface should be coated with a white or gray cement paint. Cement paints can also be used, of course, when there has been no special joint treatment.

MATERIALS LIST FOR COLONIAL HOUSE

Material	Quantity	Dimensions
Mixed cement	53 cu. yds.	
Concrete or cinder blocks	2,000	
Mortar	3 cu. yds.	
4" x 4"	2	12'
2" x 12"	3	16'
2" x 10"	149	16'
	70	20'
2" x 8"	11	16'
2" x 6"	10	16'
	10	14'
2" x 4"	32	16'
2" x 2"	50	16'

Material	Quantity	Dimensions
1″ x 6″	5,385 board ft.	
1″ x 3″	1,300′	
Finish flooring	4,757 board ft.	1″ x 3″
Roofing material	1,780 sq. ft.	
Copper flashing	104′	12″
Shelving	150′	1″ x 6″
Flue-tile	32 sections	12″ x 8″ x 2′

		Rough Openings
Entrance doors with frame and sill	2	3′4″ x 6′9½″
Casement windows with frame and trim	1	3′5½″ x 6′8″
	7	3′5½″ x 4′
	4	4′1½″ x 2′8″
	2	3′5½″ x 2′8″
	6	3′0″ x 3′0″

Insulation, 3000 sq. ft.
Wallboard, 4417 sq. ft.
Base mold, 500′
Nails: 20*d*, 36 lbs; 16*d*, 24 lbs; 10*d*, 160 lbs; 8*d*, 45 lbs; 4*d*, 108 lbs; 5*d*, 15 lbs
Louvers, 2
Gutters, 84′
Flight box stairs, 2
Closet doors, trim, jambs, stops, 11
Interior doors, trim, jambs, stops, 11
Hinges: brass, 6; interior, 44
Mortice locks, 24
Paint: water-thinned, 9 gal.; interior enamel, 1½ gal.
Common bricks, 3,000
Chimney thimble
Clean-out door
Firebricks, 180
Fireclay, 60 lbs
Hearth assembly, 2
Mixed cement, 4 cu. ft.
Mortar, 1 cu. yd.
Dampers, 2

Angleirons: 42″, 2; 36″, 2
Entrance cable, 16′
Switch box
Service head
Sill plate
Grounding bushing
Ceiling fixtures, 9
Ceiling fixtures with pull chain, 2
Wall fixtures, 3
Outside fixture
Convenience outlets, 23
Single switches, 9
Double switch
3-way switches, 2
4″ outlet boxes with plates, 11
2½″ outlet boxes with plates, 13
Cable connectors and bushings, 100
Metal hangers, 11
Door bells and buttons, 2
No. 14 2-wire, 350′
No. 12 wire, 50′
Forced warm-air heating system
Y branch

Increaser
Clean-out plug
4″ sanitary T, 2
4″ sanitary T with 2″ tapp., 3
Elbows: 2″, 4; 1½″, 14; ¾″, 22
2″ ¼-bend
Traps, 7
Closet bends, 2
Tees: 1½″, 22; ¾″, 18
4″cast-iron soil pipe, 8 sections
2″ galvanized pipe, 20′
1½″ galvanized pipe, 110′

¾″ galvanized pipe, 50′
Hot-water heater
Kitchen sink
Lavatory, 2
Water closets, 2
Bathtub
Stall showers, 2
Laundry tubs, 2
Medicine closets, 2
Towel racks, 4
Toothbrush holders, 2
Soap dishes, 2

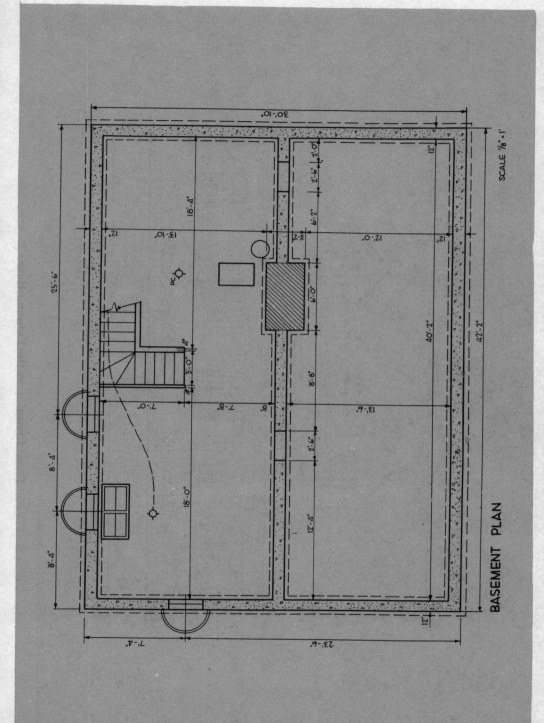

BASEMENT PLAN

Foundation Plan of the Colonial House

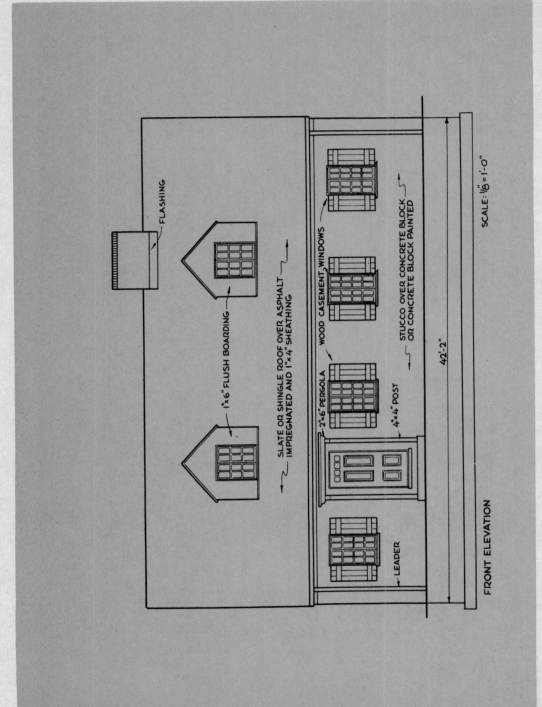

Front Elevation of the Colonial House

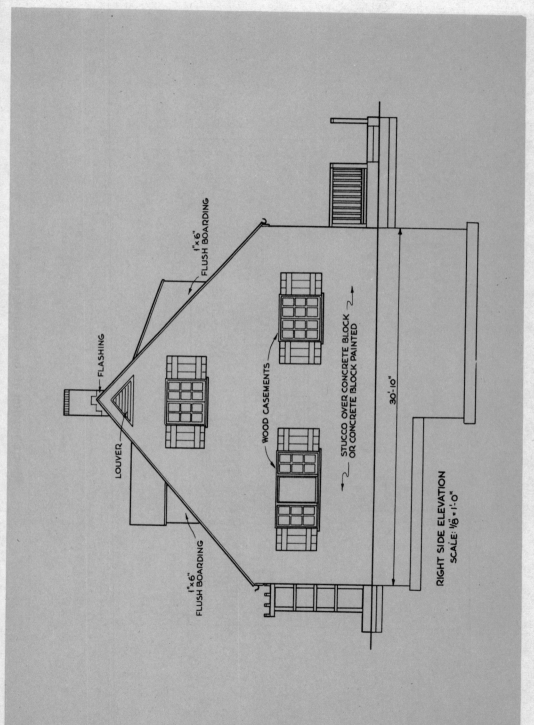

Right Side Elevation of the Colonial House

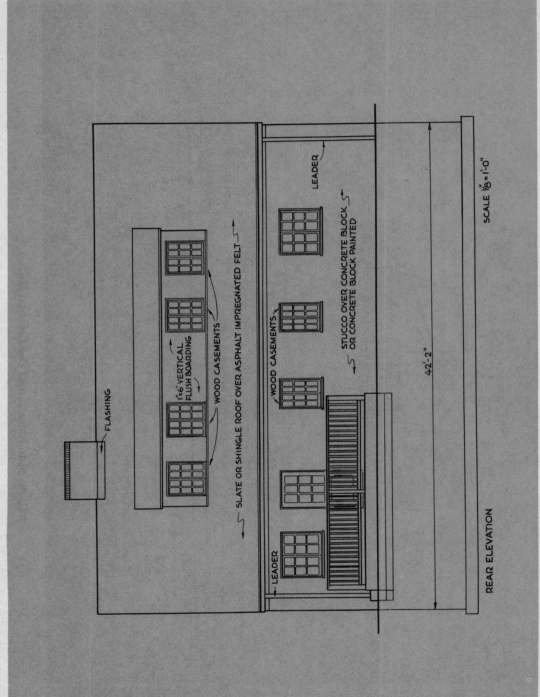

Rear Elevation of the Colonial House

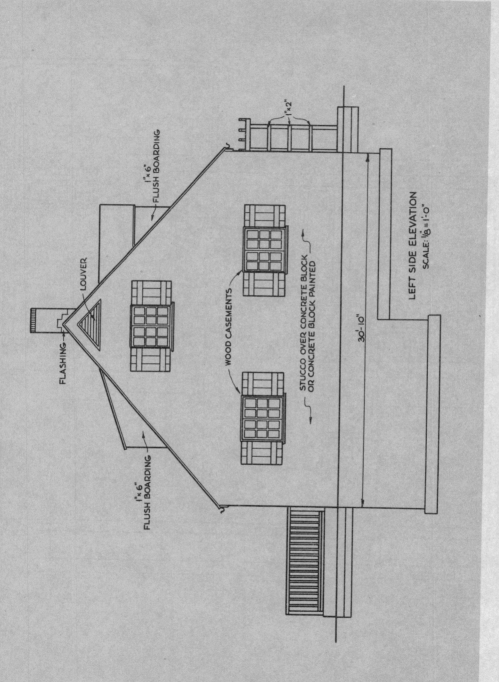

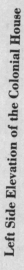

Left Side Elevation of the Colonial House

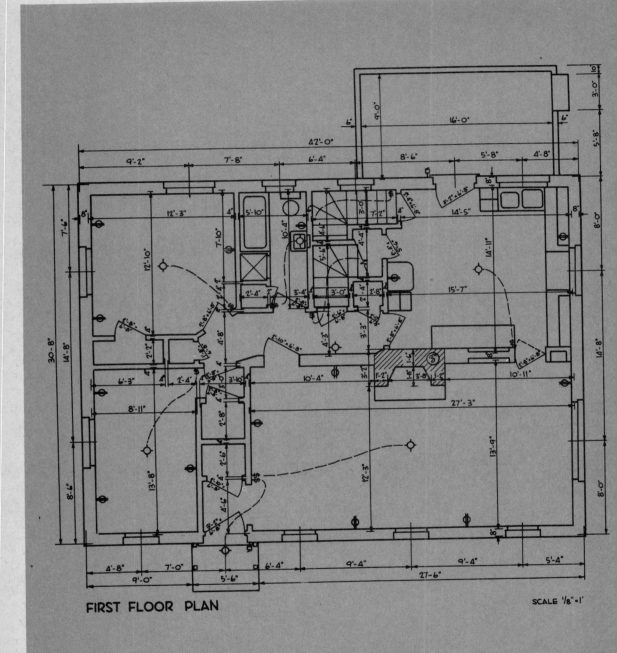

FIRST FLOOR PLAN

SCALE ⅛"=1'

Floor Plan of the Colonial House: First Floor

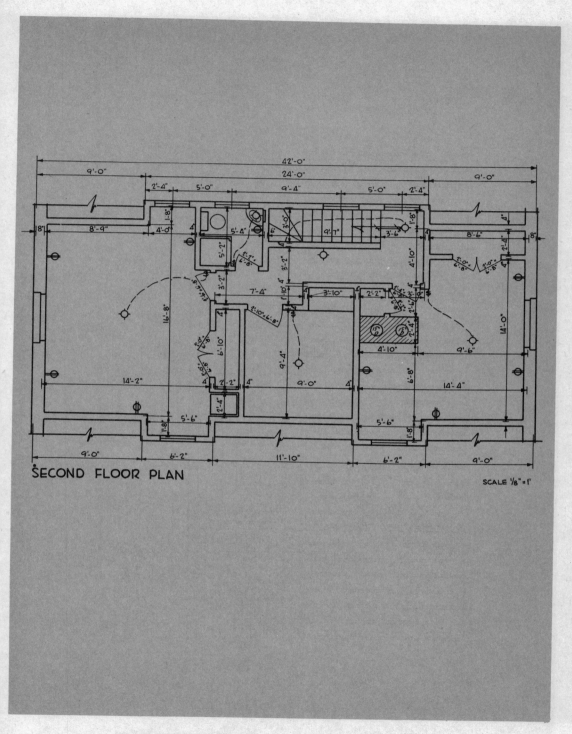

SECOND FLOOR PLAN

SCALE ⅛" = 1'

Floor Plan of the Colonial House: Second Floor

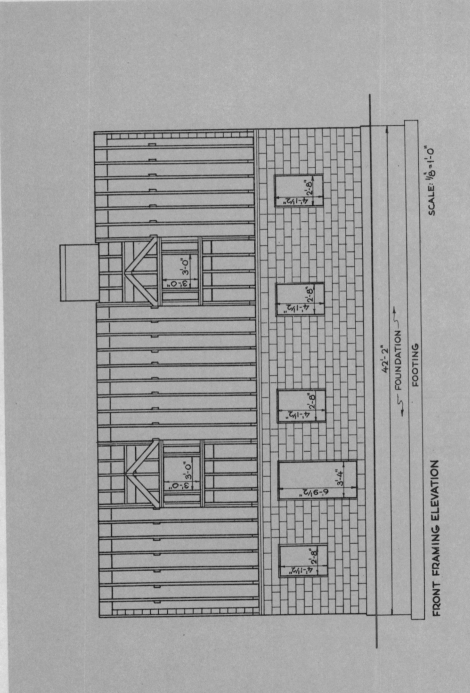

FRONT FRAMING ELEVATION

SCALE: ⅛″ = 1′-0″

Front Framing Elevation of the Colonial House

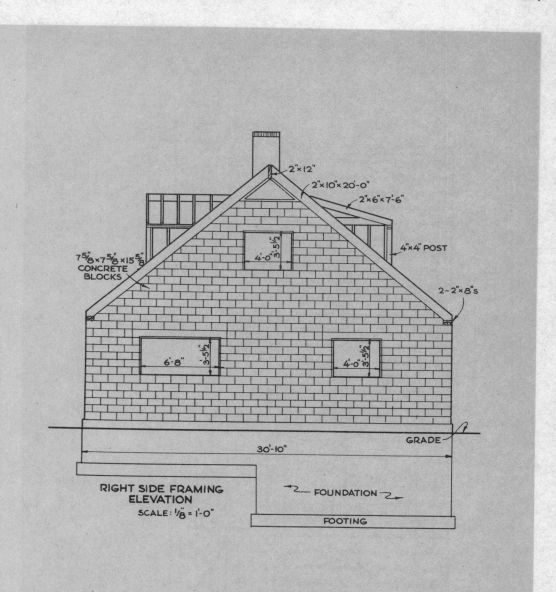

Right Framing Elevation of the Colonial House

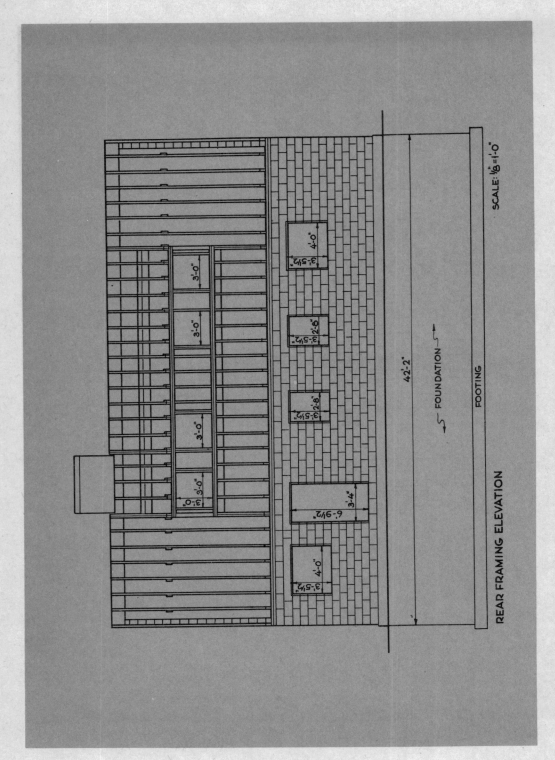

REAR FRAMING ELEVATION

Rear Framing Elevation of the Colonial House

SCALE: 1/8"=1'-0"

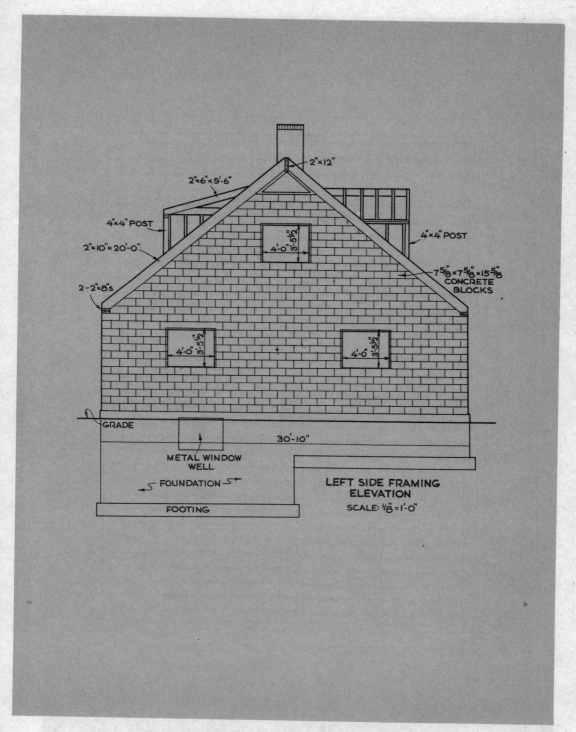

Left Framing Elevation of the Colonial House

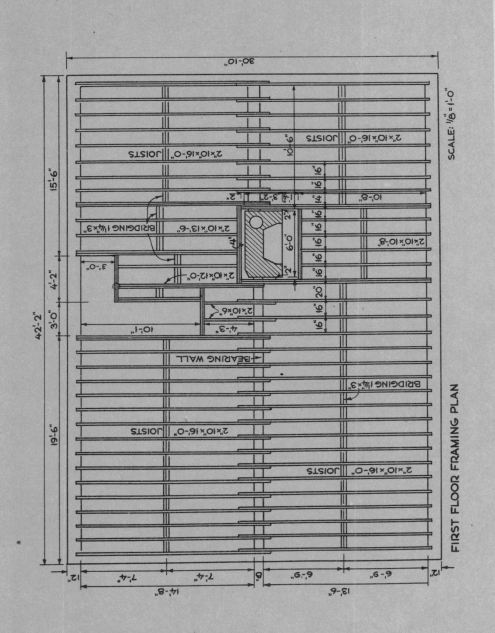

FIRST FLOOR FRAMING PLAN

SCALE: 1/8" = 1'-0"

First Floor Framing Plan of the Colonial House

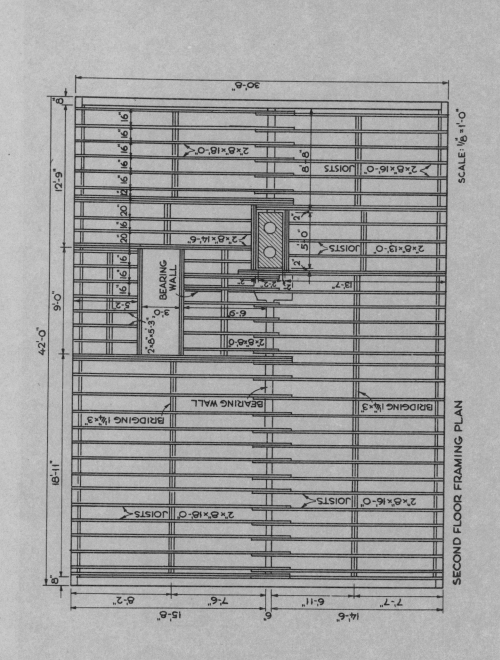

SECOND FLOOR FRAMING PLAN

Second Floor Framing Plan of the Colonial House

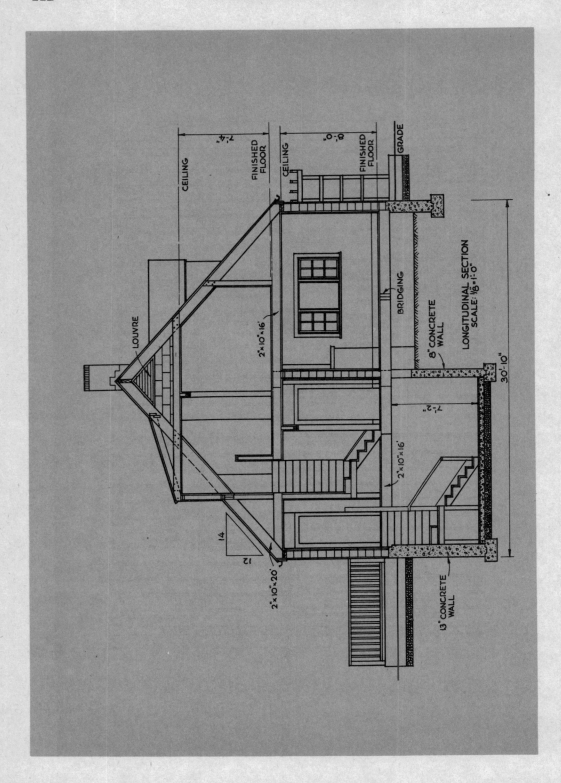

Section of the Colonial House

Chapter 26

A RANCH HOUSE

THIS particular style of architecture is at the present time the most popular type tor small and low-cost homes throughout the country, with the possible exception of the New England states, where the traditional Cape Cod cottage still remains out in front.

The ranch-house type of dwelling had its origin, of course, in the southwest part of this country, and it is to the type of terrain found there that it is most suited. It has been built, however, in every state in the union, and with a little variation here and there to suit local requirements, it makes a very efficient as well as attractive home.

Any housewife who looks at the floor plan of the Ranch House will be struck by the fact that all the rooms are on one floor. This does away with climbing up and down stairs a hundred times a day, which, as everyone knows, is extremely exhausting. The one flight of stairs that is shown in the floor plan leads to the basement. There is an access panel to the storage space in the attic.

The attic is not intended to be made into living quarters as it does not have enough headroom. As far as the basement goes, there is no reason at all to build a full basement or even a half-basement—it would simply be a waste of both time and money. A room large enough to contain the various necessary utilities will be perfectly adequate.

The floor plan indicates that this house contains three bedrooms. Two of them are single and one is double. There is a large living room, which has been designed so that a portion of it can serve as a more or less permanent dining room.

There are one large bathroom off the bedrooms and a lavatory off the kitchen. You will note that between the kitchen and the lavatory, space has been set aside for a laundry. If this is not required, the space can be rearranged so that a utility room is made out of the lavatory and the laundry becomes a lavatory that directly adjoins the kitchen. Under these conditions, there will be no need for a basement at all.

The garage has been designed for two cars, but part of it can be set aside for storage purposes.

There are many variations possible in this Ranch House. Each family will suit itself. But be sure that you have carefully considered your particular way of living before you make changes.

Designed for Outdoor Living

A ranch house requires a good-size plot, not only because of its length, which is naturally greater than that of a two-story house with the same amount of floor space, but also because it is designed for outdoor living. It is not the kind of house that can be crowded into a small plot or close up against adjoining houses. You should have sufficient room in back of the house for a good-size terrace, and you should also have a certain degree of privacy because, as you can see from the plans, almost the entire back of the house is window area. The area in front of the house is not so important as that in the back because it is not used so much for living purposes.

This is the sort of home that should appeal to a family that enjoys being outdoors as much as possible. Even during the cold weather, the large amount of window area will give the impression that you are out of doors.

One of the things about this house that might worry the owner-builder is the roof. Because of the gables over the living room and over one bedroom and bath, the roof appears to be a very complicated structure to build. This is not really the case, and you will find that when the time comes to frame the

roof, the job will not be any more difficult than when there is a dormer or two to be built in.

Foundations; the Basement

The foundations for both the house and the garage can be poured in one operation. As mentioned before, there is very little point to making an excavation for a full basement. It will be quite sufficient if enough earth is removed to allow the various utilities to be installed. The best position for the basement utility room is under the laundry and kitchen, so that access to it can be had by means of the stairs located on the first floor. The heating equipment should be located rather close to the fireplace and chimney since it will have to be connected to the latter.

One other possible arrangement is to move the basement utility room out towards the front or back wall and install a flight of outside stairs, thus completely eliminating the indoor stairs.

When the footings and foundations are being poured, be sure to install a footing for the fireplace and a foundation for the main bearing partition, which runs through the approximate center of the house. This partition, as you will note from the floor plan, forms the rear wall of the stair well and the front wall of the two rear bedrooms.

The porch at the front entrance to the house can be made of poured concrete set over a base of gravel or cin-

The Ranch House

ders. It can be poured at the same time as the foundations or finished after the house itself has been completed.

Framing

The sill used on this house can be a box sill with a 2″x6″ base. It should be securely anchored to the top of the foundation wall. The sill on the main bearing partition can be a 2″x4″. The joists used for the first floor should be 2″x10″s, and they should be spaced 16″ on center. They will rest on the foundation wall and the main bearing partition.

After the joists are in place, the sub-flooring can be installed, and you can then go on and frame the walls.

Openings for the windows and doors can be framed while the studding is being put up or they can be cut out later. In any event, before these openings can be made, you will need to get the rough-opening dimensions for the type of casement windows you intend to use.

The ceiling joists can be 2″x8″s spaced 16″ on center. If you do not feel that you will require a great amount of attic storage space, it is possible to frame the areas over the kitchen, dining room, living room, laundry and lavatory with 2″x8″s and to use 2″x6″s for the remaining portions of the house. If this is done, the direction in which the joists are laid should be varied so that they will run between the partitions that are nearest to each other. This means, of course, that before the ceiling joists can be in-

stalled, the interior partitions will have to be erected. Since these partitions are going to carry a load, the floor joists under them should be doubled.

In any case, the main bearing partition must be erected before any of the ceiling joists can be installed.

The Roof

Now comes the task of framing the roof. The best way to do this job is, for the time being, to forget about the gables over the bedroom and bath and over the living room and to proceed with the framing of the main house roof, leaving unframed the points where it will join the gables. After the main roof has been framed, install the studding at the ends.

Now you can put up the two roof rafters at the front of the living room, and then run a 2″x6″ ridge board from these to the ridge of the main roof. As you can see from the rear elevation, the ridges of the main roof and of the living-room gable join in the same plane. After the living-room ridge board is up, install the remaining common rafters for the gable. The next step is to take two 2″x6″s and run one down from each side of the point where the ridges of the living room and the main roof join. This procedure will form two valleys. The 2″x6″s are the valley rafters. Now cut short rafters and fit them between the valley rafters and the ridge of the gable.

The same method of construction is used for the gable over the bedroom and bath.

The Chimney; the Plumbing System

Once the roof has been framed, cover it with roofing boards, but leave an opening for the chimney.

Now you can go to work and cut out the openings in the walls for the windows and doors. After that, you can cover the four outside walls with sheathing.

The building of the fireplace and the chimney follows. The fireplace dimensions are the same as those used in all the other houses covered in this book, and the method of construction is identical with that given in the chapter on the fireplace and chimney.

When the chimney has been completed and the flashing has been installed, apply the roofing. Shingles of wood or asbestos or asphalt will do nicely. With the roof weathertight, the interior partitions can go up and the walls and the ceiling can be insulated.

Installing the plumbing system, and especially the drainage system, is somewhat complicated by the fact that there is a considerable distance between the main bathroom and the kitchen and lavatory. The best solution is to install two vent stacks, one for the bathroom and the other for the kitchen and lavatory. The second vent stack should be installed in the lavatory with a 2″ cast-iron line running under the floor from the kitchen sink. The equipment in the laundry can be connected into the line in the lavatory.

Siding

When it comes to the exterior siding, you have a wide choice of materials that are both suitable for construction purposes and in keeping with the architectural style of the Ranch House. It may be possible to get hold of some old, weathered boards that can be used to good advantage. If obtainable, they should be installed over the sheathing in an upright position and the vertical joints between them should be covered with strips of wood. The house pictured in the accompanying plans is covered in part with bevel siding. The remainder of the house is covered with sheets of exterior plywood. Strips of wood nailed over the plywood at 16″ intervals give the effect of wide individual boards.

RANCH HOUSE MATERIALS LIST

Material	Quantity	Dimensions
Mixed cement	55 cu. yds.	
2″ x 10″	20	18′
	33	16′
	28	14′
	35	12′
2″ x 8″	21	18′
	135	16′

Material	Quantity	Dimensions
2″ x 8″	2	14′
	64	12′
	44	10′
2″ x 6″	12	16′
2″ x 4″	12	20′
	249	16′
1″ x 3″	115	16′
Sheathing	10,070 board ft.	1″ x 6″
Finish flooring	2,400 board ft.	1″ x 3″
Shelving	150′	1″ x 6″
Copper flashing	126′	12″
Garage doors	2	8′9″ x 7′6″

		Rough Openings
Entrance doors with frame and trim	1	3′6″ x 7′
	1	3′ x 7′
	1	2′6″ x 7′0″
Windows with frame and trim	2	4′0″ x 3′9″
	1	5′0″ x 6′3″
	7	2′3″ x 3′9″
	2	2′3″ x 6′9″
	4	7′ x 4′
	1	2′3″ x 2′9″
	1	2′3″ x 6′6″
	1	2′3″ x 3′0″

1″ x 6″, 240′
1″ x 2″, 196′
Roofing material, 4,000 sq. ft.
Building paper, 1,640 sq. ft.
Beveled siding, 1,968 board ft.
Insulation, 3,350 sq. ft.
Wallboard, 5,900 sq. ft.
Base mold, 500′
Nails: 6d, 40 lbs; 8d, 50 lbs; 10d, 285 lbs; 16d, 60 lbs; 20d, 50 lbs; 4d, 240 lbs; 5d, 36 lbs
Interior doors, 15
Hinges: brass, 9; interior, 30
Mortice locks, 18

Flight box stairs, 1
Paint: exterior, 12 gal.; water-thinned, 19 gal.; interior enamel, 2 gal.
Common bricks, 6,000
Mortar, 3 cu. yds.
2-ft. flue-tile 12″ x 12″, 10; 12″ x 8″, 4
Chimney thimble
Clean-out door
Firebricks, 90
Fireclay, 30 lbs
Hearth assembly
Mixed cement, 2 cu. ft.
Damper
Angleirons: 42″, 1; 36″, 1

Forced warm-air or hot-water heating
   system

Y branches: 4″, 4; 2″, 1

Clean-out plugs, 2

Sanitary T; 4″, 2; 4″ with 2″ tapp., 6;
   2″, 2

Tees: 2″, 5; 1½″, 6; ¾″, 12

Decreasers, 2

Elbows: 2″, 6; 1½″, 7; ¾″, 4

Traps, 7

Closet bends, 2

Bathtub

5′ sections cast-iron soil pipe: 4″, 20;
   2″, 18

Galvanized pipe: 2″, 75′; 1½″, 100′;
   ¾″, 300′

Lavatories, 2

Water closets, 2

Stall shower

Laundry tub

Kitchen sink

Medicine closets, 2

Towel racks, 4

Toothbrush holder

Soap dishes, 2

Hot-water heater

Ceiling fixtures, 11

Ceiling fixtures with pull chain, 2

Wall fixtures, 2

Outside fixture

Convenience outlets, 21

Special outlets, 1

Single switches, 12

3-way switches, 2

4″ outlet boxes with plates, 13

2½″ switch boxes with plates, 21

Door bell and button

Cable connectors and bushings, 150

Metal hangers, 13

Service head

Switch box

Sill plate

Grounding bushing

Entrance cable, 16′

No. 14 2-wire, 400′

No. 14 3-wire, 75′

No. 12 wire, 50′

No. 6 wire, 30′

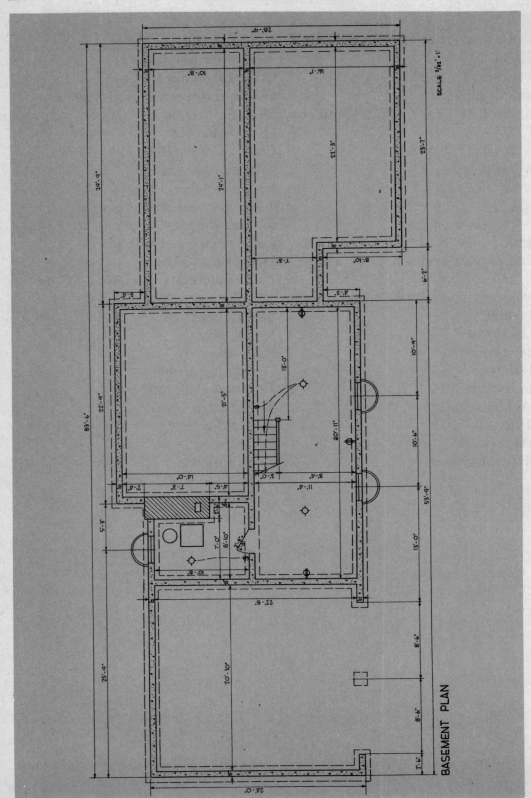

BASEMENT PLAN

SCALE 3/32"=1'

Foundation Plan of the Ranch House

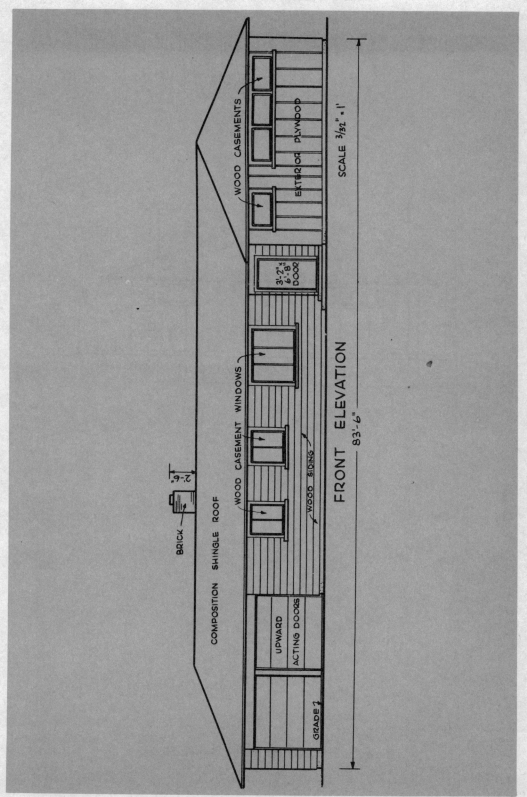

Front Elevation of the Ranch House

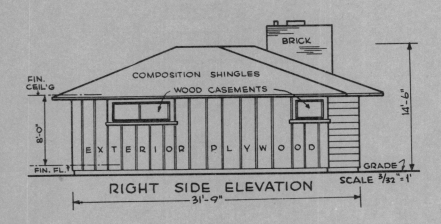

Right Side Elevation of the Ranch House

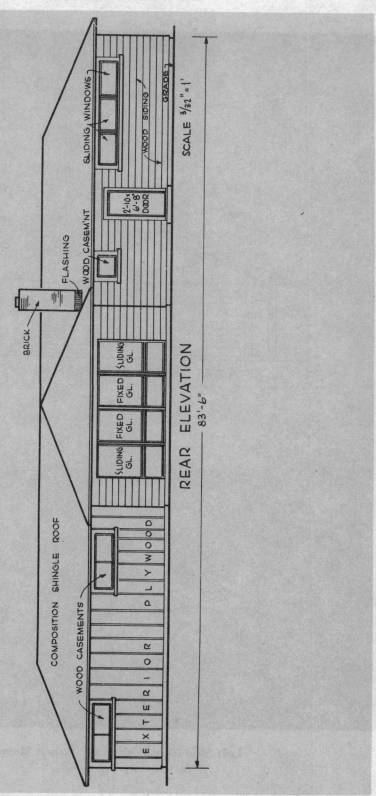

SCALE 3/32" = 1'

GRADE

WOOD SIDING

SLIDING WINDOWS

WOOD CASEM'NT

2'-10 x 6'-8" DOOR

FLASHING

BRICK

SLIDING GL. FIXED GL. FIXED GL. SLIDING GL.

REAR ELEVATION
83'-6"

COMPOSITION SHINGLE ROOF

WOOD CASEMENTS

EXTERIOR PLYWOOD

Rear Elevation of the Ranch House

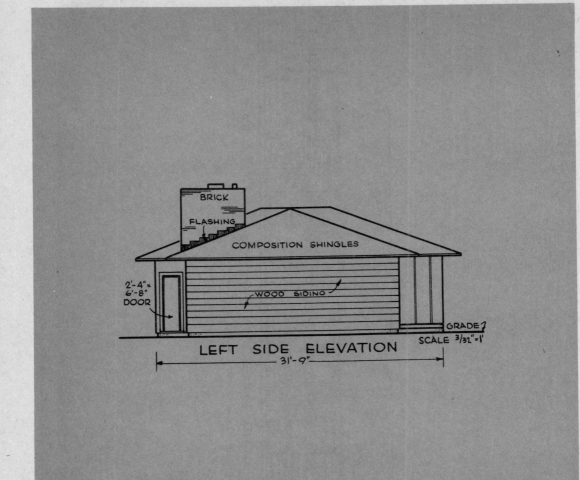

Left Side Elevation of the Ranch House

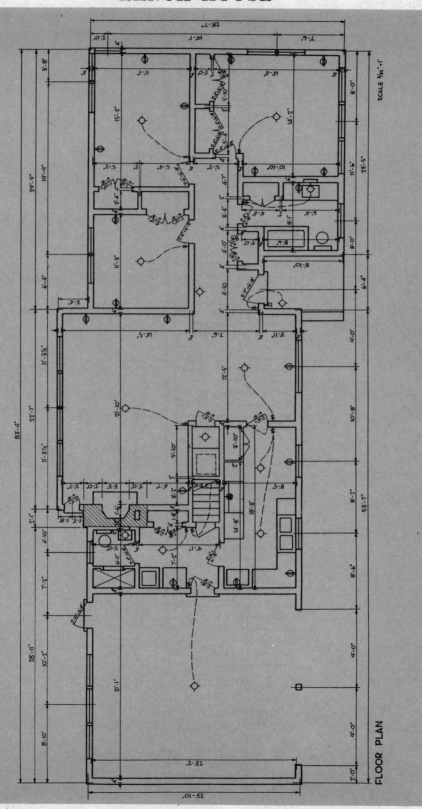

Floor Plan of the Ranch House

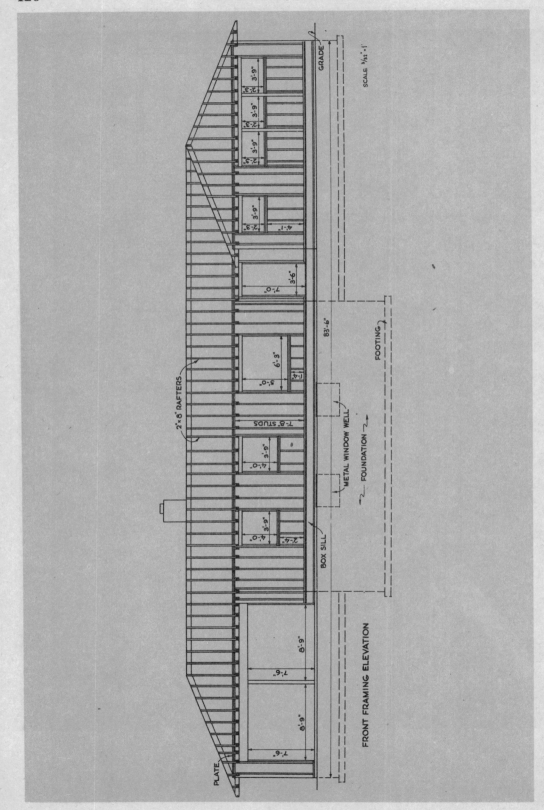

Front Framing Elevation of the Ranch House

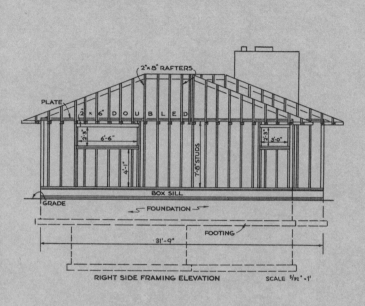

RIGHT SIDE FRAMING ELEVATION   SCALE 3/32" = 1'

Right Framing Elevation of the Ranch House

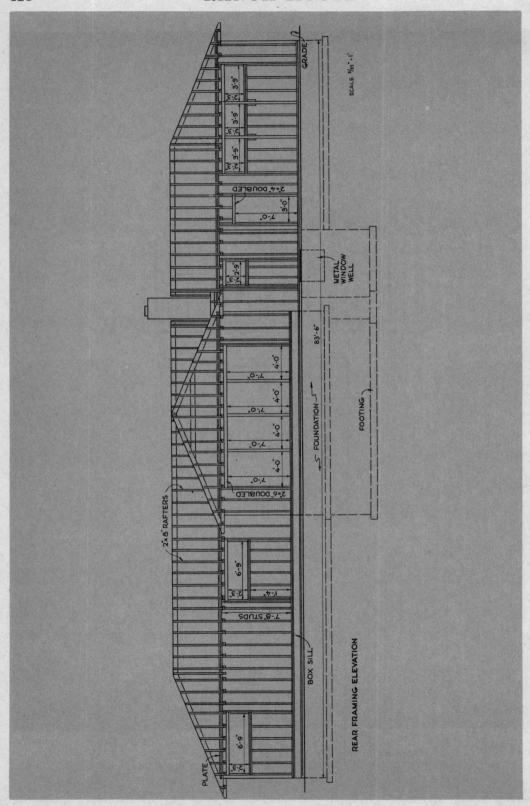

Rear Framing Elevation of the Ranch House

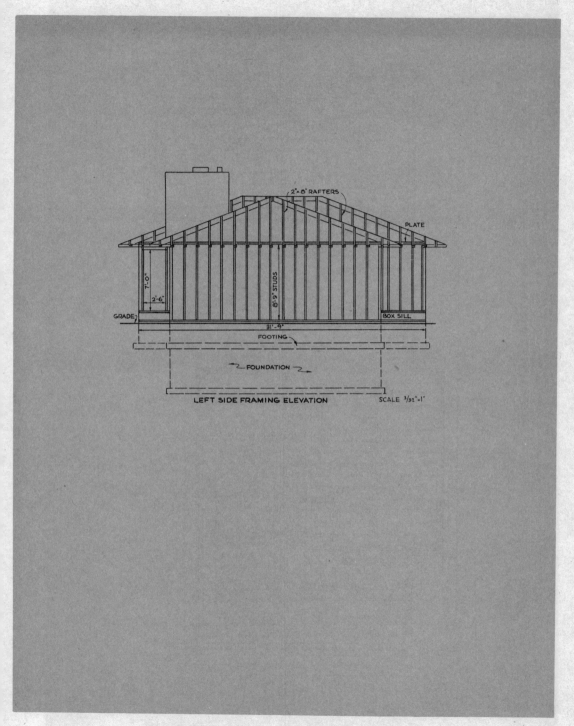

Left Framing Elevation of the Ranch House

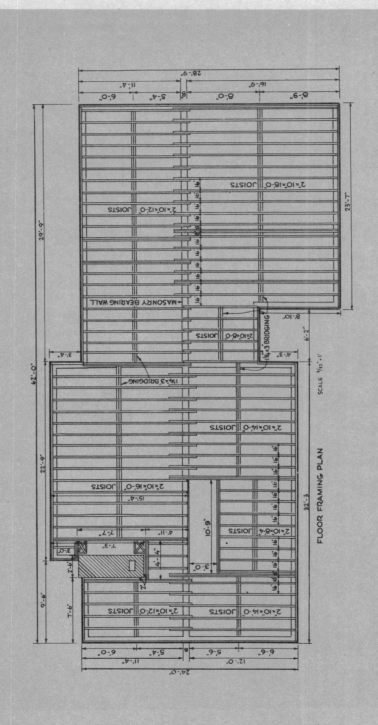

Floor Framing Plan of the Ranch House

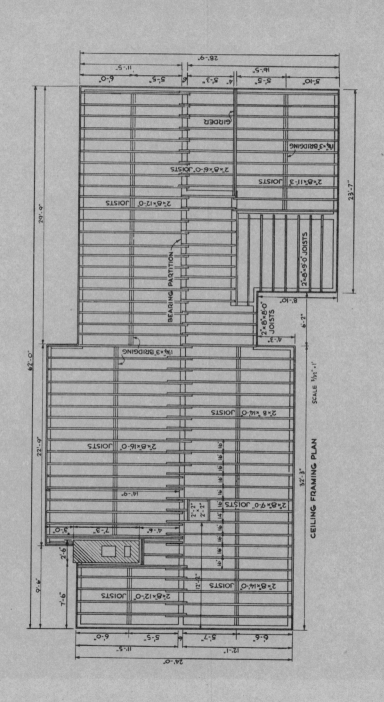

Ceiling Framing Plan of the Ranch House

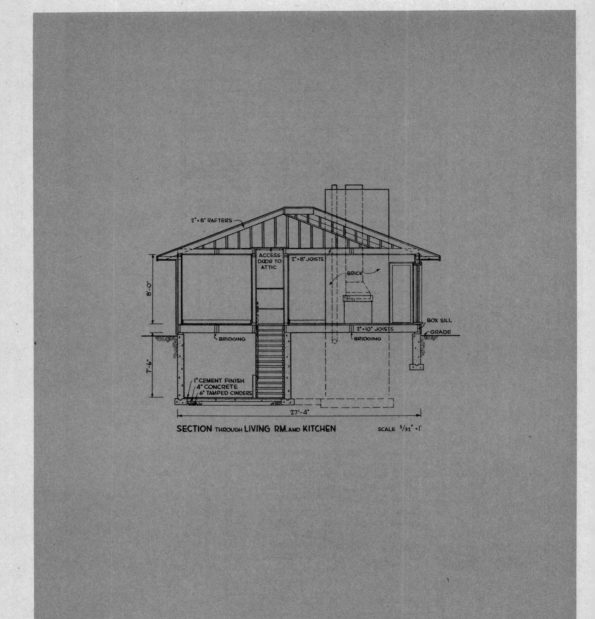

SECTION THROUGH LIVING RM. AND KITCHEN   SCALE 3/32"=1'

Section of the Ranch House

Chapter 27

A VACATION HIDEAWAY

THIS house was designed especially for the family who would like to have a home of their own for vacations or week ends. It can easily be converted, however, into a home that is quite suitable and adequate for all-year-round living. It is the sort of house that should interest someone who wants to build a house of his own but has neither the time or the money at the present to build one of the more expensive homes.

As you can see by looking at the various plans, the Vacation Hideaway gives you a great deal of living space in spite of its relatively small size. If bunks are used in the second-floor sleeping quarters, the house can easily accommodate six persons.

You will notice from the floor plan of the first floor that the house contains a good-size living room as well as a kitchen, a bath and space for heating equipment. The second floor is given over to two bedrooms.

The actual construction of the house has been planned so that it can be built with relatively light materials, which are not only easier to work with but cost far less than the heavier grades of stock required for the other homes.

Foundations and Floors

Examine the foundation plan for this house and you will see that a continuous foundation wall of concrete or masonry blocks is used. There is also a concrete footing that runs directly under the main bearing partition. As the house is relatively light, an 8"-thick foundation wall will be quite sufficient. This is indicated on the foundation plan by a heavy unbroken line. Footings for the foundations should be 8" deep and 16" wide. The outline of these footings is indicated on the plan by the light broken line. The 1'10"x 1'11" foundation at the back of the house is for the chimney base. This should have a footing under it 6" wider than the base on all sides and at least 12" deep. All footings, of course, must extend below the frost line with the exception of the one for the main bearing partition, which can be at grade level as it is not going to be exposed to heavy frost.

The 4'0"x3'1" foundation on one side of the house is for the front door-step.

Now examine the longitudinal section, which shows that the first floor of the house is a poured-concrete slab. A wood floor is placed over one portion of this floor, but it can be extended over the entire area if you wish. Instructions for making this type of floor are given in the chapter in this book covering foundations. Before the floor is poured, however, there are several things to be taken care of. One is to install the two 2″x4″s that are to serve as the house sill and the sole plate for the studding. They should be anchored to the top of the foundation wall by means of anchor bolts. The second thing to do is to determine the location of the various bathroom and kitchen fixtures, so that the drain pipes for these items can be installed in the floor before the concrete is poured.

The location of the various fixtures to be served by these lines is given in the first-floor plan, but it is well to have on hand the roughing-in dimensions for the fixtures that you intend to use in order to avoid any mistakes at this point. The installation of the plumbing system will be on the same general order as outlined in the chapter of this book dealing with house plumbing systems.

Metal clips should be installed as the flooring is poured so that the wood sleepers, to which the wood flooring will be attached, can be anchored to the concrete slab.

Framing

After the floor has been poured and has hardened, you can start framing the house. The four framing plans should give all the information necessary for this job. Most of the details of the framing will be the same as those covered in the chapter on framing.

The studding for the first floor is 6′9½″ high. It is spiked at the base to the 2″x4″ sole plate that is anchored through the house sill to the foundation wall. The wall framework can be put up piece by piece, but it will save time and work if you make up one section at a time, complete with top plate, and then hoist it into position. The top plate should be doubled after all four walls are in place. Do not take the time to make the rough openings for the doors and windows at this point. They can be cut out later on, after the entire house has been framed.

The dimensions given on the framing plans for the rough openings in the walls for windows apply only to a particular brand of wood casement window. It is wise, in view of this fact, to check with your local lumber yard before these openings are made and find out if they have casement windows in stock that are right for this size of opening. If they do not have such windows, get the rough-opening dimensions for the windows that you can get and use these instead of the dimensions given in the framing plans. You may find that different dimensions for the rough openings will throw some of the wall studding out of position so that it is no longer 16″ on center. Do not worry about this too much. It may complicate the job of installing the in-

The Vacation Hideaway

terior wallboard a little, with the result that you will need a piece of furring here or there, but a few inches one way or the other will not detract from the strength of the building. The main point to be sure of is that the windows are properly centered and that the tops come level with each other and with the top of the door opening. The exact location of the windows in relation to the other parts of the house can be seen in the elevation and framing plans.

The front framing elevation shows the location and size of the rough openings for the first- and second-floor windows. Do not let this plan confuse you. It may take a few seconds of study before the purpose of each piece of framing becomes clear.

You will note that the framework for the rear wall of the house is cut out to allow the chimney to pass up and through to the roof. There must be a clearance of at least 2" between the framework and chimney. To make the job of framing easier, it is best not to bother with this opening at the present time. Frame the wall just as if there were not to be a chimney, and, when the time comes to build the chimney, the necessary sections of the framework can be cut out then.

After the first floor has been framed and the top plate has been doubled, the ceiling rafters can be installed. Refer to the second-floor plan for the location of the opening for the stairs to the second floor. This opening must be framed with double joists. Due to their relatively short span and the fact that they will be supported from below by the partitions, the ceiling joists can be 2"x6"s. They should be spaced 16" on center. You will need joists across only that portion of the first-floor ceiling that is to be under the two bedrooms. The area over the living room does not require any joists.

If you do not want the ceiling of the living room to extend right up to the roof, you can lay 2"x4"s over the top plate and attach to them a ceiling of wallboard or plywood.

Now the studding for the second floor can be installed. You will note from the side framing elevations that at the front of the bedroom and directly under the windows, the studding has been doubled and two 2"x6"s have been set on edge and run horizontally over to the corner posts on either side. These provide a support for the roof rafters of the living room. The same arrangement of two 2"x6"s is used at the back of the house at the top of the wall studding to support the rear ends of the roof rafters.

After the framework has been installed, the bedroom rafters can be installed. These are 2"x6"s notched at front and rear so that they will fit over the front and rear framework. The amount of overhang is optional.

The rafters should be spaced 16" on center.

The next step is to install the side studding for the living-room framework before you go on to the living-room rafters.

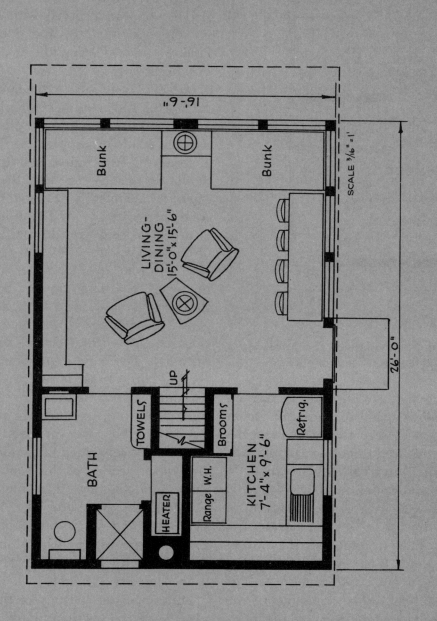

General Floor Plan of the Vacation Hideaway: First Floor

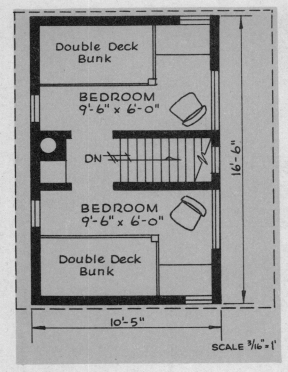

Double Deck
Bunk

BEDROOM
9'-6" x 6'-0"

DN

BEDROOM
9'-6" x 6'-0"

Double Deck
Bunk

16'-6"

10'-5"

SCALE 3/16"=1'

**General Floor Plan of the Vacation
Hideaway: Second Floor**

As the living-room rafters have a considerable span, to construct them it will be necessary to use two lengths of stock spliced together at the approximate center point of the span. To provide additional support for this joint as well as for the rafter as a whole, three 2"x6"s are set on edge and run directly under all the rafters at this point. The rafters themselves are notched out so that they will fit over the 2"x6"s. The rear ends of the living-room rafters rest on the horizontal 2"x6"s set under the windows of the bedroom. The front ends of the rafters are notched out to fit over the top plate at the front of the house.

Sheathing

Once the framework has been completed, you can proceed with cutting out the openings for the doors and windows and covering the framework with sheathing.

If you plan to occupy the house only during the warm summer months, you can save considerable money by using a heavy grade of drop siding in place of sheathing and regular siding. If you should do this, be sure that the framework is adequately covered with a good, heavy grade of building paper in order to keep air and moisture out of the house.

If you plan to use regular drop siding over sheathing, do not bother to sheathe that portion of the framework where the chimney is to run. After the sheathing is on, roof boards should be installed. The least expensive type of roofing you can use is roll roofing, but it should be installed only over a good tight deck-roof, so take care to install the roofing boards with care.

Chimney construction has been covered in the section of this book on fireplaces and chimneys. The chimney pictured in the plans for the Vacation Hideaway is a single-flue chimney for the heating system. There should be little difficulty with its construction as it is perfectly straight with only one opening near the bottom for the smoke pipe from the heating plant.

The window and outside-door frames can now be installed, along with the necessary flashing. Flashing should be used at the top of window and door frames and at the joint formed by the living-room roof and the front wall of the bedrooms.

Now the interior partitions should be installed. The main-floor partitions will rest on a sole plate that is anchored to the concrete floor. Their location is shown on the first-floor plan. Once they are in place, you can install the partitions in the bedroom according to the second-floor plan.

Roofing and Siding

The house is now ready for the roofing and siding. As was mentioned before, the least expensive type of roofing is roll roofing, which is perfectly adequate as far as keeping out moisture goes but which is not very attractive. Asphalt shingles are considerably more pleasant looking—and also more expensive.

If the house is to have sheathing, bevel siding is quite sufficient for the outside covering. Put building paper over the sheathing before you apply the siding.

You will note from the elevation plans that bevel siding has been used on the lower portion of the house while the upper half has been covered with shiplap siding that is put on vertically. This is only one of the many variations that can be made with siding.

Finishing Off

With the house weathertight, you can go about the job of finishing off the interior. The first question is whether or not to insulate the walls and ceilings. If the house is to be used only during the summer months, insulation is not vital, but it will certainly help to make the house more comfortable during the hot weather. It is well worth the few added dollars of cost to insulate the roof in the bedrooms and living room. Insulation in the walls will also help to keep out the heat.

The location of the various outlets, fixtures and switches for the electrical system are given in the two floor plans. The wiring and the plumbing equipment should be installed at this time.

The wood flooring can also be installed now, and this, as you can see, consists of a rough flooring nailed to 2″x4″ sleepers anchored to the masonry floor. The rough sub-flooring can be covered with plywood; the latter in turn can be covered with either linoleum or sanded smooth and then painted.

The interior walls and ceilings can be covered with any of the many types of wallboard or with plywood. Vertical strips of wood paneling would also be suitable.

The stairs to the bedrooms need not be fancy. Two 2″x12″ stringers cut out for treads and risers and spiked to the partition studding will be perfectly adequate. The method of building stairs is covered in Chapter 16.

The interior trim—the trim around the interior of the doors and windows and at the baseboard—should be very simple. 1″x3″ stock fitted with a butt joint is quite suitable.

HIDEAWAY MATERIALS LIST

Material	Quantity	Dimensions
Mixed cement	19 cu. yds.	
2″ x 12″	24′	
2″ x 8″	3	16′
2″ x 6″	23	18′
	17	14′
2″ x 4″	13	18′
	83	16′
	36	10′
Flooring	413 board ft.	1″ x 6″
Shelving	50 board ft.	1″ x 6″
Entrance doors with frame and trim	1	3′0″ x 6′8″
	1	2′2″ x 6′8″
Interior doors with trim, jambs and stops	3	2′4″ x 6′8″
	1	2′0″ x 6′8″
Windows with frame and trim	9	4′2⅜″ x 3′1¾″
	3	3′2³⁄₁₆″ x 3′1¾″
	6	3′2³⁄₁₆″ x 18″

1″ x 4″, 103′
Roof sheathing, 620 sq. ft.
Roofing material, 620 sq. ft.
Building paper, 1,050 sq. ft.
Drop siding, 1,250 sq. ft.
Wallboard, 1,200 sq. ft.
Nails: 6d, 22 lbs; 8d, 45 lbs; 16d, 15 lbs; finish, 20 lbs; 4d, 36 lbs; 5d, 8 lbs
Hinges: brass, 6; interior, 8
Mortice locks, 6
2-ft. flue-tile, 12″ x 8″, 8
Common bricks, 1,000
Mortar, 14 cu. ft.
Chimney thimble
Clean-out door
8″ copper flashing, 16′
Paint: exterior, 9 gal.; interior enamel, 1 gal.

Space-heater
4″ Y branch
Clean-out plug
Sanitary T: 4″, 1; 4″ with 2″ tapp., 2
Tees, 5
Increaser
Elbows, 6
Traps, 3
Closet bend
5′ sections 4″-cast-iron soil pipe, 5
Galvanized pipe: 2″, 20′; 1½″, 30′
Kitchen sink
Lavatory
Stall shower
Water closet
Hot-water heater
Ceiling fixtures, 5
Ceiling fixtures, with pull chain, 2

Outside fixture
Convenience outlets, 11
Special outlet
Single switches, 6
Double switch
4″ outlet boxes with plates, 8
2½″ switch boxes with plates, 20
Cable connectors, 60

Fibre bushings, 60
Metal hangers, 7
Service head
Sill plate
Grounding bushing
Switch box
Entrance cable, 10′
No. 14 2-wire, 200′

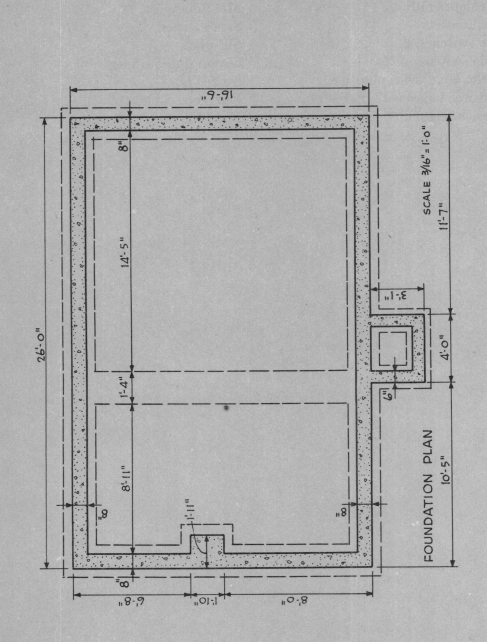

FOUNDATION PLAN

SCALE 3/16" = 1'-0"

Foundation Plan of the Vacation Hideaway

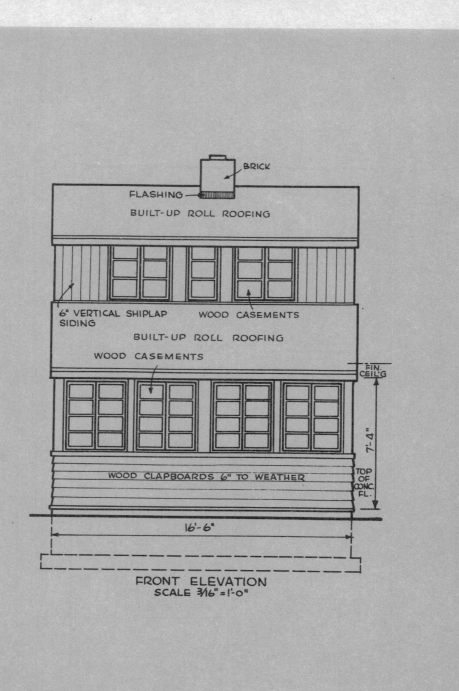

BRICK

FLASHING

BUILT-UP ROLL ROOFING

6" VERTICAL SHIPLAP SIDING

WOOD CASEMENTS

BUILT-UP ROLL ROOFING

WOOD CASEMENTS

FIN. CEIL'G

7'-4"

WOOD CLAPBOARDS 6" TO WEATHER

TOP OF CONC. FL.

16'-6"

FRONT ELEVATION
SCALE 3/16"=1'-0"

Front Elevation of the Vacation Hideaway

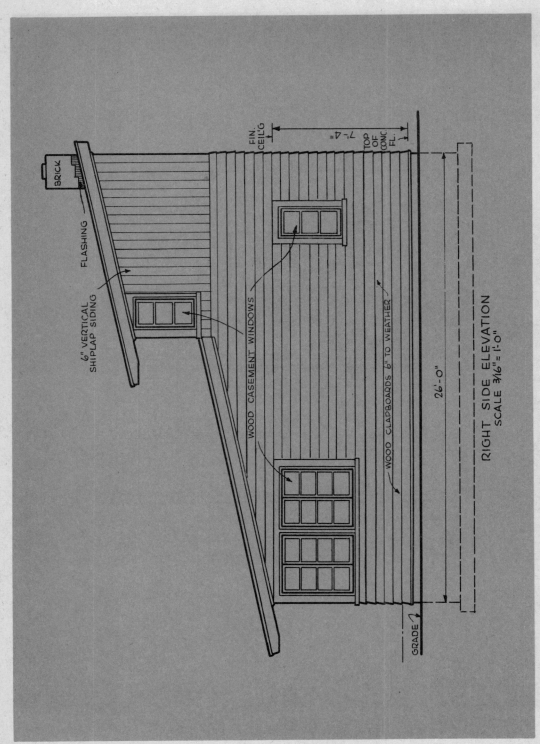

Right Side Elevation of the Vacation Hideaway

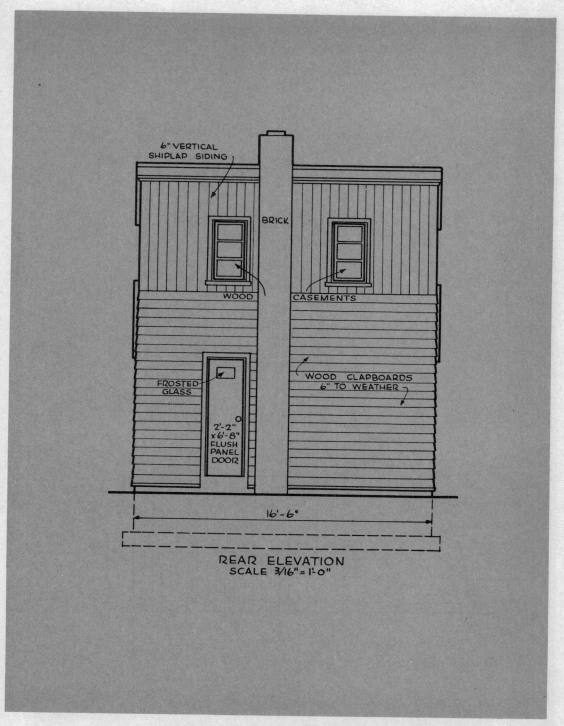

Rear Elevation of the Vacation Hideaway

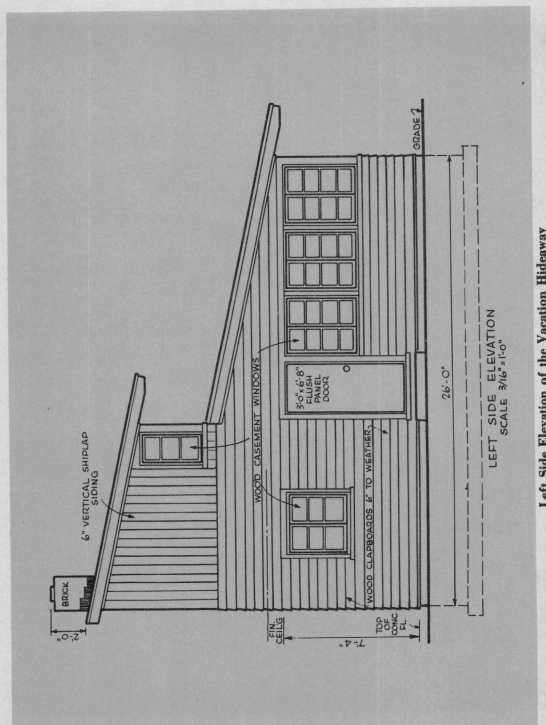

Left Side Elevation of the Vacation Hideaway

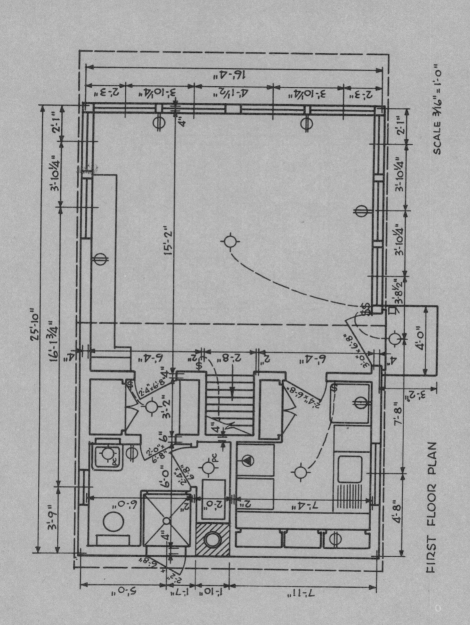

FIRST FLOOR PLAN

Floor Plan of the Vacation Hideaway: First Floor

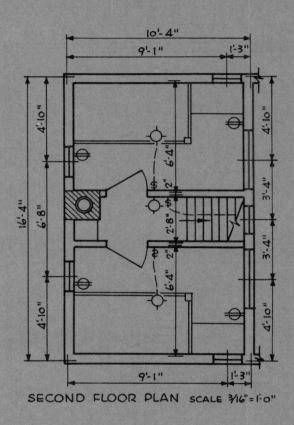

SECOND FLOOR PLAN SCALE 3/16"=1'-0"

Floor Plan of the Vacation Hideaway: Second Floor

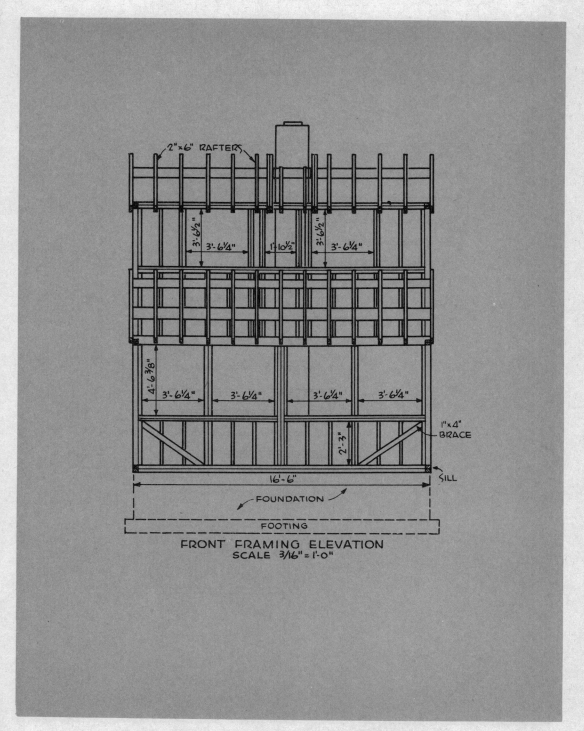

Front Framing Elevation of the Vacation Hideaway

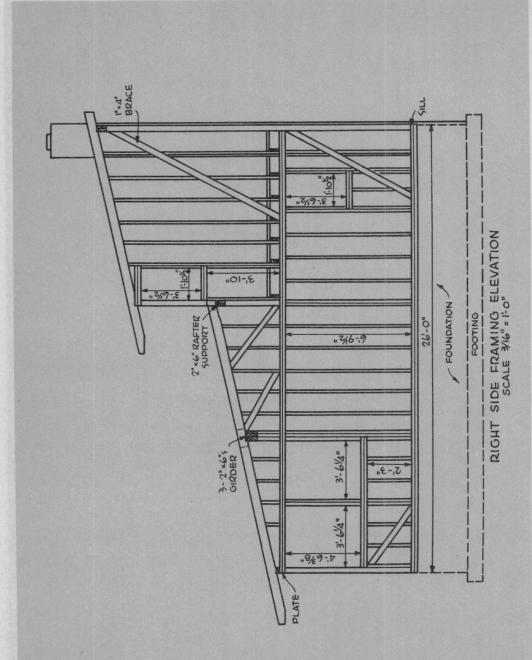

RIGHT SIDE FRAMING ELEVATION

SCALE 3/16" = 1'-0"

Right Side Framing Elevation of the Vacation Hideaway

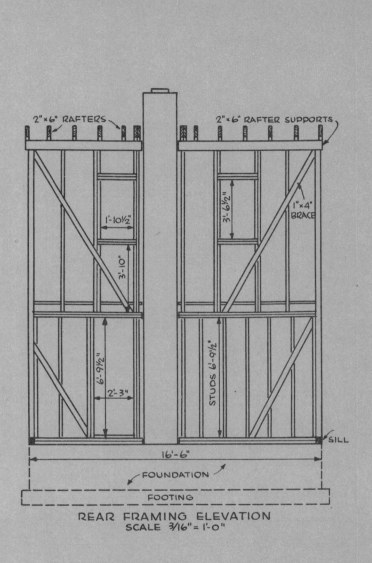

Rear Framing Elevation of the Vacation Hideaway

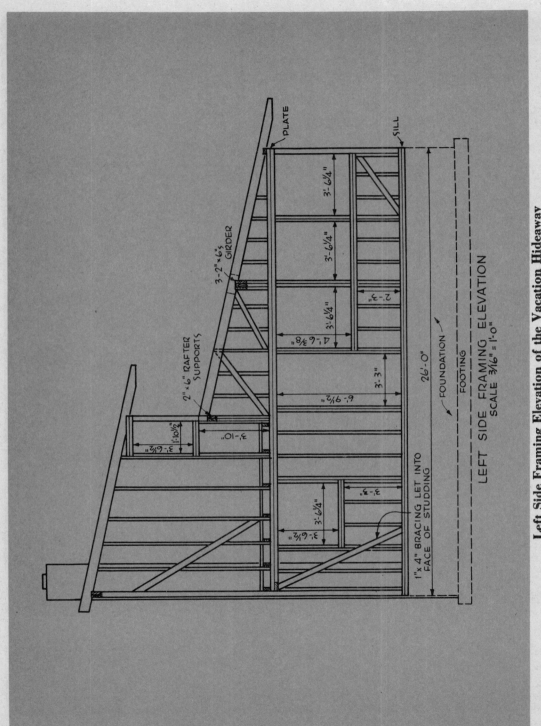

Left Side Framing Elevation of the Vacation Hideaway

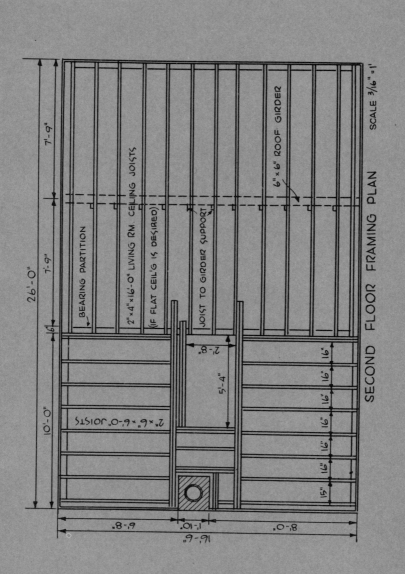

SECOND FLOOR FRAMING PLAN

SCALE 3/16" = 1'

Framing Plan of the Vacation Hideaway

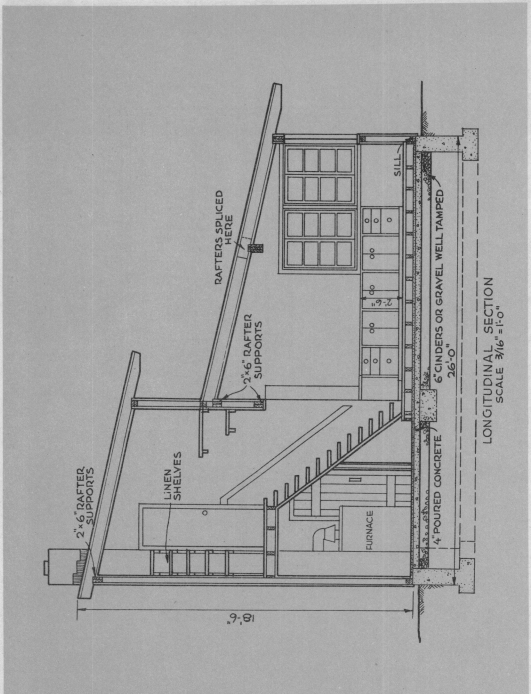

Longitudinal Section of the Vacation Hideaway

Chapter 28

A COTSWOLD COTTAGE

THIS cottage, like the Tudor cottage, is of English tradition. It is of such a design that it can be built in a thickly settled residential area or, like many of the English originals, it can stand alone in the countryside. In either case, this cottage has a knack for fitting in perfectly with its surroundings, and its definite English flavor will not make it appear out of place in a definitely American neighborhood.

Exterior Materials

The traditional design of this type of house calls for an exterior wall of stone, but masonry-blocks, bricks or stucco can also be used, just as is the case with the Tudor Cottage.

The house pictured in the plans in this book has the upper portion of the gable ends covered with sheets of exterior plywood with the joints running on the horizontal. Plywood is not the only material than can be used for this purpose. Bevel siding or shingles of either asbestos or wood will do nicely and, for that matter, so will stucco. The stonework or masonry-blocks can, if you wish, be brought right up to the roof peak, but this complicates construction considerably. Moreover,

many persons find that a house made entirely of masonry or stone is a little too massive in its appearance and often looks more like a fortress than a home. A little woodwork at the gable ends will help to soften the appearance of the house considerably.

The Floor Plan

As you can easily see from the floor plan, this is a very compact house. The first floor contains two good-size bedrooms, a living room, a kitchen and a bathroom. As you will note, while the over-all dimensions of the house are not great, the rooms are all rather spacious and there is ample closet and storage space at convenient locations.

One thing that will immediately catch your eye is the fact that the kitchen is located at the front of the house rather than at the rear. The front entrance runs past the kitchen into a hall that leads directly into the living room, which is located at the rear of the house. Off to the left of the hall near the bathroom is a coat closet. Locating the kitchen at the front of the house permits the construction of the large bay window at the back of the living room, which, aside from increasing the size of the living room, allows the entrance of a maximum amount of light and air without disturbing the privacy of the household.

The living room must, of course, also serve as a dining room, and for this purpose there is a door to the kitchen on the opposite side from the hall so that one can get directly from the kitchen to the living-dining room.

In the back of the kitchen is a utility room for the heater and hot-water equipment. This room eliminates the need for any basement at all unless one is required for a game room or laundry. If you decide to have a basement, the heating equipment can be moved into the basement and the utility room can be turned into a breakfast bar.

The side door between the kitchen and the living room opens on the breezeway and this will serve as a back entrance to the house for deliveries.

The stairs off the hall on the first floor lead to the attic. The attic can be converted into a bedroom with bath. This attic room will get plenty of light and air by means of the three dormer windows in the roof and the large window in the left-hand gable end.

The area over the garage and breezeway can be used for storage purposes. The dormer window over the garage will provide the necessary degree of light and ventilation for this storage space.

The dormer windows at the rear of the house are each of a different style, one having a peaked roof while the other has a shed-type roof.

Windows

The Right Side Elevation shows clearly the relation of the garage and breezeway roof to the main house roof as well as the location of the four dormer windows. From this plan and the Left Side Elevation plan, you can also see the distance that the large bay window at the rear of the living room extends out past the outside wall. This window should be constructed at the same time that the outside walls are being erected. The remaining windows can be put in after the house framework or masonry walls have been completed. All windows are of the casement type, either metal or wood, and, when possible, windows with small panes of glass should be used, as this is in keeping with the Cotswold tradition.

Garage and Breezeway

To simplify the construction of this house, when it is to be made out of either masonry or stone, the breezeway and garage should be constructed at the same time as the main house. Many persons have made the mistake of building the house first and then trying to add the garage and breezeway. This is not too practical when masonry is used because it will be necessary to take down some of the finished work so that the new work can be joined to it with interlocking bonds. If the house is made of wood, this is unnecessary.

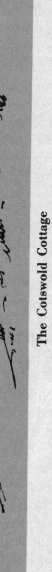

The Cotswold Cottage

Foundation

The type of footing and foundation required for this house will, of course, depend on the type of materials used for construction. They must be wide enough to carry the weight of the walls and, therefore, will be wider if masonry is used than if the house is built of wood and covered with stucco. The footing for the main bearing partition should run directly under the partitions between the bedroom and living room and between the second bedroom and the stairway. With this arrangement, you will have relatively short spans for the joists and, therefore, you will save on both material costs and labor.

If the house is to have a full basement, support for the main bearing partition can be made out of masonry-blocks, which will also divide the basement into the required number of rooms. Due to the location of the stairs, you will need a doorway through this wall to allow for entrance into the portion of the basement directly under the two bedrooms and bath. The top of this opening should be covered with a reinforced concrete lintel to provide the necessary support for the floor joists.

Excavation for the breezeway and garage should be done at the same time as that for the main house. The finished floor of the breezeway should be one step below the finished floor of the house and the garage floor should be one step below the floor of the breezeway.

The fireplace footing should be installed at the same time as the other footings. If you plan to have a basement game room, it is quite practicable to have a fireplace here as well as in the living room. The basement fireplace should be located directly under the living-room fireplace and a flue for the heating system should be incorporated in the chimney.

Use of Timbers

For those who are interested in keeping strictly to the Cotswold tradition, it is suggested that the top of the masonry walls be capped with old timbers. These run around the four walls of the house and around the garage and breezeway too. The ends of the breezeway can also be framed with heavy timbers, as is indicated on the Front and Rear Elevations. It is often possible to pick up timbers of a suitable size and age from second-hand lumber dealers or from house-wreckers. There are many old barns in this country that contain fine hand-hewn beams, and these can often be purchased for a small sum. A little cleaning up and some staining will be all that is required to make them ready for use.

Joists and Rafters

The ceiling joists for the second floor can rest directly on the cap of heavy timbers. If no timbers are used, a wood sill should be installed at the top of the wall to provide a nailing base and a level surface for the joists to rest upon.

From here on out, the work is done with wood. The ceiling joists should be 2" x 8"s if the attic is to be used for living purposes. The joists over the breezeway and garage can be reduced to 2″ x 6″s if the area is to be used for limited storage. Roof rafters can be 2″ x 6″s, providing collar beams are installed. If the rafters are to be without collar beams or some other type of brace, they should be increased to 2″ x 8″s.

Once the roof has been framed and covered with sheathing, the windows should be installed. The home-builder should be reminded that if masonry walls are used, it is absolutely essential that he have the size of openings required for the windows selected before the walls are put up. In many instances, openings have been left in walls for windows that are no longer in stock; the only alternatives in this case are either to have windows made to order, an expensive undertaking at best, or to undo the work and remake the openings to the required size.

The joints between window frames and outside walls must be carefully flashed so there is no chance that air or moisture will penetrate to the finished wall surface.

The Roof

The roof of the house can be covered with slate, wood or asbestos shingles. Wood shingles should be stained before they are installed because the light shade of new shingles is hardly in keeping with the Cotswold style of architecture. Asbestos shingles that meet the requirements for this style can be purchased, and slate, of course, is the perfect roofing except for its high cost. An interesting little touch can be added by not coating the copper flashing used on the roof and at other points. In time the copper will tarnish to a greenish color that gives the house the appearance of age.

If the house is to be stuccoed, it is well worth the trouble to break up some of the large wall surfaces with heavy timbers. These beams should be spiked through the sheathing into the studding. Timbers are especially desirable along the gable ends, where they can be arranged to form a brace in addition to making the wall look more interesting.

The Interior

As far as the interior walls go, either plaster, plasterboard, wallboard or some type of wood paneling is suitable. The living room will look very well, of course, if it is paneled with wood— either plywood or planks. The living-room floor can be of wood as well, either hardwood or plank; linoleum of the right shade and pattern is also acceptable.

Too much wood in a home is not always desirable, and it will probably be best to use in the other rooms either plaster or some other form of dry-wall construction that can be papered or painted. The kitchen and bathroom walls can be covered with one of the many wall materials that are suitable where color and an ability to withstand soiling and constant cleaning are required.

Floors for the bedrooms can be of wood or linoleum, and the latter can be used for both kitchen and bathroom. The utility room should be covered with asbestos board on walls and ceiling since a fire-resistant material is required in this area.

The fireplace in the living room can be made out of bricks, but many persons may prefer native stone with a heavy oak mantel. Of course, the outside dimensions of the fireplace cannot be increased too much without cutting off the entrance from the hall into the living room.

Hardware for this house should be either wrought iron or solid brass. The front door should be of oak and the side door from kitchen to breezeway should be a panel door.

COTSWOLD COTTAGE MATERIALS LIST

Material	Quantity	Dimensions
Mixed cement, or	61 cu. yds.	
Concrete blocks	2,500	
2″ x 10″	20	14′
	23	12′
	11	10′
2″ x 8″	55	18′
	18	14′
	14	12′
	13	10′
2″ x 6″	4	18′
	41	16′
	34	14′
2″ x 4″	29	16′
	60	12′
2″ x 2″	55	16′
1″ x 6″	2	16′
	3,972 board ft.	
1″ x 3″	768′	
Shelving	100′	1″ x 6″
Beveled siding	681 board ft.	6″
		Rough Openings
Window with frame and trim	1	3′9″ x 4′
	2	2′3″ x 1′6″
	2	3′9″ x 2′
	1	3′9″ x 3′6″
	1	3′6″ x 2′6″

Material	Quantity	Rough Openings
Window with frame and trim	3	2'6" x 4'6"
	4	3'6" x 2'3"
	1	1'3" x 4'3"
	3	4'6" x 2'9"
	4	2'3" x 2'3"
	3	4'6" x 3'

Roofing material, 1,500 sq. ft.
Building paper, 576 sq. ft.
Insulation, 2,405 sq. ft.
Copper flashing, 208 sq. ft.
Wallboard, 3,497, sq. ft.
Base mold, 328'
¾" plywood, 1,141 sq. ft.
Linoleum, 1,141 sq. ft.
Exterior doors with frame and trim, 3
Interior doors with trim, jambs and stops, 17
Nails: 6d bevel siding, 10 lbs; 8d, 72 lbs; 8d furring, 10 lbs; finishing, 6 lbs; 10d, 60 lbs; 16d, 20 lbs: 20d, 25 lbs; 4d, 90 lbs; 5d, 15 lbs
Louvers, 2
Gutters, 60'
Flight box stairs, 2
Hinges: brass, 9; interior, 34
Mortice locks, 13
Paint: exterior, 6 gal.; water-thinned, 11 gal.; interior enamel, 2½ gal.
2-ft. flue-tile: 12" x 12", 7; 12" x 8", 7
Common bricks, 2,000
Mortar, 1 cu. yd.
Chimney thimble
Firebricks, 90
Fireclay, 30 lbs
Clean-out door
Hearth assembly
Mixed cement, 2 cu. ft.
Damper

Angleiron: 42", 1; 36", 1
Hot-water heating system
4" Y branch, 3
Clean-out Plug
Sanitary T: 4", 1; 4" with 2" tapp., 3; 2", 2
Tees, 1½", 8; ¾", 12
4"-2" reducer
2" ¼-bend
Elbows: 1½", 9; ¾", 12
Traps, 3
Increaser
Decreaser
Closet bend
5' sections cast-iron soil pipe: 4", 8; 2", 15
Galvanized pipe: 2", 12'; 1½", 100'; ¾", 270'
Kitchen sink
Stall shower
Bathtub
Laundry Tubs, 2
Lavatory, 2
Water closet
Medicine closets, 2
Towel racks, 5
Toothbrush holders, 2
Soap dishes, 2
Hot-water heater
Ceiling fixtures, 13
Ceiling fixtures with pull chain, 3
Wall fixtures, 2

Outside fixture
Single switches, 12
Double switches, 2
Convenience outlets, 20
4″ outlet boxes with plates, 16
2½″ outlet boxes with plates, 19
Door bell and button
Cable connectors and bushings, 150

Metal hangers, 16
Switch box
Service head
Sill plate
Grounding bushing
Entrance cable, 16′
No. 14 2-wire, 300′
No. 12 wire, 50′

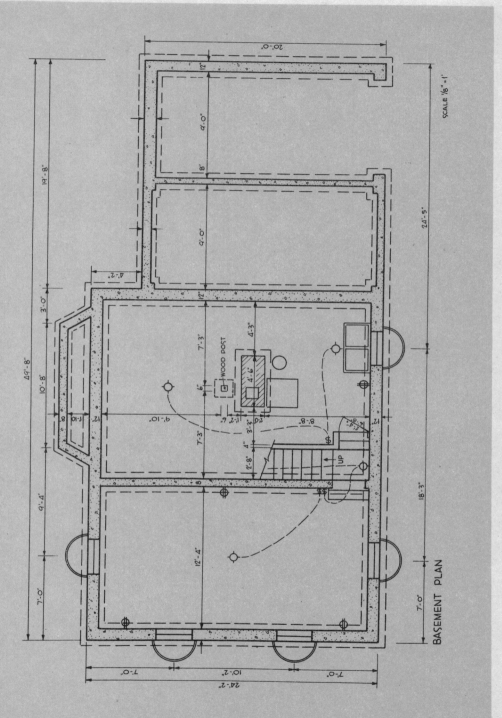

BASEMENT PLAN

Foundation Plan of the Cotswold Cottage

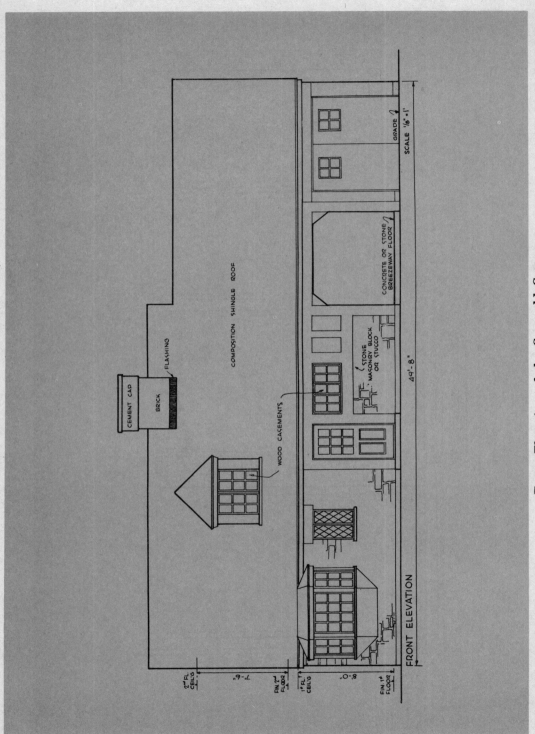

Front Elevation of the Cotswold Cottage

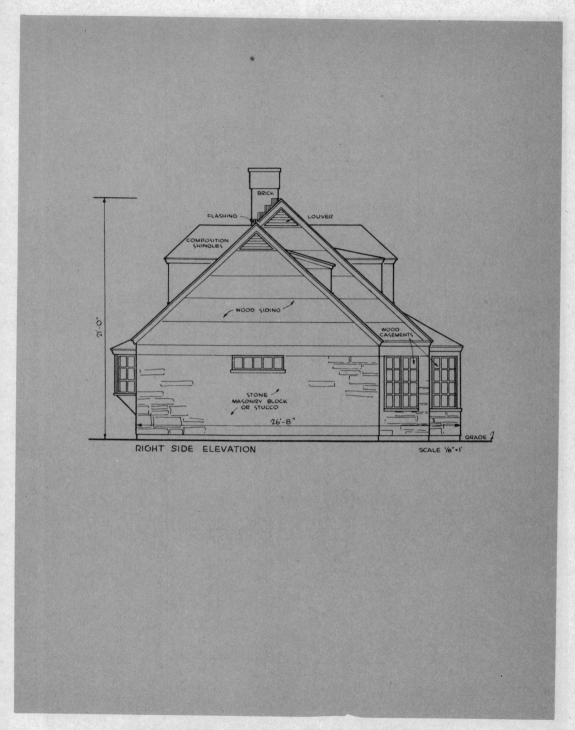

Right Side Elevation of the Cotswold Cottage

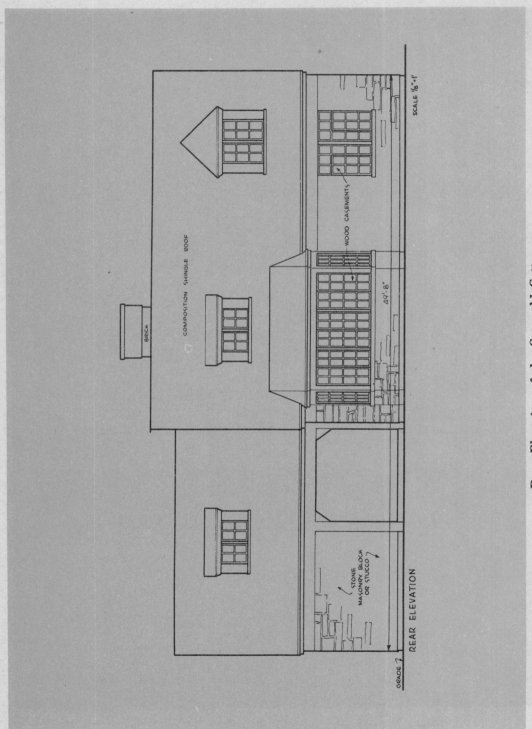

Rear Elevation of the Cotswold Cottage

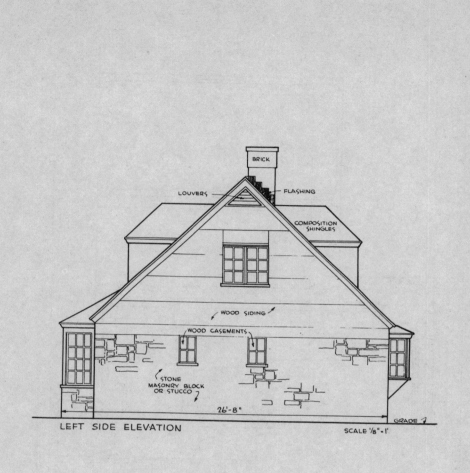

LEFT SIDE ELEVATION

SCALE 1/8" = 1'

Left Side Elevation of the Cotswold Cottage

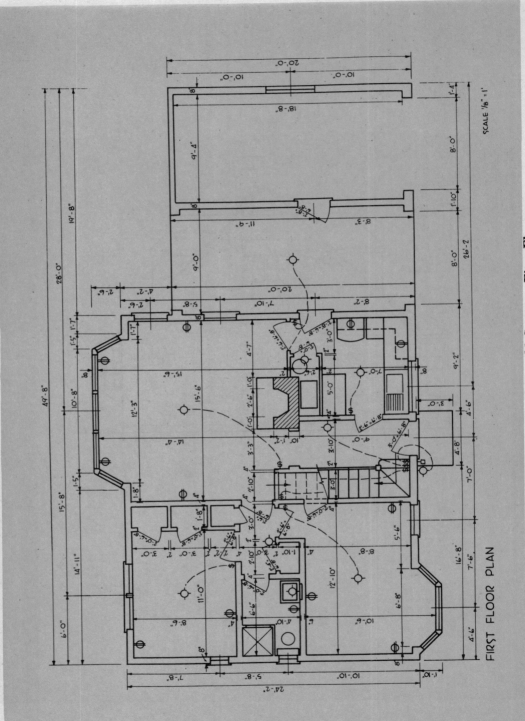

FIRST FLOOR PLAN

SCALE ⅛ = 1

Floor Plan of the Cotswold Cottage: First Floor

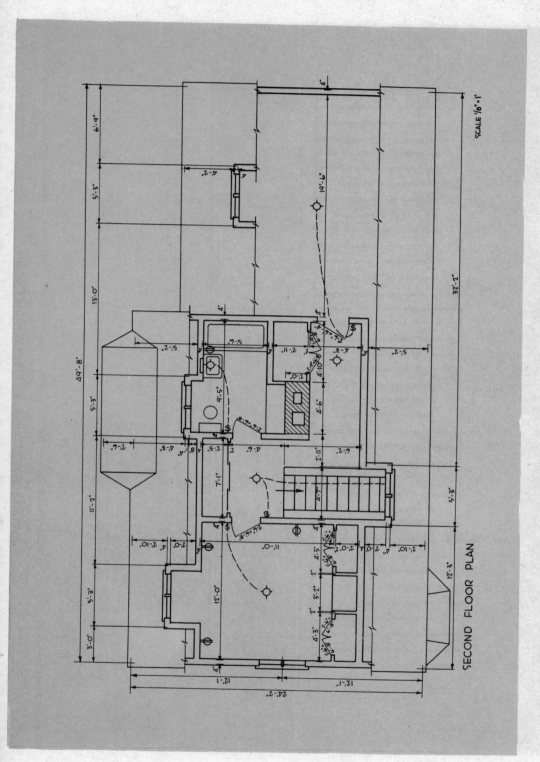

SECOND FLOOR PLAN

SCALE 1/8" = 1'

Floor Plan of the Cotswold Cottage: Second Floor

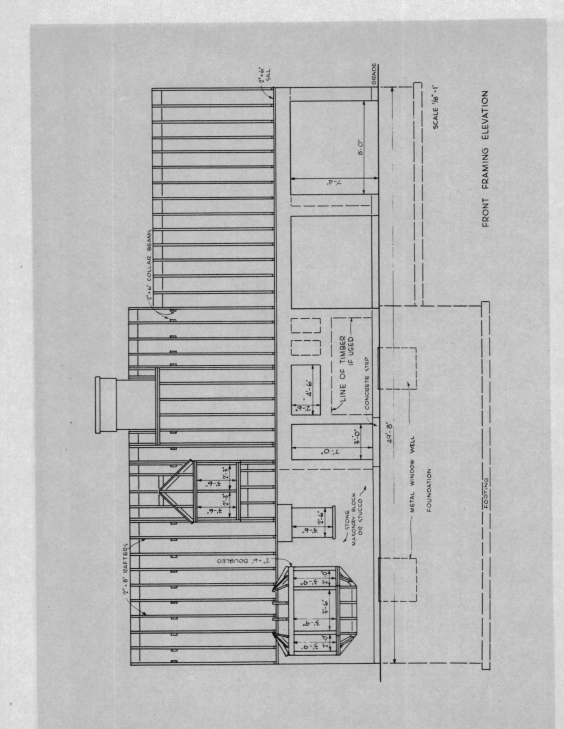

Front Framing Elevation of the Cotswold Cottage

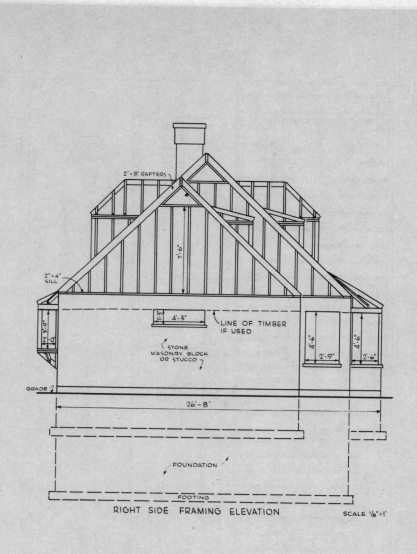

RIGHT SIDE FRAMING ELEVATION

SCALE ⅛"=1'

Right Framing Elevation of the Cotswold Cottage

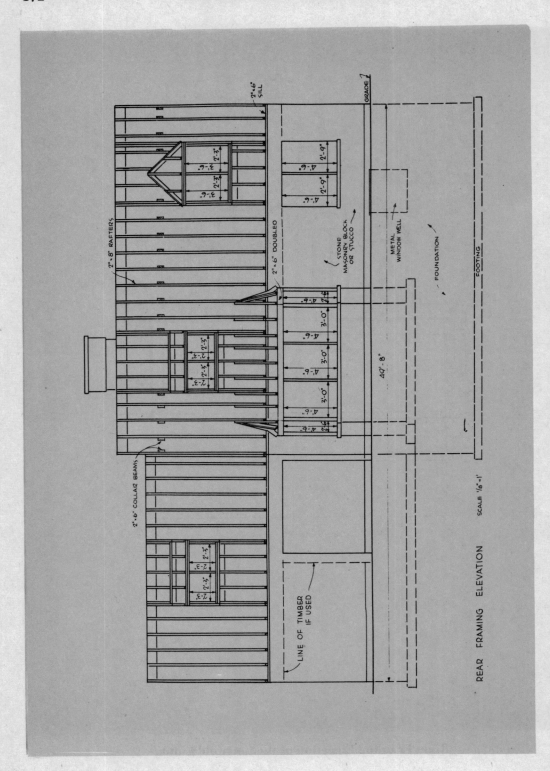

Rear Framing Elevation of the Cotswold Cottage

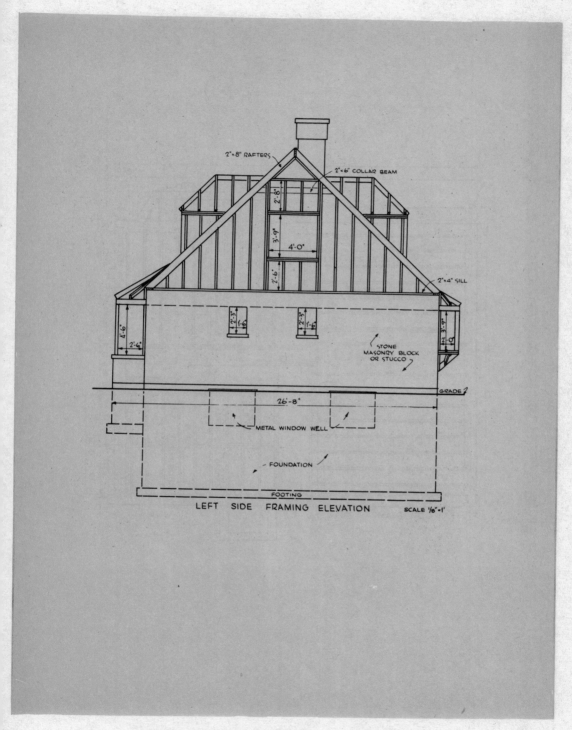

Left Framing Elevation of the Cotswold Cottage

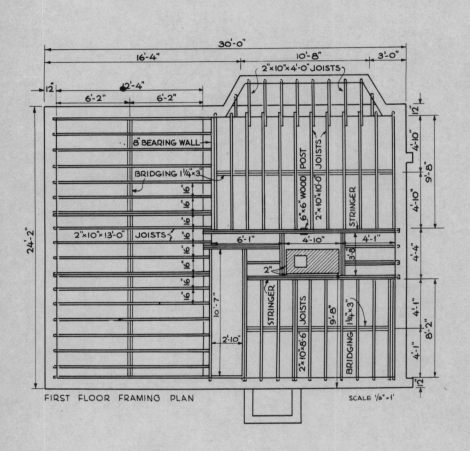

FIRST FLOOR FRAMING PLAN

SCALE ⅛"=1'

First Floor Framing Plan of the Cotswold Cottage

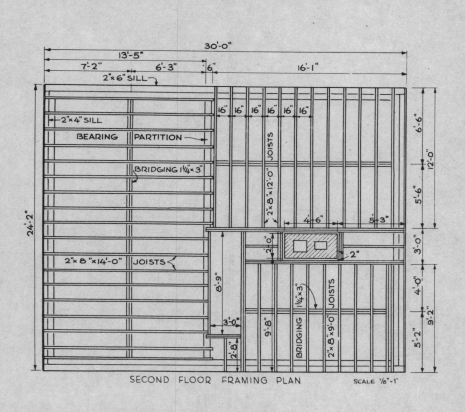

Second Floor Framing Plan of the Cotswold Cottage

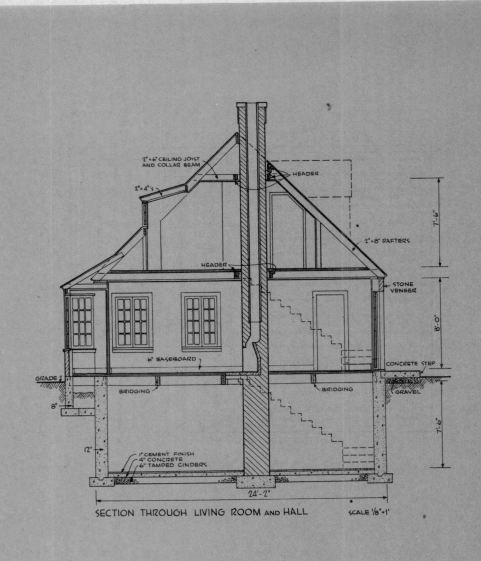

SECTION THROUGH LIVING ROOM AND HALL   SCALE ⅛"=1'

Section of the Cotswold Cottage

Chapter 29

A TUDOR COTTAGE

SINCE its origin in England during the reign of the House of Tudor, this particular style of architecture has been popular for both country and suburban homes. Tudor architecture was brought to this country by the early settlers, and many fine examples of it can be found here in both old and modern homes.

One of the most outstanding features of Tudor architecture is the feeling of permanence that it produces. The massive walls of masonry or stucco with exposed heavy timbers give one the feeling that here is a house that will stand for many a year.

The Tudor Cottage covered in this section will make an ideal country or suburban home for the average family. While it is only one story, the first floor provides ample space for two good-size bedrooms along with a spacious living room and dining room as well as a kitchen, a bathroom and several large closets.

The large bay windows help increase the size of the two bedrooms and the living room considerably. In fact, the bay window in the living room is large enough to serve as a dining alcove, so that the dining-room table and chairs

can be left in place without detracting from the over-all size of the living room proper.

The utility room off the kitchen provides sufficient space for the furnace and hot-water heater, so there is no need for a basement of any sort, unless one is desired for a game room or for additional storage space.

Choice of Materials

As far as the construction of this type of house goes, the builder is somewhat limited in his choice of materials. Wood siding or wood or asphalt shingles are not satisfactory. Native field stone is excellent, but the work goes rather slowly. Cut stone can be used with very good results, but this will run up construction costs considerably.

Special masonry blocks can also be used for the job, and they can be laid up in coursed ashlar or random ashlar or a combination of the two. They are much less expensive than the cut stone and can be laid up a good deal more easily. After they are in place, they can be painted.

Ordinary masonry blocks can also be used and, after the wall is finished, they can be coated with stucco, which is marked off before it is hard to give the appearance of a wall of stone. Still another method of construction is to build with masonry blocks and then cover them with a veneer of stone.

Brick veneer is also suitable for the outside walls of the Tudor Cottage. In this type of construction, the house frame is built out of wood and then covered with wood sheathing and waterproof paper. After this has been done, a veneer one brick thick is laid up and tied to the house framework by means of metal straps.

Another method of building is to use stucco for the walls. Before the stucco is applied, the wall can be divided up into sections by attaching heavy timbers to the house framework. While these timbers will give the impression that they provide structural strength to the house, actually they do not, and therefore it is possible to use rather light-weight stock, just thick enough, in fact, so that it will stick out beyond the finish surface of the stucco. The outside face of these timbers can be worked over with a hatchet to give the appearance that the wood was hand-hewn.

Windows should be of the casement type, of either metal or wood, with small-size panes of glass. Lead windows are very much in keeping with the Tudor style but, of course, they are more expensive than some of the other windows available.

The perfect material for the roof is slate, but this is not only very expensive as compared with other roofing materials but is also difficult for anyone other than a skilled roofer to install satisfactorily. Asbestos or asphalt shingles made to resemble a slate roof will be adequate in most cases.

If stone or concrete blocks are to be used for the outside walls, the gable ends of the house can be covered with some other type of siding since to cut stone or blocks to go under the end rafters and produce a tight fit would be difficult and time consuming. The house shown here has its gable ends covered with plywood or wide boards with the horizontal joints exposed.

Foundations

Before the footing and foundations can be installed, you must decide what sort of siding you are going to use. If you select either stone, blocks or blocks with stone veneer, the footings and foundations must be wide enough to carry the load. The minimum thickness for a stone wall is 16", and for one made out of blocks, 8". If you plan to use brick veneer, the foundation walls must extend far enough beyond the house framework and sheathing to provide a base on which to lay up the bricks. This is important because unless the bricks are set on a solid base, the wall will not last long since the house framework cannot support it.

At the same time that the foundations are installed, a footing for the main bearing partition and one for the fireplace and chimney should be installed.

The Tudor Cottage

Framing

If you are using brick veneer or stucco for the outside walls, the construction of the house framework is not very difficult. The sills, the walls, the main bearing partition and the roof are framed exactly as if the house were to be covered with wood siding. Use 2″ x 10″s for the floor joists; the ceiling joists can be 2″ x 8″s, and 2″ x 6″s will be suitable for the roof rafters if collar beams are installed at the midpoint between the rafters. If no collar beams are used, the rafters should be increased to 2″ x 8″s.

Windows

After the walls have been framed, the openings for the doors and windows can be cut and the framework for the bay windows can be constructed. Because of the great width of these windows, their tops should be constructed out of 2″ x 6″s on edge. These beams will provide sufficient support so that there will be no chance of the roof's sagging. After the bay windows have been framed, the sheathing should be applied.

Building with concrete masonry blocks should present no great difficulty except for framing the large bay window that is on the right side of the house. This, as you will note from the Right Side Elevation, has a base constructed with masonry, and, therefore, this base must be built at the same time as the outside walls of the house. The other bay windows are constructed with wood, and your main problem here will be fastening their framework into the masonry. This can be done with masonry anchors.

If you wish to save time but also spend some extra money, you can buy complete windows of this type that require no work other than installing the unit in the wall opening.

Building with Stone or Blocks

Building with stone, even cut stone, will prove much more difficult than with masonry blocks because it will be virtually impossible to get the inside face of the wall perfectly flush and, therefore, the furring for the interior walls will have to be set up plumb and then fastened into the mortar joints between the stone with masonry anchors.

You will also have to leave openings in the wall into which the floor joists and ceiling joists will fit. These joists must be spaced 16″ apart and must be level with each other. Be sure to cut the end of each joist that fits into the masonry at a bevel, so that if the joist should fall, it will not damage the wall above it.

While you may be able to get hold of stone long enough to serve as lintels or headers over the small windows, it is doubtful if you can find anything along this line to serve for the large bay windows. What you can do in this case is to use two reinforced-concrete lintels. They should be set at the rear of the window opening and you can use thin stones for veneer in front of the lintels.

Once the house frame has been built and the roof is on, the interior wall partitions can go up.

The location of these is shown on the first-floor plan.

Insulation and Flashing

Insulation should be installed on the four outside walls; this is especially important if stone has been used. Be sure that the insulation does not come into direct contact with the masonry because if it does, there is a chance that it will be damaged by moisture's coming through a leak in the wall.

After the bay windows have been constructed, but before the siding is installed, the bottom of the windows and the joints between the sides of the bay windows and the house wall must be flashed with metal flashing to eliminate the possibility that moisture will enter at the seams. Joints between the window frame and masonry walls can be made tight by first packing the seam with oakum and then using caulking compound. Flashing at the base of the window should be bent over and turned into one of the horizontal mortar joints in the masonry.

Keeping the Tudor Style

When finishing off this type of house, care must be taken not to ruin its style. As far as the hardware is concerned, the most suitable type is rough wrought iron. This is coated with asphaltum paint, which is black and in keeping with the design of the house. Solid brass hardware is also suitable.

The front door should be of oak and rather heavy. It can be given a stain to darken the wood and then a coating of spar varnish to protect it from the weather. Woodwork around the outside window frames and door frames should be treated in a similar fashion. Where possible, woodwork should be left natural, with, of course, a protective coating of varnish.

Exterior fixtures, such as the front-door electric light, should be selected to fit in with the architectural style. Fixtures of suitable types are on the market and are no more expensive than other kinds.

In considering the interior of the house, do not think that it has to be dark. Light colors or natural wood are quite proper. In the strictest tradition of Tudor architecture, of course, the living room is best finished off with a hardwood floor of oak or planks and walls covered with wood paneling.

An excellent material to use for the living-room walls is grained plywood, which, when stained, resembles very closely the type of walls found in the original Tudor homes. A rough-textured plaster wall, however, is likewise very effective, and plaster can also be used with good results on the ceiling.

The fireplace opening in the living room may be of Tudor design, of course, but a conventional type of fireplace is perfectly suitable under most conditions.

The bedrooms should be finished off for comfort and cheerfulness and need not by any means follow the Tudor style. The same holds true for the bathroom and kitchen, which should, in fact, be finished in a modern fashion.

Do not use ultra-modern furniture or furnishings if you can possibly avoid them, because they will clash with the house itself and the effect of both will be ruined. This does not mean, of course, that only heavy, massive, Tudor furniture can be used, but you should steer clear of too much present day, modern furniture.

Interior woodwork in the living room and halls can be stained. Doors can be either of the panel or flush type, but the flush is more in keeping with the general style.

Interior hardware, with the exception of the bathroom and kitchen, should be wrought iron or solid brass.

TUDOR COTTAGE MATERIALS LIST

Material	Quantity	Dimensions
Mixed cement	4.5 cu. yds.	
Concrete blocks	1,406	
2″ x 10″	18	14′
	22	16′
2″ x 8″	6	12′
	18	14′
	21	16′
	46	18′
2″ x 6″	19	14′
2″ x 4″	43	16′
2″ x 2″	32	16′
1″ x 6″	2	16′
Sheathing	2,359 board ft.	1″ x 6″
Beveled siding	300 board ft.	1″ x 6″
Shelving	100′	1″ x 6″
Copper flashing	50′	24″
Entrance doors with frame and trim	2	7′0″ x 3′3″
Windows with frame and trim	2	2′4″ x 4′6″
	3	3′3″ x 4′6″
	2	3′3″ x 3′3″
	3	1′8″ x 2′6″
	4	2′0″ x 3′3″
	1	3′4″ x 2′6″
	1	2′9″ x 4′6″
	1	4′6″ x 7′2″

1″ x 3″, 288′

Building paper, 250 sq. ft.

Roofing material, 700 sq. ft.

Flooring, 600 sq. ft.

Insulation, 1,400 sq. ft.

Wallboard, 1,520 sq. ft.

Base mold, 173′

Nails: 4d, 42 lbs; 5d, 9 lbs; 6d, 8 lbs; 8d, 7 lbs; 8d finishing, 3 lbs; 10d, 57 lbs; 16d, 15 lbs; 20d, 25 lbs

Louvers, 2

Gutters, 60′

Interior doors with trim, jambs and stops, 8

Hinges: brass, 6; interior, 24

Mortice locks, 10

Paint: exterior, 3 gal.; water-thinned, 5 gal.; interior enamel, 1½ gal.

Ceiling fixtures, 5

Ceiling fixture with pull chain

Wall fixtures, 2

Outside fixture

Single switches, 5

Double switch

Convenience outlets, 13

Special outlet

4″ outlet boxes with plates, 6

2½″ outlet boxes with plates, 20

Cable connectors, 60

Fibre bushings, 60

Metal hangers, 6

Doorbells and buttons, 2

Switch box

Service head

Sill plate

Grounding bushing

Entrance cable, 16′

No. 14 2-wire, 250′

No. 12 wire, 50′

No. 6 wire, 30′

Hot-water heating system

Common bricks, 1,800

Mortar, 1 cu. yd.

2-ft. flue-tile: 12″ x 12″, 6; 12″ x 8″, 6

Clean-out door

Firebricks, 90

Fireclay, 30 lbs

Hearth assembly

Mixed cement, 2 cu. ft.

Damper

Angleirons: 42″, 1; 36″, 1

4″ Y branch, 2

Clean-out plug

Sanitary T: 4″, 1; 4″ with 2″ tapp., 2; 2″, 2

2″ ¼-bends, 2

4″-2″ reducer

Increaser

Closet bend

Traps, 3

Elbows: 1½″, 3; ½″, 6

Tees: 1½″, 3; ½″, 6

Kitchen sink

Shower stall

Water closet

Lavatory

Medicine closet

Towel racks, 2

Toothbrush holder

Glass holder

Soap dish

Hot-water heater

5′-sections cast-iron soil pipe: 4″, 7; 2″, 6

Galvanized pipe: 1½″, 60′; ¾″, 100′; ½″, 30′

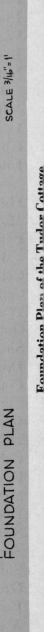

FOUNDATION PLAN

Foundation Plan of the Tudor Cottage

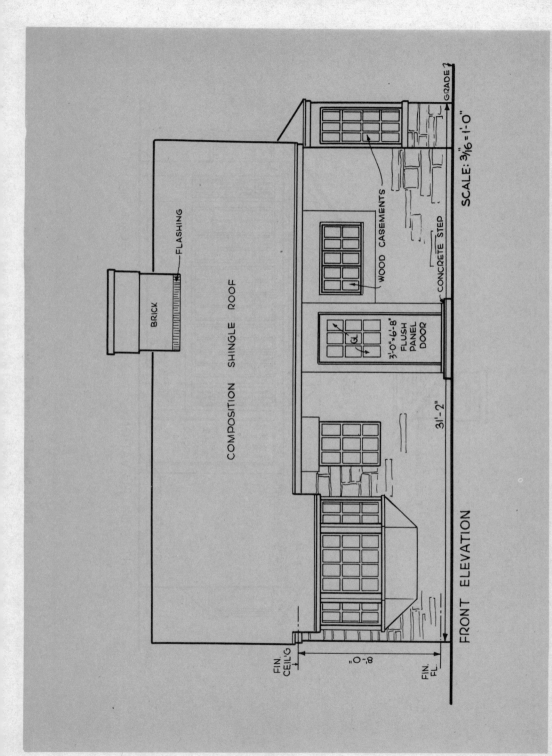

Front Elevation of the Tudor Cottage

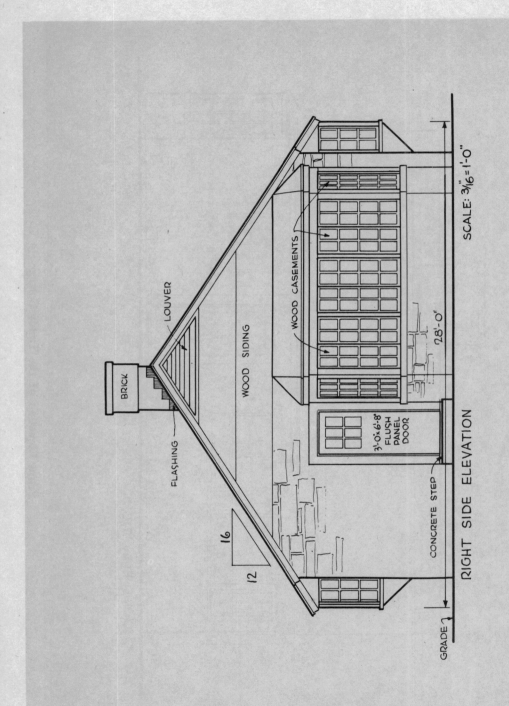

Right Side Elevation of the Tudor Cottage

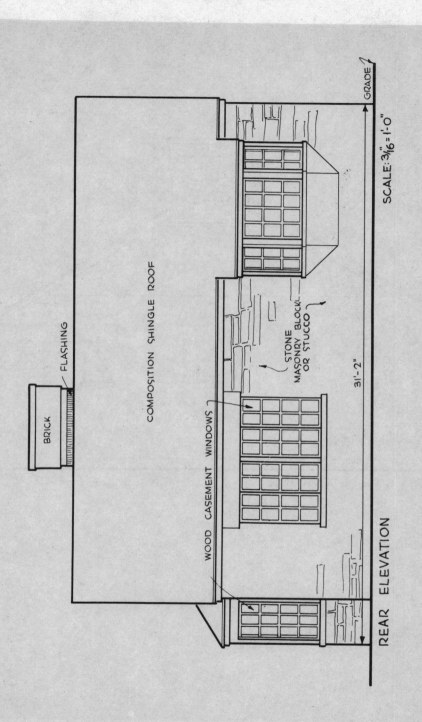

Rear Elevation of the Tudor Cottage

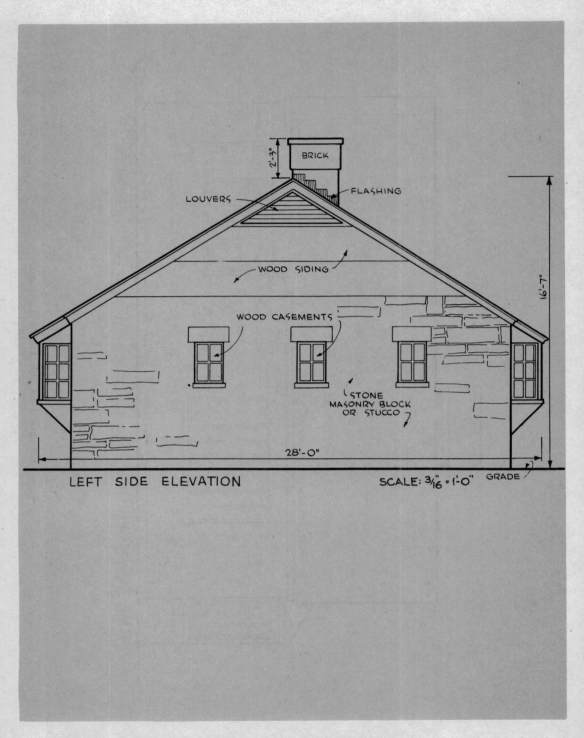

Left Side Elevation of the Tudor Cottage

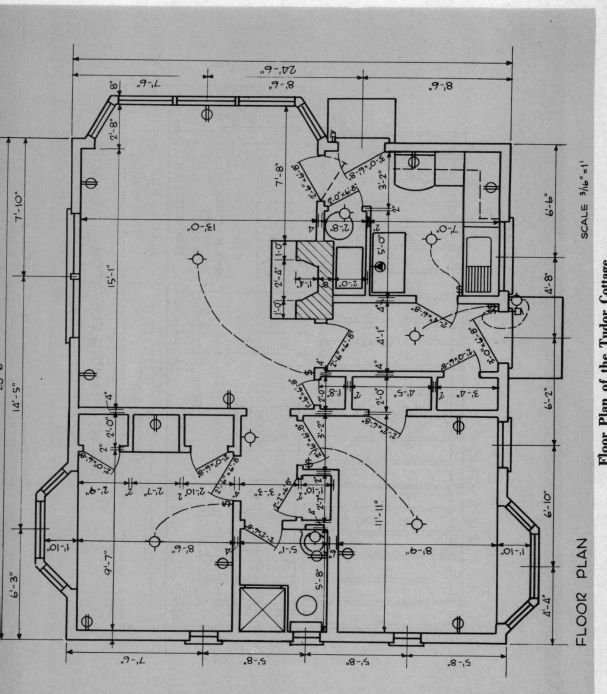

Floor Plan of the Tudor Cottage

FLOOR PLAN

SCALE 3/16"=1'

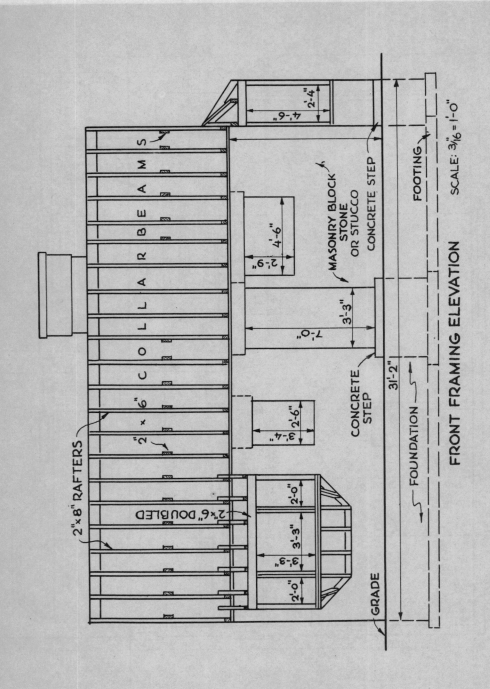

FRONT FRAMING ELEVATION

SCALE: 3/16" = 1'-0"

Front Framing Elevation of the Tudor Cottage

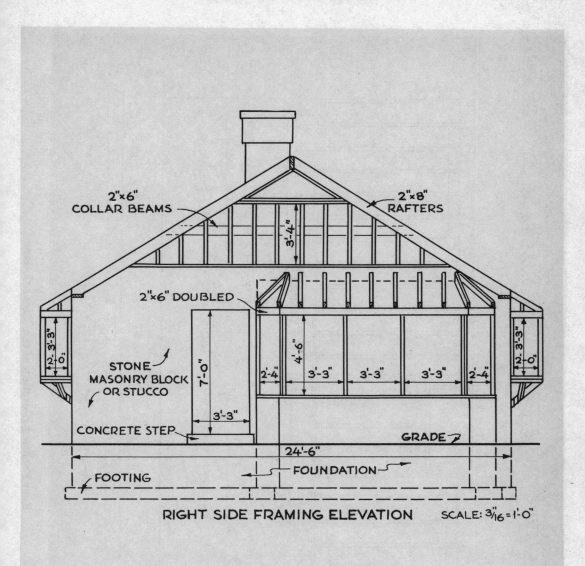

2"×6"
COLLAR BEAMS

2"×8"
RAFTERS

3'-4"

2"×6" DOUBLED

STONE
MASONRY BLOCK
OR STUCCO

3'-3"
2'-0"

7'-0"

4'-6"

2'-4"   3'-3"   3'-3"   3'-3"   2'-4"

3'-3"
2'-0"

CONCRETE STEP

3'-3"

GRADE

24'-6"

FOOTING

FOUNDATION

RIGHT SIDE FRAMING ELEVATION   SCALE: 3/16"=1'-0"

Right Framing Elevation of the Tudor Cottage

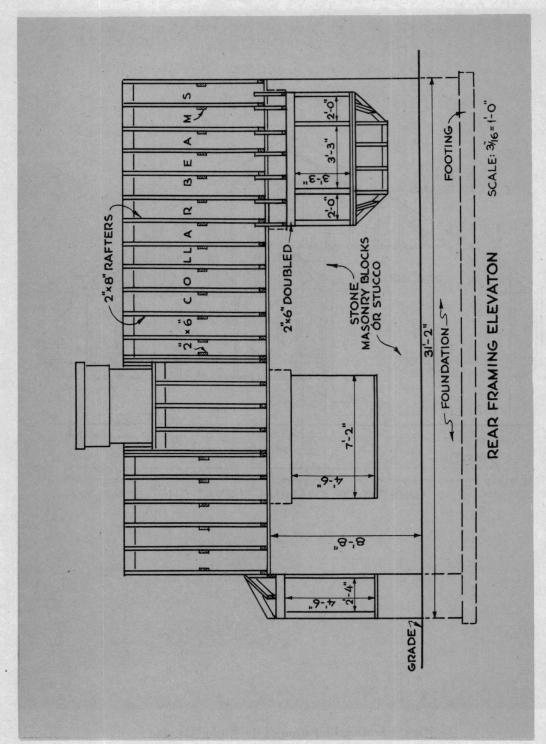

Rear Framing Elevation of the Tudor Cottage

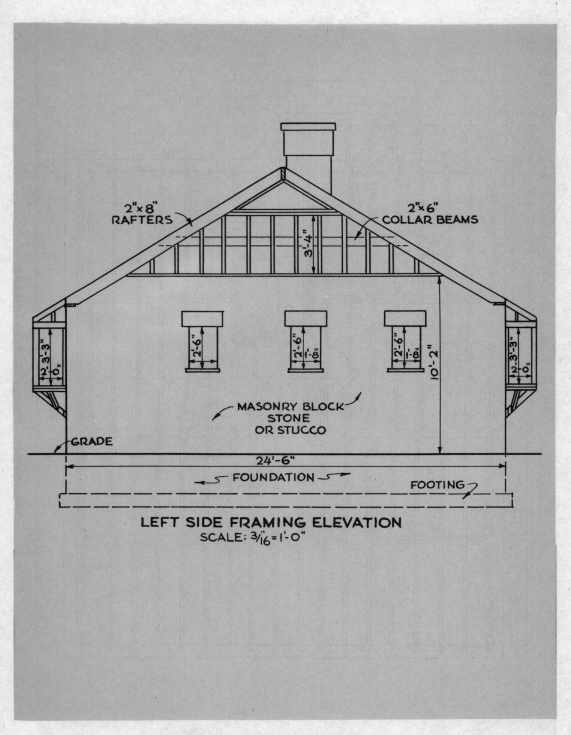

2"x 8" RAFTERS

2"x 6" COLLAR BEAMS

3'-4"

2'-6"

2'-6"
1'-8"

2'-6"
1'-8"

2'-3'-3"
0"

2'-3'-3"
0"

10'-2"

MASONRY BLOCK STONE OR STUCCO

GRADE

24'-6"

FOUNDATION

FOOTING

LEFT SIDE FRAMING ELEVATION
SCALE: 3/16" = 1'-0"

Left Framing Elevation of the Tudor Cottage

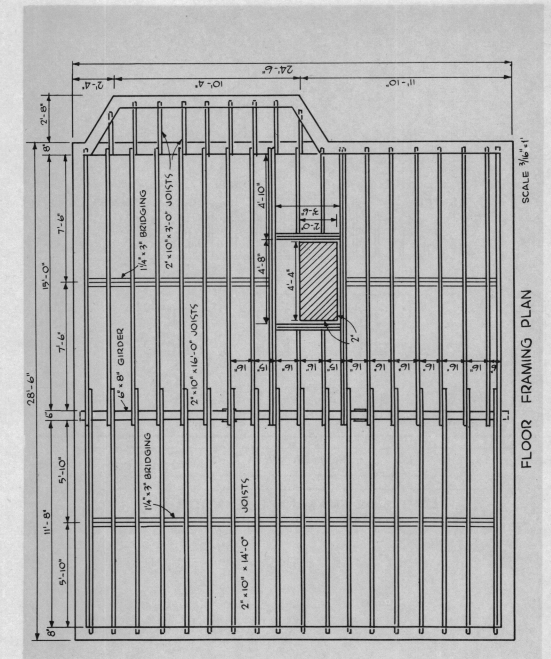

FLOOR FRAMING PLAN

SCALE 3/16" = 1'

Floor Framing Plan of the Tudor Cottage

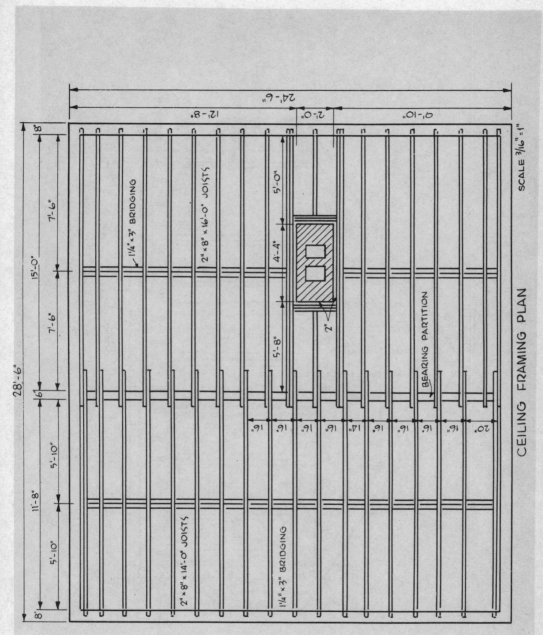

CEILING FRAMING PLAN

Ceiling Framing Plan of the Tudor Cottage

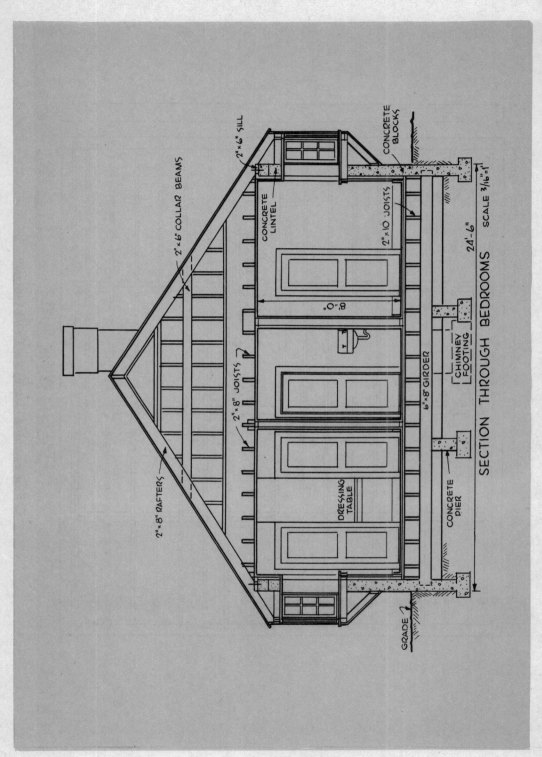

Section of the Tudor Cottage

Chapter 30

A SUBURBAN HOME

This is an ideal house for a growing family in a growing community. Its conventional design makes it acceptable in almost every kind of residential zone but at the same time it has sufficient character of its own not to look like "just another house on the block." This is an important point, for far too many homes these days have no character of their own and might just as well have been poured from a mold. Of course, this home does just as nicely out in the country as in a well settled community.

The Suburban Home, when fully completed, can easily accommodate a large family. The attic is large enough to contain two full-size bedrooms as well as a bathroom and ample closet and storage space besides. The large dormer window in the roof insures that these rooms are both light and airy. They will be perfect for two or more older children, or they can be used as guest rooms.

The Floor Plan

The first floor, as you can see from the floor plan, includes a large master bedroom and a somewhat smaller second bedroom. Each room has ample

closet space, and there is additional closet space that can be used for linens or the like. There is a large living room with a dining alcove off to the rear as well as a large kitchen and bathroom. The kitchen has been located so that there is easy access from it to the dining alcove. There is enough extra room in the kitchen for a breakfast bar, so that the dining alcove need only be used for the main meals or when there is company. The layout of the fixtures in the kitchen is the conventional L-type arrangement, which is considered most efficient.

An interesting feature of the first floor is the location of the front door, which, as you can see from the plans, is located in an off-set on the front wall. This door opens into a coat entry or foyer. Its location—protected on two sides by walls—makes it highly desirable in cold climates where there is a tendency for houses to become chilled by strong winds each time the front door is opened. The rear door of the house is located in the rear of the dining alcove. A stoop in front of this door leads directly to the door of the garage. While there is no outside door to the kitchen, it is only a matter of a few steps from the kitchen to the outside dining-room door.

The front of the living room is almost entirely taken up by large picture windows and there is another window that looks out on the side over the driveway.

The corners of the two bedrooms consist entirely of windows, and there are windows as well over the kitchen sink and in the bathroom.

The Basement

Some sort of a basement will be required for this house since no provision has been made on the first floor for a utility room for the furnace and other necessary equipment. You have a choice here either of making a half- or quarter-basement—enough to take care of this equipment—or of building a full basement and dividing it up into a utility room, a laundry room and a good-size game room. If the family is large, it might well be worth the added expense of having a full basement with a decent-size rumpus room.

Partitions between the rooms in the basement can be made out of masonry-blocks. This will eliminate the need for a heavy girder or lintel and will also make it possible to use a lighter size of joist than would be required if there was no support for the joists other than the main girder running through the approximate center of the floor.

Access to the basement is by means of the stairs located in the hall between the bathroom and bedroom. In planning the basement, be sure that these

steps lead down into the game room rather than into the utility room or laundry.

The one-car garage is incorporated directly in the house. If a two-car garage is desired, this can easily be constructed by extending the far wall of the garage the required distance.

The Foundation

If this house is to be built with a full basement, the foundation walls should be of either poured concrete or masonry-blocks and all precautions should be taken to insure that the basement will be adequately drained. If a laundry is to be located in the basement, there should be a floor drain at some point and the necessary provisions should be made for drainage pipes for the laundry equipment. In many instances the basement will come below the sewer line or septic tank, and in this case a sump pump will have to be installed to pump the waste water into the house sewer line.

Many basement game rooms are provided with a powder room or half-bathroom located under the basement stairs. Such fixtures will also have to be served by a sump pump if the basement is below the grade of the sewer.

Many persons, of course, will not wish to complete the entire house at one time but will put off finishing the attic and the basement until some later date. This is an excellent plan, but provisions for the attic bath and the basement laundry and bath should be made when the main house plumbing system

The Suburban Home

is put in or else you will find that these additions later on can be unduly expensive.

When the house foundations are poured, the garage foundations must be poured as well. This is absolutely necessary, because the garage framework will have to be built right along with that of the house. If you want, the garage *can* be added later on, but this will complicate construction considerably.

The Framework

The erection of the house framework will, in general, be just the same as for any of the other homes covered in this book. As there is no single partition that runs the entire width of the first floor, the various room partitions should be erected before the ceiling joists are installed. They will serve as bearing partitions and allow you to use somewhat smaller joists than are needed for a large span. On the other hand, bearing posts or masonry walls will be required under the partitions carrying joists so that the load of the second floor can be adequately supported. This load can sometimes be compensated for merely by increasing the joists under the partitions by one or even two additional joists spiked to the side of the main joist.

There should not be any problem in building the larger dormer in the roof as its design is very simple, but it is most important that the windows in this dormer be centered directly over the ones on the floor below. They should

also be exact duplicates of the windows used on the first floor.

If the garage is built along with the house, the construction of the roof at the point where the garage and house meet will not be difficult. As you can see from the Rear Elevation, the rear portion of the garage roof has exactly the same pitch as the house roof. Consequently, after the main house has been framed, you can simply install one of the rear garage rafters and spike it to the end house rafter. Install a rafter on the rear of the garage at the opposite end and then run a ridge board between the two. Now the intermediate rafters can be put up, running from ridge board to garage plate.

As you can see from the floor plan, the chimney for the heating system runs up past the linen closet. There is no fireplace, but one can be installed if you wish. It can be located in the front of the wall between the living room and kitchen or in the right wall of the living room.

Windows for the Suburban Home are metal or wood casement windows except for the picture window in the living room. The picture window is fixed but is flanked on both sides by single-pane movable sashes. These are necessary in order to provide the necessary cross-ventilation in the living room during warm weather.

The Exterior

As far as exterior siding goes, plywood or bevel siding or wood or asbestos shingles are suitable. A combination of two kinds of siding, one on the lower portion and one on the gable ends, is very desirable and breaks up surfaces that would otherwise become monotonous.

The roof should be shingled with either wood or asbestos shingles. Slate can be used, but it is expensive and difficult to install.

The Interior

As this is basically a light and cheerful house, care should be taken in selecting the covering for the interior walls. Without a doubt the most suitable material would be either plaster or plasterboard, as either of these can be painted or papered. A light-color wood or plywood paneling would be suitable in the living room with a somewhat darker paneling used in the dining room. It is best not to make the walls of both these rooms with paneling of the same color, as too much of a good thing can often ruin the entire effect.

Bedrooms should have walls that will take either paper or paint and the bathroom and kitchen walls should be of a type that can be covered with paper, linoleum or metal or plastic wall tile.

The living-room floor should be of either wood or linoleum in a light color. A softwood plank floor finished in a light color would be most suitable.

Finishing Off

The Suburban Home is an American house in design, and this fact must not be forgotten when it comes to finishing it off. Too many homes are neither fish nor fowl when completed, not through any fault of the design but because little items such as the hardware and fixtures were selected without any thought of the style of the house in which they were to be used.

As far as hardware goes, simple wrought iron of Colonial style or solid brass is suitable. Many persons with a love for all that is nautical may want to choose hardware with a ship motive and this too is suitable if not carried to an extreme.

The exterior walls should be painted white or grey with the same color used for the outside trim around window and doors or with blue or green trim. Green trim is in keeping with Colonial style but many persons prefer to have the trim the same color as the siding.

· The front door should be in Colonial style and painted the same color as the siding. A heavy oak door with a dark natural finish would be somewhat out of place. The door at the rear of the dining room should be a panel door with lights, as this will give an almost solid wall of glass at the back of the house.

SUBURBAN HOME MATERIALS LIST

Material	Quantity	Dimensions
Mixed cement	48 cu. yds.	
6″ x 6″	3	6′6″

Material	Quantity	Dimensions
2″ x 10″	16	18′
	29	16′
	57	14′
	20	12′
2″ x 8″	18	14′
	9	16′
	7	18′
	24	22′
2″ x 6″	13	18′
	14	16′
	18	14′
2″ x 4″	84	20′
	157	16′
1″ x 6″	3	20′
	10	16′
Sheathing	6,160 board ft.	1″ x 6″
Shelving	250′	1″ x 6″
Base mold	522′	1″ x 3″
Copper flashing	18′	12″

	Quantity	Rough Openings
Entrance door with frame and trim	2	7′ x 3′
	1	7′ x 2′9″
Overhead door	1	7′2″ x 8′3″
Windows with frame and trim	1	3′3″ x 5′0″
	2	3′3″ x 3′3″
	2	4′9″ x 3′3″
	1	3′3″ x 5′3″
	1	3′3″ x 2′9″
	10	3′3″ x 4′0″
	1	3′6″ x 4′6″
	1	3′6″ x 2′9″
	2	6′0″ x 1′8″
	1	4′3″ x 6′0″

1″ x 3″, 654′

Beveled siding, 2,444 board ft.

Building paper, 2,000 sq. ft.

Roofing material, 1,800 sq. ft.

Insulation, 3,353 sq. ft.

Wallboard, 4,873 sq. ft.

⅜″ plywood, 2,424 sq. ft.

Linoleum, 2,424 sq. ft.

Nails: 6d, 45 lbs; 8d, 128 lbs; 8d finishing, 37 lbs; 10d, 70 lbs; 16d, 24 lbs; 20d, 36 lbs; 4d, 104 lbs; 5d, 18 lbs

Interior doors, trim, jambs, stops, 12

Hinges: brass, 9, interior, 24

Mortice locks, 15

Louvers, 3

Gutters, 140'

Flight box stairs, 2

Paint: exterior, 12 gal.; water-thinned, 12 gal.; interior enamel, 2½ gal.

Common bricks, 1,885

Mortar, 1 cu. yd.

2-ft. flue-tile 12″ x 12″, 12

Chimney thimble

Clean-out door

Forced warm-air heating system

Medicine cabinets, 2

Towel racks, 5

Soap dish and toothbrush holder, 2

Sanitary T: 4″, 1; 4″ with 2″ tapping, 5; 2', 2; 1½″, 6

Y branch: 4″, 2; 2″, 1

Clean-out plug: 4″, 1; 2″, 1

Increaser

4″-2″ reducer

4″ closet bends, 3

Drain traps, 10

Elbows: 2″, 1; 1½″, 7; ¾″, 3; ½″, 14

2″ ¼-bend

Tees: ¾″, 3; ½″, 21

5' sections cast-iron soil pipe: 4″, 10; 2″, 3

Galvanized pipe: 2″, 10'; 1½″, 120'; ¾″, 30'; ½″, 80'

Kitchen sink

Laundry tubs, 2

Bathtubs with shower and fittings, 2

Lavatories with fittings, 3

Water closets with flush tank, 3

30-gal. hot-water heater

Ceiling fixtures, 13

Ceiling fixtures with pull chain, 3

Wall fixtures, 3

Outside fixture

Convenience outlets, 25

Special outlet

Single switches, 13

3-way switch

4″ outlet boxes with plates, 16

2½″ switch boxes with plates, 40

Cable connectors and bushings, 190

Door bells and buttons, 2

Metal hangers, 16

Service head

Sill plate

Grounding bushing

Switch box

Entrance cable, 16'

No. 14 2-wire, 500'

No. 12 wire, 75'

No. 6 wire, 25'

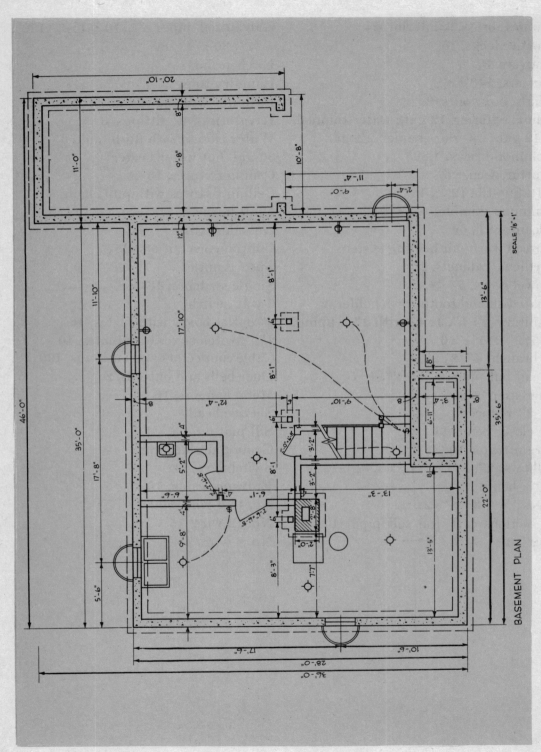

BASEMENT PLAN

SCALE 1/8"=1'

Foundation Plan of the Suburban Home

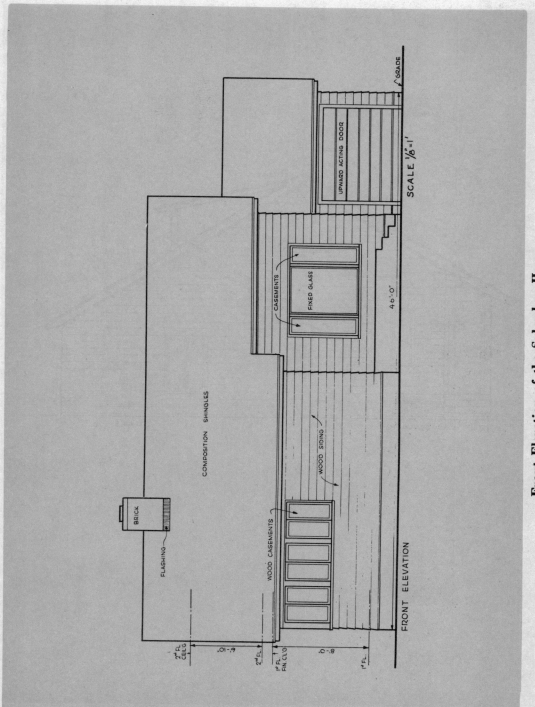

Front Elevation of the Suburban Home

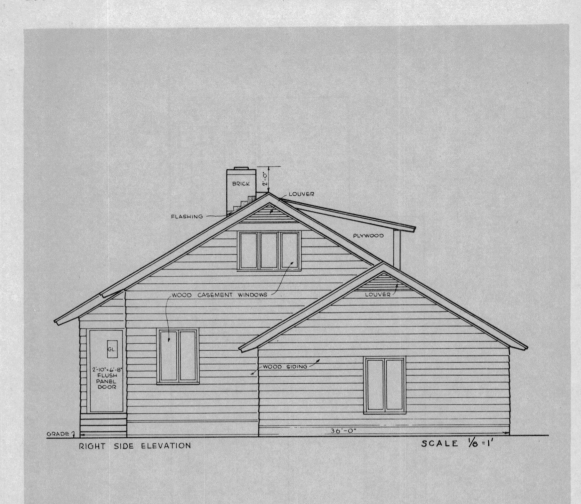

Right Side Elevation of the Suburban Home

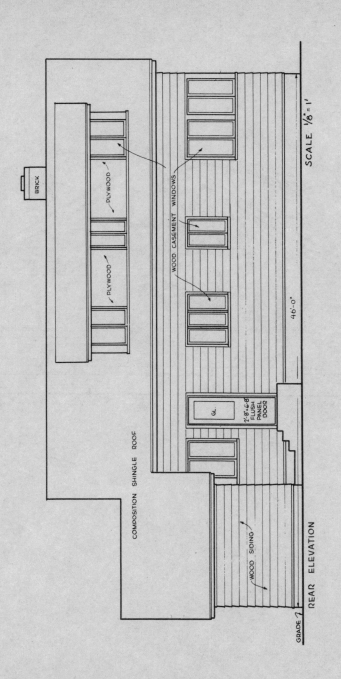

Rear Elevation of the Suburban Home

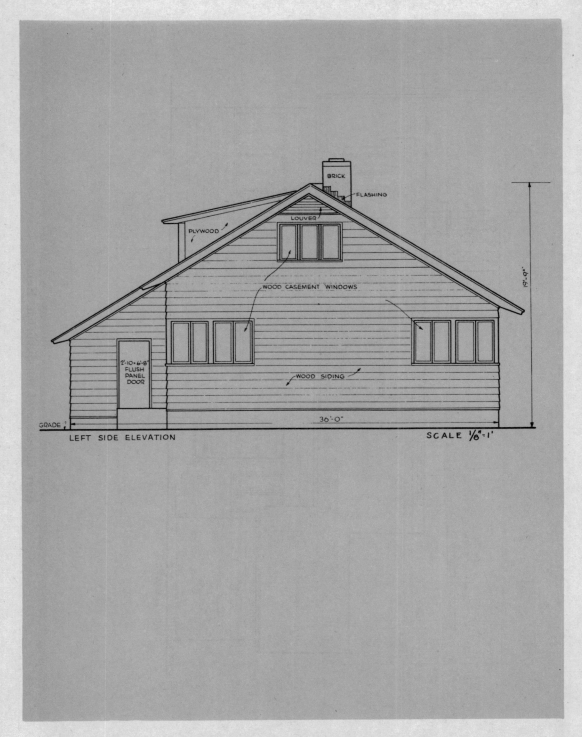

Left Side Elevation of the Suburban Home

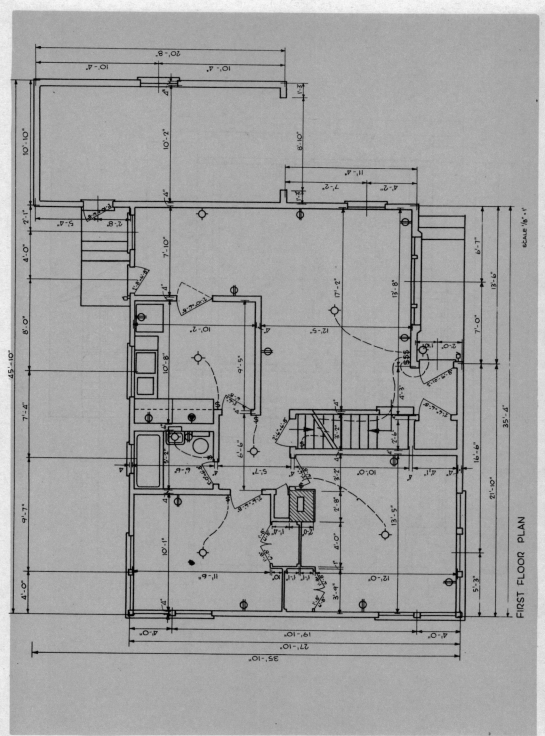

Floor Plan of the Suburban Home: First Floor

FIRST FLOOR PLAN

SCALE 1/8" = 1'

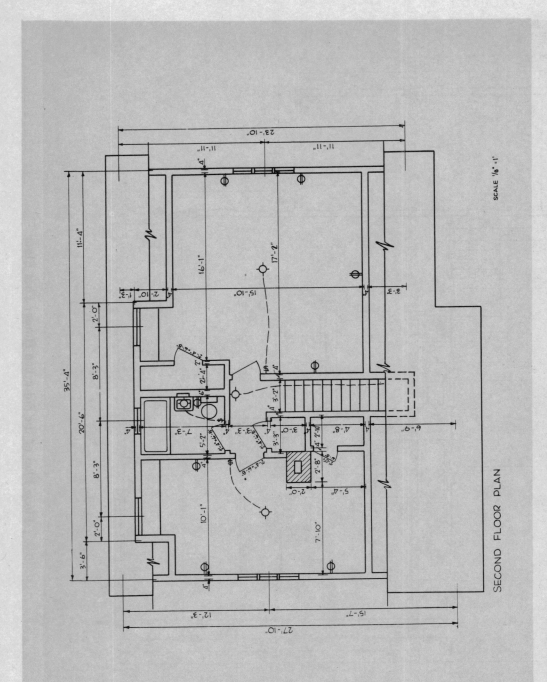

Floor Plan of the Suburban Home: Second Floor

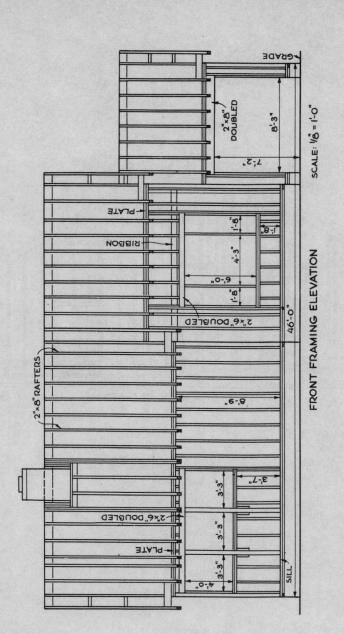

Front Framing Elevation of the Suburban Home

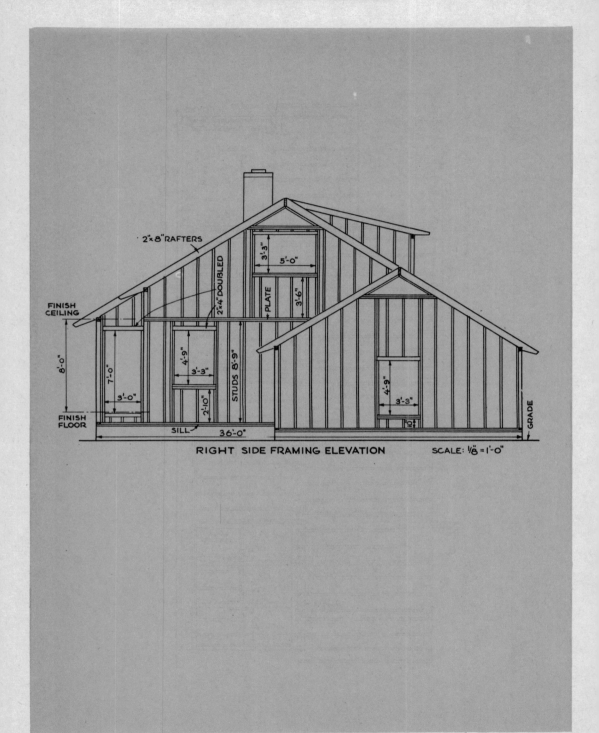

Right Framing Elevation of the Suburban Home

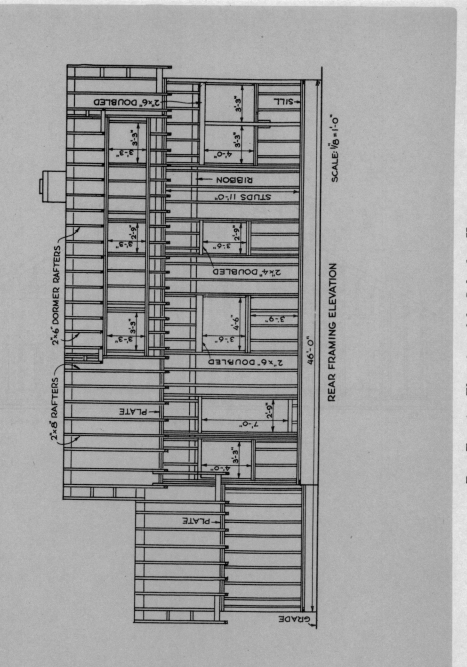

Rear Framing Elevation of the Suburban Home

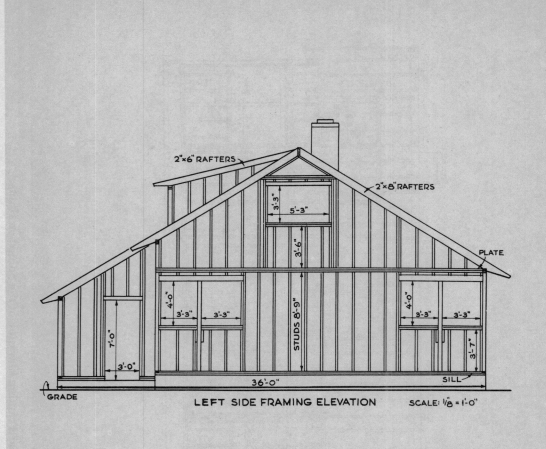

Left Framing Elevation of the Suburban Home

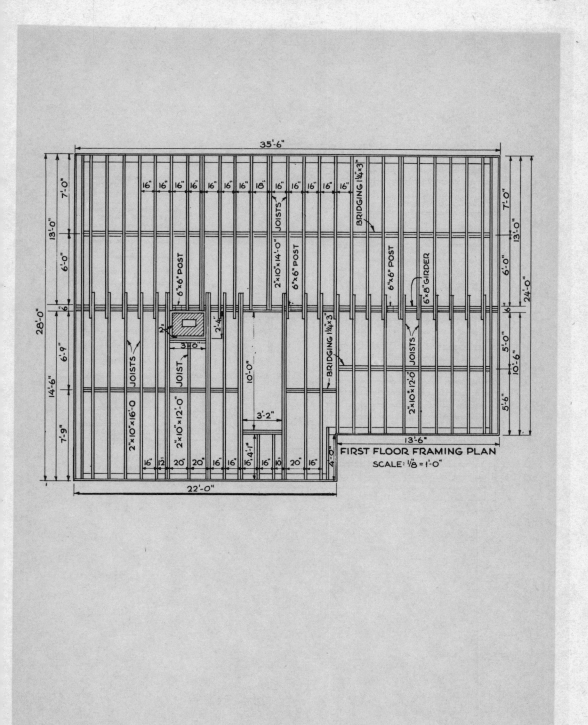

First Floor Framing Plan of the Suburban Home

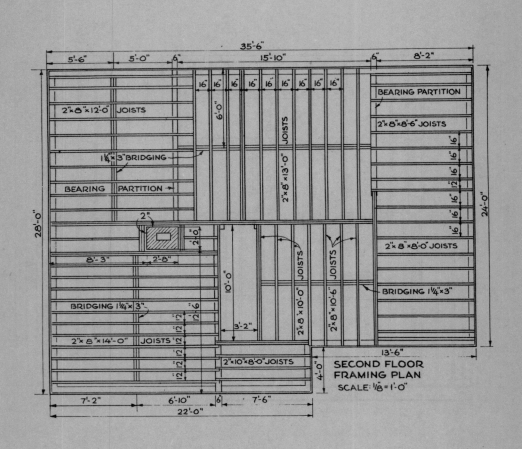

Second Floor Framing Plan of the Suburban Home

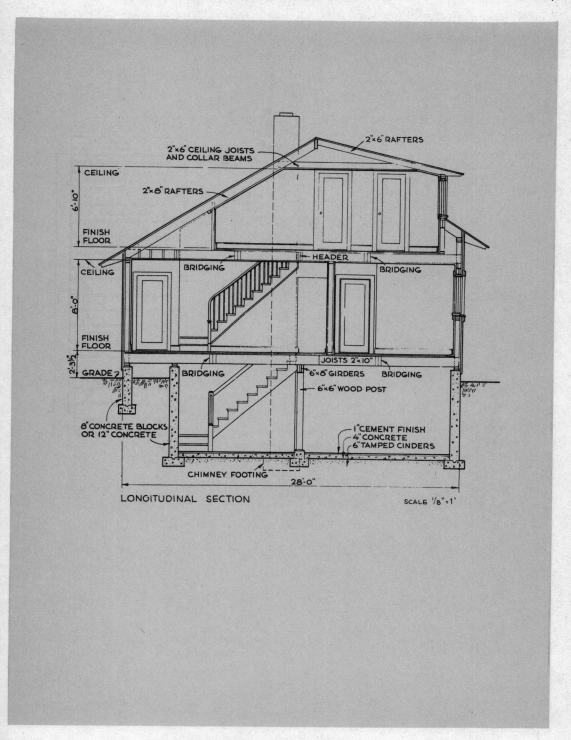

Section of the Suburban Home

GLOSSARY

ABRASIVE

Material such as sandpaper, pumice, or emery, used for polishing, sanding, and grinding.

ABUTTALS

The boundings of a piece of land on other land or on a street, river, etc.

ACOUSTICS

Having to do with the transmission of sound through air and building materials.

ACROSS THE GRAIN

At right angles to the run of the wood grain.

ADDITION

Any change whereby the exterior dimensions of a structure are increased.

ADOBE

(1) Aluminous earth; (2) brick made from such earth without fire; (3) with "the" or "an," a single brick of this kind; (4) a house built of these materials.

AGGREGATES

The materials (sand and gravel) mixed with Portland cement to produce concrete.

AIR DRIED

Lumber that has been allowed to season in the air rather than in a kiln.

AIR SPACE

The area between the inner and outer wall of the house. Any cavity.

ALCOVE

Any large recess in a room, usually separated by an arch.

ALL LENGTHS

Lumber cut in many different lengths.

ALL WIDTHS

Lumber cut in many different widths.

ALTERATION

Any change or rearrangement in the structural parts of a building.

AMPERE

Unit used to measure the rate of flow of electrical current.

ANCHOR

To secure one object to another; a device used to attach two objects together.

ANCHOR BOLT

A bolt set into masonry to secure woodwork, machines, etc., as opposed to a bolt that is inserted into masonry that has hardened.

ANGLE IRON

A piece of iron or metal in the shape of a right angle; used in carpentry and brickwork to reinforce joints.

APRON

A piece of finish, plain or molded, that is put under a window sill to cover the rough edge of the plastering.

AQUASTAT

A control device used to regulate the temperature of the hot water supply when heated by the furnace.

ARCH

An arrangement of building materials in the form of a curve. This arrangement preserves a given form and, when supported by piers, sustains weights and resists pressures.

ARCHITECT

One who designs a building, prepares the building plans, and supervises the workers who do the actual building.

ARCHITECTURE

The art of building, or designing a building, in such a way as to best enable it to fulfill its purpose and in such a way as to give it the qualities of beauty, interest, harmony, and strength.

ARCHITRAVE

Wooden casing or trim.

AREA

(1) The total surface of a floor or wall. (2) A court or open space within a building.

AREAWAY

A sub-surface space left around the foundation walls to permit light or air to reach the cellar or basement or for other purposes.

ARMORED CABLE

Electric wires encased in metal.

ARRIS

The point at which two surfaces meet to form an angle, such as the corner of a board.

ASBESTOS

A fireproof mineral.

ASBESTOS BOARD

A sheet of building board made of asbestos fibers and cement. It is fire-resistant and moisture-resistant and can be used for interior or exterior work.

ASBESTOS PAPER

Heavy paper which will not burn and is a poor conductor of heat.

ASBESTOS SHINGLES

Roof or siding shingles made of Portland cement and asbestos.

ASHLAR

A type of stonework. A facing made of squared stones or of thin slabs; it is used to cover walls of brick or rubble. *Coursed* ashlar means that the stones are laid in level courses all around the building; *random* ashlar means that the stones are of different heights but that the beds are level. (2) Small common freestones.

ATTIC

A low story above the main part of a building; that part of the building that is immediately below the roof.

BACKFILL

To replace earth in the pit, trench, or other excavation from which it was removed.

BACK OF A WINDOW

That piece of wainscoting that is between the bottom of the sash frame and the door.

BACK-PAINTING

Painting the back side or unexposed surface of lumber to prevent the wood from absorbing moisture.

BACK PUTTY

A thin layer of putty placed between the glass and the rabbet of a window.

BACKING OF A RAFTER OR RIB

An upper or outer surface that is added to any rafter or rib in order to make it extend as far as the rafters or ribs on either side.

BACKING OF A WALL

The rough inner surface of a wall; earth that is deposited behind a retaining wall, etc.

BACKSAW

A fine-toothed saw with a thin blade, reinforced with a steel back. Used for chamfering, mitering, etc. Also called a tenon saw.

BALCONY

A projection from the face of a wall, supported by columns or consoles, usually surrounded by a balustrade.

BALLOON FRAMING

A system of framing wooden buildings in which the corner posts and studs are continuous in one piece from sill to roof plate. The intermediate joists are carried by girts spiked to, or let into, the studs; the pieces are secured only by nailing, without the use of mortises, tenons, and the like. This system is used in modern building wherein relatively light lumber is used.

BALUSTERS

The vertical posts on stair railings.

BARGE BOARD

See Verge Board.

BASEBOARD

The molding used to cover the joint between the floor and wall. It is sometimes called skirting.

BASEMENT

The lower part of a building, partly but not more than one-half below the level of the lot or street. *See* Cellar.

BASE MOLDINGS

The moldings immediately above the plinth of a wall, pillar, or pedestal.

BASE PLATE

Another name for Sole or Sole Plate.

BAT

A part of a brick. A type of insulation.

BATTENS

Small strips of board. Among other purposes, they are used over the joints of sheathing in order to keep out the weather.

BATTEN DOOR

A door made of sheathing secured by strips of board, placed crossways, and nailed with clinched nails.

BATTER

A wall, or a piece of timber or other material, that does not stand upright but leans away from you when you stand in front of it. When, on the contrary, it leans toward you, it is called an overhang.

BATTER BOARDS

Horizontal boards set in pairs a short distance back from each corner of an excavation. The boards are each nailed to two upright stakes, and are used to indicate the building level, and as a support for various guide lines that are stretched between them.

BAY

Any division or compartment of an arcade, roof, etc.

BAY WINDOW

Any window that projects outward from the wall of a building. These windows may be square or polygonal in shape, and they rise from the ground.

BEAD

A circular molding. When several are joined, the result is called reeding; when flush with the surface, it is called quick-bead; when raised, it is called cock-bead.

BEADING

Small wooden molding used for decorative purposes.

BEAM

A heavy timber or other material that is placed horizontally, either from post to post or over an opening, to support a load; for example, a beam under the floor of a house.

BEARING

That portion of a beam, truss, etc., that rests on the supports.

BEARING PARTITION

A partition which supports any vertical load in addition to its own weight.

BEARING WALL

A wall which supports the floors and roofs in a building.

BED

(1) A specially prepared surface, usually of mortar, sand, or cinders, on which the bricks or stones of walls, walks, etc., are to be laid. (2) A course of stones or bricks on which another course is to be laid. (3) Applied to the underside of a stone or brick that is to be laid, or the upper surface of a stone or brick that is to support another.

BED OF A SLATE

The under side.

BELLY

To bulge out.

BELT

A course of stones or brick projecting from a brick or stone wall, generally in a line with the window sills. It may be molded, fluted, plane, or ornamented.

BENZINE

A liquid used to clean paint brushes and sometimes to thin paint.

BEVEL

(1) Instrument used to adjust surfaces of work to any given angle. (2) To cut on a slant, so the angle formed is not a right angle. One side of a solid body is said to be beveled with respect to another when the angle contained between the two sides is either greater or less than a right angle.

BEVEL SIDING

Siding made by "resawing" dry, square-surfaced boards diagonally to produce two wedge-shaped pieces. It is used as the finish siding on the exterior of a house.

BIBB

A faucet with the nozzle threaded so that a hose can be attached.

BLEED

Wood is said to bleed when the liquid contained in it works its way to the surface.

BLOCKING OR BLOCKING-COURSE

A course of stones placed on top of a cornice crowning the walls.

BLUEPRINT

A photographic print showing white lines against a blue background, commonly used to reproduce architect's drawings, plans, etc.

BOARD FOOT

A unit for the measurement of lumber. It refers to a piece of lumber measuring one square foot on the surface and one inch in thickness or to its equivalent (144 sq. in.).

BOND

A connection between bricks or stones that is designed to form an inseparable mass of building. It is formed by overlapping the bricks one upon another instead of allowing the vertical joints to fall over one another. There are several kinds of bond in brickwork. In common brick walls, in every sixth or seventh course the bricks are laid crossways of the wall. In face work, the back of the face brick is clipped so as to get in a diagonal course of headers behind. In Old English bond, every alternate course is a header course. In Flemish bond, a header and stretcher alternate in each course.

BOND-STONES

Stones running through the thickness of the wall at right angles to its face, in order to bind it together.

BOND-TIMBERS

Timbers placed horizontally in tiers in the walls of a brick building, and to which the battens, laths, etc., are secured. In rubble work, walls are better plugged for this purpose.

BORDER

A series of useful ornamental pieces which are placed around the edge of anything.

BOX SILL

A foundation sill in which the sole plate rests on the floor joists rather than on the sill proper.

BRACE

In carpentry, an inclined piece of timber. Braces are used in trussed partitions or in framed roofs to form a triangle and thereby stiffen the framing. A brace that is used to support a rafter is called a strut. Braces in partitions and span-roofs should always be disposed in pairs and introduced in opposite directions.

BRACING

A system of framing a building in which all vertical structural elements of the bearing walls and partitions, except the corner posts, extend for only one story. They start at the foundation sill for the first-story framing and at the top plate of the story below for all stories above the first. Corner posts extend from foundation sill to roof plate and are braced by diagonal members usually extending the full height of each story and crossing several of the studs in each outer wall.

BRACKET
A projecting ornament carrying a cornice.

BRAD
A small nail.

BREAK
Any projection from the general surface of a building.

BREAKING JOINTS
Arranging stones or bricks so that the mortar joints are staggered and no one joint is allowed to fall immediately over another. *See* Bond.

BREAST OF A WINDOW
The masonry forming the back of the recess and the parapet under the window sill.

BREEZEWAY
A passageway between two buildings that is covered, but is open on both sides.

BRICK COURSE
A layer of bricks.

BRICK VENEER
A thin layer of bricks used as a finish.

BRIDGING
A method of stiffening floor joists and partition studs by placing small wooden braces in between in a diagonal position.

BROWN COAT
The second coat of either plaster or stucco.

B.T.U. (BRITISH THERMAL UNIT)
A unit used in measuring heat. One B.T.U. is equal to the amount of heat required to raise the temperature of one pound of water one degree F.

BUCKLE
To heave up, lift, or warp.

BUILDING CODES
Local laws or ordinances regulating various phases of construction work.

BUILDING LINE
A line of demarcation between public and private property. A line beyond which no building or part thereof can be extended without the approval or permission of the authorities.

BUTT
To join end to end without overlapping.

BUTTER
In masonry, to apply mortar to a brick.

BUTT-JOINT
The point at which two pieces of timber or molding butt together.

BX CABLE
Electric wires in flexible metal covering.

CALCIUM CHLORIDE
A chemical that absorbs moisture from the air. It is used to dry out damp rooms and also to melt ice.

CALIBER OR CALIPER
The diameter of any round body.

CAMBER
The convexity of a beam upon the surface, in order to prevent its becoming concave by its own weight or by the burden it may have to hold.

CANTILEVER
A structural member which is supported at only one end and which supports a projecting load. A beam or truss projecting from a pier.

Cant Strip

Wood strip used to give the first course of shingles or siding the same slant as the other courses.

Cap

The cement finish as used on top of a brick wall or chimney.

Carriage

The timber or iron joist that supports the steps of a wooden stair.

Cased

Covered with other materials, usually of better quality.

Casement

A glass frame that is made to open by turning on hinges attached to its vertical edges.

Casement Windows

Windows with the sash hinged to open like a door.

Casing

The wooden trim around doors and windows.

Cast-iron Pipes

Soil pipes made of cast iron and used for the sewage system.

Caulk

To fill a crack or seam with oakum.

Caulking Compound

A soft plastic used for caulking. It sets soft, and can be painted.

Ceiling

That covering of a room which hides the joists of the floor above or the rafters of the roof.

Ceiling Joists

Lumber used to support the ceiling.

Cellar

When there is a basement, the cellar is that part of a building below the basement. When there is no basement, it is the story or portion thereof, more than one-half of which is below the level of the street.

Cement

An adhesive used to bind objects together. There is also Portland cement, used in concrete.

Cement Plaster

A mixture of Portland cement and sand, used as a finish coat.

Chamfer

To cut off a corner to form a bevel. To cut a groove or channel in. Also, the surface formed when the angle made by adjacent faces of a piece of timber, masonry, metal, etc., is cut away.

Chase

A recess or frame consisting of sides, sill, and head.

Check Valve

A valve used in plumbing to prevent a reverse flow of water in a pipe.

Cinders

Ashes from coal used as fill or mixed with cement to produce cinder blocks.

Clapboard

Board having one edge thicker than the other. Used for exterior siding of houses.

Clinch

To bend over.

Clinch Nail

A nail made of soft steel, which bends over easily at the end.

Close String or Box String

A method of finishing the outer edge of stairs by building up a sort of curb string on which the balusters set. The treads and risers stop against it.

COAT

A thickness or covering of paint, plaster, or other material applied at one time. The first coat of plaster is called the scratch coat; the second coat (when there are three coats) is called the brown coat; and the last coat is called the slipped coat, skim-coat, or white coat.

COFFER

A deep panel in a ceiling.

COLLAR BEAM

A piece of lumber running horizontally between two rafters to provide additional support. It is placed above the lower ends of the rafters and spiked to them. Also called rafter tie.

COMMON

A line, angle, surface, etc., that is shared by more than one object. Common centering is a centering without trusses, having a tie beam at the bottom. Common joists are the beams in naked flooring to which the joists are attached. Common rafters in a roof are those to which the laths are attached.

COMMON BOARDS

Boards one inch thick and up to twelve inches wide. Also a grade of lumber.

COMMON BRICKS

Ordinary red bricks of standard size.

COMPASS SAW

A saw with narrow, tapering blade. Used to cut curves, circles, and fine cuts.

COMPOSITION WOOD

Flexible building material made by pressing wood fibers into thin sheets of building board.

CONCRETE

A mixture of Portland cement, sand, gravel, and water.

CONCRETE PAINT

A mixture composed of cement, water, and coloring matter, for use on concrete and cement surfaces. Any paint formulated for use on concrete or cement.

CONDUIT

A channel, canal, or pipe for the conveyance of water or the protection of electric wires.

COPING

The capping or covering of a wall. It is made of stone and weathered to throw off moisture.

COPING SAW

A saw with an extremely narrow blade which can be turned in the frame to saw at various angles.

CORBEL

A short piece of stone or wood projecting from a wall to form a support, generally ornamented.

CORBEL OUT

To build one or more courses of brick or stone out from the face of a wall in order to form a support for timbers.

CORNER BEADS

Thin metal beads having rounded corners. They are used to protect plaster at corners and to guide the plasterer.

CORNER BLOCK
A masonry block having one square end.

CORNICE
The projection at the top of a wall finished by a blocking-course. Usually, the portion of a wall directly under the eaves.

COUNTER FLASHING
Flashing applied over flashing.

COUNTERSINK
To make a cavity for the reception of a plate of iron, or the head of a screw or bolt, so that it will not project beyond the face of the work.

COUPLING
In plumbing, a device used to join sections of pipe or hose.

COURSE
A layer of bricks or stones in buildings; applied to slates, shingles, etc.

COVE CEILING
A ceiling springing from the walls with a curve.

COVED AND FLAT CEILING
A ceiling in which the section is the quadrant of a circle, rising from the walls and intersecting in a flat surface.

CRADLING
Timber work for sustaining the lath and plaster of vaulted ceilings.

CREOSOTE
Wood or coal tar used as a wood preservative.

CRICKET
A small, sloped roof structure which is placed where two larger surfaces meet at an angle. Its function is to divert drainage.

CROSS BRIDGING
Strips of wood nailed between the floor joists to form an "X."

CROWN
The top part of an arch, or of an arched surface.

CROWNING
To raise the center of a flat surface so that water will drain off.

CURB ROOF OR MANSARD ROOF
A roof formed of four contiguous planes, each pair having an external inclination.

CURTAIN WALL
See Wall, Curtain.

DADO
A rectangular, flat-bottomed groove cut in wood.

DADO JOINT
A joint made by cutting a tongue on the end of one member to fit into a dado cut in the other member.

DADO PLANE
A plane used to cut dados.

DARBY
A flat tool used by plasterers, especially when working on ceilings. It is usually about seven inches wide and forty-two inches long, having two handles on the back.

DENATURED ALCOHOL
In painting, a liquid used to thin shellac.

DESIGN
The plans, elevations, sections, and whatever other drawings may be necessary to exhibit the design of a building. The term *plan* has a restricted application to a technical portion of the design.

DETAIL

As used by architects, detail means the smaller parts into which a composition can be divided. It is generally applied to moldings and other adornments.

DETAIL DRAWING

A separate sketch made of a portion of a plan or drawing to show more clearly the construction details of that portion.

DIAGONAL SHEATHING

Sheathing applied in diagonal, rather than horizontal or vertical, lines.

DIAMETER

The line passing through a circle at its thickest part; the length of this line. The diameters of the lower and upper ends of the shaft of a column are called its *inferior* and *superior* diameters, respectively. The former is the greatest, the latter the least diameter of the shaft.

DIMENSION STUFF

Lumber two inches thick and up to twelve inches wide.

DIVISION WALL

See Wall, Division.

DOMESTIC ARCHITECTURE

That branch of architecture which relates to private buildings.

DOOR FRAME

The surrounding case into and out of which the door shuts and opens. It consists of two upright pieces, called jambs, and a head. The pieces are usually fixed together by mortices and tenons.

DORMER WINDOW

A window built into the side of a roof. It, consequently, projects from the roof and has a valley gutter on each side.

DOUBLE HUNG WINDOW

A window consisting of an upper and lower sash in a frame.

DOUBLE STUDDING

Two pieces of studding spiked together to form the openings for doors and windows.

DOVETAILING

In carpentry and joinery, the method of fastening boards or other timbers together by letting one piece into another in the form of the extended tail of a dove.

DOWEL

(1) A round piece of wood. (2) A pin let into two pieces of wood or stone where they are joined together. (3) A piece of wood driven into a wall so that other pieces can be nailed to it. This is also called plugging.

DOWEL JOINT

A joint made by gluing a dowel into two pieces of wood.

DRAIN COCK

A device which permits water to be drained from the coils when the heating system is not operating.

DRAIN TILE

Sectional tile pipe designed to be laid in drainage ditches to carry surface water away from the outside of the foundation wall of a house.

DRESSING

The operation of squaring and smoothing stones or lumber for building.

DRIFTBOLT

(1) Metal rod used to fasten heavy timbers. (2) Bolt used to drive other bolts or pins out of their lodging places.

DRIP

The member of a cornice that has a projection beyond the other parts for the purpose of throwing off small quantities of water, drop by drop.

DRIP-STONE

The label molding that serves for an opening on a canopy and also serves to throw off the rain. It is also called weather molding.

DROP SIDING

Siding which is usually ¾″ thick and 6″ wide and which can be machined into various patterns. It has tongue-and-groove or shiplap joints, is heavier and has more structural strength than bevel siding.

DRY ROT

A rapid decay of timber in which its substance is converted into a dry powder which issues from small cavities and resembles the borings of worms. It is usually caused by alternating dryness and dampness.

DRY-WALL CONSTRUCTION

Any interior wall or ceiling material that does not have to be mixed with water before it can be applied. A plaster wall or ceiling, on the other hand, is called wet-wall construction.

DRY WELL

A hole in the earth filled with stones or gravel, used to collect water from the roof of a house.

D. S. GLASS

Double-strength glass, used for glazing large windows.

DUTCH DOOR

A door so constructed that the lower part can be shut while the upper part remains open.

DWELLING

A building intended for the residence of not more than two families.

EAVES

That portion of the roof which extends beyond the walls.

EFFLORESCENCE

The appearance of a white crust or powder on the surface of stone or brick walls. It is caused by the presence of mineral salts in the wall.

ELEVATION

(1) The front facade of a structure; (2) a geometrical drawing of the external upright parts of a building.

ELEVATION DRAWING

One which shows one side of the outside of the finished house, from the ground floor to the roof. It indicates door and window sizes, height of each floor, kind of sizing used, etc.

EMERY PAPER

An abrasive paper used on metal.

END-MATCH LUMBER

Boards having the ends as well as the sides tongued and grooved.

ENSEMBLE

The work or composition considered as a whole and not in parts.

ENTRY

A hall without stairs or vestibule.

Escutcheon
The metal plate on doors around the knobs and keyhole.

Excavate
To dig out.

Expansion Bolt
A bolt designed for anchoring in masonry.

Expansion Joint
An open joint between sections of concrete. It allows for expansion and contraction.

Facade
Generally speaking, all of the exterior side of a building that can be seen at one view; strictly speaking, the principal front.

Face
The front of a wall or brick.

Face Mold
A pattern for making the board from which ornamental hand railings and other works are to be cut.

Face Nailing
To nail perpendicular to the initial surface or to the junction of the pieces being joined.

Felt Paper
Heavy paper used in construction work for insulating purposes.

Ferrule
The metal portion of a paint brush at the base of the bristles.

Field Stones
Rough, uncut local stones.

Filler
In painting, a material used to fill the wood pores. Also, a gravel or cinder base for laying concrete.

Finish
The final surface when completed.

Fire Brick
Special bricks used in fireplaces and furnaces because of their ability to withstand heat.

Fire Clay
A special heat-resisting cement used to bond fire bricks.

Fireplace
That part of a building designed to permit the making of open fires. It is a recess in the wall or chimney-breast which connects directly with a flue for smoke. The recess or space is enclosed on the sides by two jambs or cheeks, and it terminates in the flue above. The decoration of the fireplace is important because that one part is wholly different in its uses, and probably in materials as well, from the rest of the room.

Fire Resistant
A material that will resist fire but is not absolutely fireproof.

Fire Stop
A piece of studding used in wall construction to prevent fire from rising through the air space between inner and outer wall.

Fire Wall
See Wall, Fire.

First Story
The story, the floor of which is at or first above the level of the sidewalk.

Fish Joint
A splice where two pieces are joined butt-end to end. The connection is made by pieces of wood or iron placed on each side and firmly bolted

to the timbers or other pieces being joined.

FISH TAPE

A length of steel wire that can be pushed around bends or through a rigid conduit.

FLAGSTONES

Stone or concrete slabs, from one to three inches thick, used for floors or walks.

FLANGE

A projecting edge, rim, or rib. Flanges are often cast on the top or bottom of iron columns, to fasten them to those above or below. The top and bottom of I-beams and channels are called the flange.

FLASHING

(1) Strips of lead, tin, or copper that are let into the joints of a wall so as to lap over gutters or other pieces; (2) pieces worked in the slates or shingles around dormers, chimneys, and other rising parts, to prevent leaking.

FLATTING

Painting finished without leaving a gloss on the surface.

FLIGHT

A run of steps or stairs from one landing to another.

FLOATING

The equal spreading of plaster or stucco on the surface of a wall by means of a board called a float. As a general rule, only rough plastering is floated.

FLOOR PLAN

A drawing which shows the arrangement of rooms and partitions on a single floor. It also indicates the location of each door, window, stairway, fireplace, and the like.

FLOW OUT

In painting, the ability of some paints to dry without brush marks.

FLUE

The space or passage in a chimney through which the smoke ascends. Each passage is called a flue, while all together make the chimney.

FLUSH

The continued surface, in the same plane, of two contiguous masses.

FLUX

A composition used in soldering. It cleans the metal and helps the solder to flow.

FOOTING

The lower part of a foundation that rests on the ground; the base.

FORM

Mold used to shape poured masonry.

FOUNDATION

The supporting portion of a structure, below the first-floor construction or grade, including the footings.

FOUNDATION WALL

See Wall, Foundation.

FRAMING

See Balloon Framing, Braced Framing, and Platform Framing.

FRENCH DOOR

A door in which panes of glass are substituted for wooden panels.

FRONT

That face of a building which contains the principal entrance.

FROST LINE

The depth to which the earth freezes.

FURRING

Strips of wood or metal that are attached to a wall or other surface to even it, form an air space, make it appear thicker, or serve as a base for laths, wallboard, or insulation.

GABLE

The triangular portion at the end of a building. That portion of a wall contained between the slopes of a double-sloped roof; on a single-sloped roof, that portion contained between the slope of, and a line projected horizontally through, the lowest elevation of the roof construction.

GAIN

A beveled shoulder on the end of a mortised brace, for the purpose of giving additional resistance to the shoulder.

GALVANIZE

To coat a metal with zinc in order to prevent rusting.

GALVANIZED

Coated with zinc.

GALVANIZED NAILS

Zinc-coated nails for use in objects that will be exposed to weather.

GAMBREL ROOF

A roof with two pitches, similar to a Mansard or curb roof.

GAUGE

(1) To mix plaster of Paris with common plaster to make it set quickly. The result is called gauged mortar. (2) A tool used by carpenters in order to strike a line parallel to the edge of a board.

GIRDER

A large timber or iron beam, either single or built-up, used to support concentrated loads at particular points along its length. Used to support either joists or walls over an opening.

GLASS BLOCKS

Translucent or transparent blocks of glass used in building.

GLAZED BRICKS

Bricks with a glazed surface.

GLAZING

The process of putting a pane of window glass into a sash.

GRADE

The slope or pitch of the ground. As distinct from the natural grade, the established grade is the level of the street curb as fixed by the municipality.

GRADING

Modifying the ground surface by filling, cutting, or both.

GRAIN

(1) The lines in wood; (2) the direction, size, arrangement, appearance, or quality of the fibers in wood.

GRAVEL

Small stones used in making concrete or used as fill.

GREEN LUMBER

Lumber that has not been properly seasoned.

GRILLE

Iron-work in the form of an enclosure screen. Grilles are made of wrought iron, ornamented by the swage and punch, and put together by either rivets or clips. They are used extensively to protect the lower windows in city houses and to protect the glass of outside doors.

GROOVE

In joinery, a term used to signify a sunk channel whose section is rectangular. It is usually used on the edge of a molding, stile, or rail, etc., into which a tongue corresponding to its section, and in the substance of the wood to which it is joined, is inserted.

GROUND FLOOR

That floor of a building which is level, or nearly so, with the ground.

GROUND JOIST

A joist that is blocked up from the ground.

GROUNDS

Pieces of wood embedded in the plastering of walls to which skirting and other joiner's work is attached; also used to stop the plastering around door and window openings.

GROUT

A thin cement mortar used for pointing. It is made so thin by the addition of water that it will run into all the joints and cavities of the masonwork and fill it up solid.

GUTTER

Channel for carrying off rain water.

HALL

A room or passageway at the entrance to a house or to a group of rooms.

HALVING

The joining of two pieces of timber by letting one into the other.

HANGER

An iron support used for attaching beams.

HANGING STYLE

That part of a door to which the hinges are attached.

HARDBOARD

See Composition Board.

HARDWARE

The metal work in a house, such as hinges, locks, etc.

HARDWOOD FLOORS

Floors made out of hardwoods, such as oak and maple.

HATCHING

Drawing parallel lines close together for the purpose of indicating a section of anything. The lines are usually drawn at an angle of 45° with a horizontal.

HEAD

The top portion of a door or window opening.

HEADER

A beam placed perpendicular to joists and to which joists are nailed in framing for a chimney, stairway, or other opening. More generally, a piece or member that makes a T-joint with other members; often a short piece extending between other members and at right angles to them; often used instead of lintel.

HEADERS

In masonry, stones or bricks extending over the thickness of a wall.

HEADING COURSES

Courses of a wall in which the stones or bricks are all headers.

HEADWAY
Clear space or height under an arch or over a stairway, and the like.

HEARTH
That portion of a fireplace which extends into the room.

HEEL
End cut on a rafter. The foot of the rafter that rests on the wall plate.

HERRINGBONE WORK
Bricks, tiles, or other materials arranged diagonally in building.

HIP RAFTER
A rafter that forms the intersection of an external roof angle.

HIP ROOF
A roof that rises by equally inclined planes from all four sides of the building.

HIPS
Those pieces of timber placed in an inclined position at the corners or angles of a hip roof.

HOOD-MOLD
The drip-stone or label over a window or door opening, whether inside or out.

HOT WIRE
An electric wire through which a current is passing; a live wire.

HOUSING
The space made in one solid to permit the insertion of another. The base on a stair is generally housed into the treads and risers.

I-BEAM
A steel structural member rolled to the shape of the letter "I."

INCISE
To cut in, carve, or engrave.

INDENTED
Toothed together.

INLAYING
Inserting pieces of ivory, metal, or choice woods, or the like, into a groundwork of some other material, for the purpose of ornamentation.

INSULATE
Generally speaking, to insulate means to detach, separate, or isolate; the word has several applications. (1) to equip a building with materials that will prevent the passage of heat, cold, or sound. (2) To cover electric wires with materials that will prevent the passage of electricity. (3) To devise a system for preventing the entrance of termites, mice, and other annoying rodents and insects into a building. (4) Detached from another building; or standing free from the wall.

INTERIOR
The inside of a house or other building.

JACK
An instrument for raising heavy loads, either by crank, lever, and pinion, or by hydraulic power. Jacks are always worked by hand.

JACK RAFTER
A short rafter, used especially in hip roofs. It spans the distance from a wall plate to a hip or from a valley to a ridge.

JAMB
The side post or lining of a doorway or other opening. The jambs of a window outside the frame are called reveals.

JAMB SHAFTS

Small shafts to doors and windows with caps and bases. When in the inside arris of the jamb of a window, they are sometimes called esconsons.

JOGGLE

A joint between two bodies which is so constructed by means of jogs or notches as to prevent their sliding past one another.

JOINER

A V-shaped steel implement used to tool mortar in order to compress it and make a waterproof joint.

JOINERY

That branch of building which is confined to the finer and more ornamental parts of carpentry.

JOINT

To fit two pieces of material together; the point at which two pieces of material are joined to one another.

JOINTER

Any of various tools used in making joints.

JOIST

A small timber to which the boards of a floor or the laths of a ceiling are nailed; one of a series of parallel beams, supported in turn by larger beams, girders, or bearing walls.

JOIST HANGER

A metal strap used to suspend floor joists.

KEYHOLE SAW

A keyhole saw resembles a compass saw but has an even more narrow and tapering blade. It is designed for cutting out keyholes.

KEYSTONE

The stone placed in the center of the top of an arch.

KILN-DRIED

Term used to describe material that has been seasoned in a kiln oven rather than in the air.

KINGPOST

The middle post of a trussed piece of framing, for supporting the tie-beam at the middle and the lower ends of the struts.

KNEE

A piece of timber naturally or artificially bent to receive another in order to relieve a weight or strain.

KNUCKLES OF A HINGE

The rounded portion of a hinge plate that takes the hinge pin.

LAG SCREWS

Heavy wood screws used on timbers and heavy beams.

LANDING

A platform in a flight of stairs between two stories, or at the termination of a stairway.

LAP JOINT

A joint formed by lapping the edge of one piece of material over the edge of another.

LAP SIDING

See Bevel Siding.

LATHS

Thin strips of wood four feet long, nailed to studding as supports for plaster. Also, wire-mesh or composition plasterboard.

LATTICE

(1) Any work of wood or metal that is made by crossing laths, rods, or

bars to form a network. (2) A reticulated window, made of laths or slips of iron separated by glass windows. These are used only where air rather than light is to be admitted.

LAVATORY

A place for washing the person.

LEADER

The pipe from the gutter to the ground; a downspout.

LEAN-TO

A small building whose rafters pitch or lean against another building or against a wall.

LEDGE OR LEDGEMENT

A projection from a plane, as slips on the sides of window and door frames to hold them steady in their places.

LEDGERS

The horizontal pieces that are fastened to the standard poles or timbers of scaffolding raised around buildings during their erection. Those which rest on the ledgers are called putlogs, and the boards are laid on these.

LEDGER STRIP

A strip of lumber nailed along the bottom of the side of a girder on which joists rest.

LIGHT

(1) A division or space in a sash for a single pane of glass; (2) a pane of glass.

LINING

(1) Covering for the interior, as casing is covering for the exterior, surface of a building; (2) linings for doors, windows, shutters, etc.

LINTEL

The horizontal piece which covers the opening of a door or window and supports the load over it.

LOAD-BEARING WALL

See Wall, Bearing.

LOT

A subdivision of a block, or another portion of land that is considered as a unit of property and is described by metes and bounds. If one or more lots are built upon as a single unit of property, they are considered as a single lot.

LOOKOUT

A short wood bracket or cantilever which supports an overhanging portion of a roof or the like, usually concealed from view.

LOUVER

A kind of vertical window, frequently in the peaks of gables and in the tops of towers. It is equipped with horizontal slats which permit ventilation and exclude rain, but does not have glass panes.

LUGS

Projections at the ends of door stiles.

MANHOLE

A hole through which a man can creep into a drain, boiler, etc.

MANSARD ROOF

See Curb Roof.

MANTEL

The work over a fireplace in front of a chimney. It usually consists of an ornamented shelf above the fireplace.

MASKING TAPE

A tape with an adhesive on one side,

used for painting and decorating. The tape can be removed without damage to a painted surface.

MASONRY

Brick, stone, tile, or terra-cotta laid in mortar or concrete.

MASONRY BLOCK

A building block of concrete or cinder, usually 7⅝″ x 7⅝″ x 15⅝″.

MASTIC

A type of composition cement used for linoleum and asphalt flooring.

MATCHED BOARDS

Boards cut with tongue and groove.

MEMBERS

The different parts of a building or an entablature, the different moldings of a cornice, and the like.

MITER

A molding returned upon itself at right angles is said to miter. In joinery, when the ends of any two pieces of wood of corresponding form are cut off at 45°, they necessarily abut to form a right angle and are said to miter.

MITER BOX

An apparatus for guiding a handsaw at the proper angle in making a miter joint in wood.

MITER JOINT

A joint made by cutting the ends of two matched pieces so that they join to form a right angle.

MOLDING

Wood that has been milled into special shapes and designs for use as trim. When any work is wrought into long regular channels or projections, forming curves, rounds, hollows, or the like, it is said to be molded, and each separate member is a molding.

MORTAR

A mixture of cement and sand used for bonding bricks and stone.

MORTAR JOINT

That point where two bricks or masonry blocks are joined together with mortar.

MORTICE

A hole cut into a piece of wood to receive a tenon or tongue shaped at the end of another piece of wood. The resulting fit is called a mortice and tenon joint.

MULLION OR MUNION

(1) The perpendicular pieces of stone, sometimes like columns, sometimes like slender piers, which divide the bays or lights of windows or screen-work from each other; (2) a wooden or iron division between two windows.

MURIATIC ACID

Hydrochloric acid used for cleaning cement.

NATURAL BEDS

In stratified rocks, the surface of a stone as it lies in the quarry. If not laid in walls in their natural bed, the layers separate.

NATURAL FINISH

Wood that is left with the natural coloring.

NEWEL POST

The post, plain or ornamented, placed at the first or lowest step so that the beginning of the hand-rail can be placed upon it.

NICHE

A recess sunk in a wall, generally for the reception of a statue.

NON-BEARING PARTITION

A partition extending from floor to ceiling but which supports no load other than its own weight.

NOSINGS

The rounded and projecting edges of the treads of a stair.

NOVELTY SIDING

Wood siding cut into special designs.

OAKUM

A hemp fiber used for caulking.

OFFSETS

When the face of a wall is not one continuous surface but rather sets in by horizontal jogs, the jogs are called offsets.

ON CENTER

From center to center.

ORANGE SHELLAC

Shellac with natural coloring.

ORIEL WINDOW

A projecting, angular window, commonly triagonal or pentagonal in form. These windows are divided by mullions and transoms into different bays and compartments.

OUT OF PLUMB

Not plumb; in other words, not level or vertical.

OWNER

Any person having title to, or control as guardian or trustee of, a building or property.

PALE

A fence picket that is sharpened at the upper end.

PANE

A term applied to each of the pieces of glass in a window; they are also called lights.

PANEL

(1) A piece of wood framed within four other pieces of wood, as in the styles and rails of a door, to fill an opening; (2) the whole square frame and the sinking itself; (3) the ranges of sunken compartments in wainscoting, cornices, corbel tables, groined vaults, ceilings, etc.

PANTRY

An apartment or closet in which bread and other provisions are kept.

PAPIER-MACHÉ

A hard substance made of pulp from rags or paper mixed with size or glue and molded into any desired shape. This material is widely used for architectural ornamentations.

PARALLEL

Running side by side in the same direction.

PARGING

A thin coat of plastering applied to smooth off rough brick or stone walls.

PARTING STRIP

A thin strip of wood nailed between the upper and lower sashes in a double hung window.

PARTITION

A wall that subdivides space within any story of a building. *See* Bearing Partition and Nonbearing Partition.

PENNY (abbreviated *d*)

A measure of nail length. Originally, it indicated the price per hundred.

PENT ROOF

A roof that is sloped on only one side.

PERCH

A unit of measure for stone work. In some localities a perch is equal to 24¾ cu. ft.; in others, 16⅔ cu. ft.

PERPENDICULAR

A line running at right angles to another line, such as a wall to a floor. A vertical line.

PERSPECTIVE DRAWING

The art of drawing an object on a plane surface so that it appears to the eye the same as the object itself would; that is, so that the drawing appears to have a third dimension.

PICKET

A narrow board, often pointed, used in making fences.

PICTURE MOLDING

Special molding attached to the walls and from which pictures are hung. It can be made of either wood or plaster.

PIER GLASS

A large high mirror.

PIERS

(1) The solid parts of a wall between windows and other openings. (2) Masses of brickwork or masonry that are insulated to form supports to gates or to carry arches, posts, girders, etc.

PILE

A large stake or trunk of a tree driven into soft ground, as at the bottom of a river, or in made land, for the support of a building.

PILLARS

The round or polygonal piers, or those surrounded with clustered columns, which carry the main arches of a building.

PIN

A cylindrical piece of wood, iron, or steel, used to hold two or more pieces together by passing through a hole in each of them, as in a mortise and tenon joint or a pin joint of a truss.

PITCH

The slope of a surface, such as a roof or the ground.

PITCH OF A ROOF

The proportion obtained by dividing the height by the span; thus, we speak of it as being one-half, one-third, etc.

PITCHING PIECE

A horizontal timber, with one of its ends wedged into the wall at the top of a flight of stairs, to support the upper end of the rough strings.

PIT SAND

Sand taken directly from the pit.

PLACE

An open piece of ground surrounded by buildings; a place is usually decorated by a statue, column, or other ornament.

PLANE

(1) Of a surface, flat. (2) In joinery, a tool used to smooth the surface of wood to make moldings and the like.

PLANK

A heavy board.

PLASTER

A mixture of sand, water, lime or some other binder, and perhaps a fiber for added strength. The mixture hardens on drying. It is used to coat walls and ceilings.

PLASTER GROUNDS

Wood strips which are attached along the bases of walls and around windows, doors, and other openings where wood trim is to fit over the edge of plaster. They provide a nailing base for the trim.

PLASTERING

Covering walls or ceilings with plaster or a similar material. The plaster is applied to laths which have been nailed to the walls.

PLATE

The piece of timber that supports the end of the rafters in a building. Usually, the 2"x4" timbers running horizontally on the top of wall studding.

PLATE GLASS

Heavy glass used for large areas, such as store display windows.

PLATFORM FRAMING

A system of framing a building in which floor joists of each story rest on the top plates of the story below (or on the foundation sill for the first story) and the bearing walls and partitions rest on the sub-floor of each story.

PLINTH

The square block at the base of a column or pedestal. In a wall, the term plinth is applied to the projecting base or water table.

PLUMB

Perpendicular or in a perfectly upright position; standing according to a plumb line. For example, the post of a house or wall is said to be plumb.

PLUMB CUT

The top cut, where the rafter joins the ridge board.

PLUMBING

The system of pipes and other apparatus employed in conveying water and sewage in a building.

PLUMB LINE

A line or cord weighted at one end used to determine verticality.

PLY

Term used to denote the number of thicknesses of roofing paper, as three-ply, four-ply, etc.

PLYWOOD

A piece of wood made of three or more layers of veneer joined with glue and usually laid with the grain of adjoining plies at right angles. Almost always an odd number of plies are used to secure balanced construction.

POINTING

Filling joints in masonry with mortar and then striking or troweling the joint with the point of the trowel to give a finished appearance. Also, the material used for pointing.

PORCH

A floor extending beyond the exterior walls of a building. It may be enclosed or unenclosed, roofed or uncovered.

PORTLAND CEMENT

A hydraulic cement made by burning and grinding a mixture of pure limestone and clay, or of other aluminous material.

POST

A piece of timber, metal or similar material that is fixed firmly upright, especially when it is meant to serve as a support.

PRIMING

The laying on of the first coat of paint. This coat is usually high in oil content; its purpose is to protect and fill the wood.

PROFILE

(1) The outline or contour of a part or of the parts composing an order. (2) The perpendicular section.

PROTRACTOR

A mathematical instrument designed for laying down and measuring angles on paper. It is used in drawing or plotting.

PUDDLE

Clay, or similar material, worked, when wet, in order to render it impervious to water.

PUGGING

A coarse kind of mortar laid on the boarding between floor joists to prevent the passage of sound; also called deafening.

PUMICE STONE

A finely ground stone used for polishing.

PURLINS

Those pieces of timber which support the rafters to prevent them from sinking.

PUTLOG

Horizontal pieces which support the floor of a scaffold. One end is inserted into a putlog hole that was left in the masonry for that purpose.

PUTTY

(1) A plastic made of powdered whiting and linseed oil. (2) Lump lime slacked with water to the consistency of cream and then left to harden by evaporation until it resembles soft putty. It is then mixed with plaster of Paris or sand for the finishing coat.

PYRAMID

A solid having a particular form. One side, called a base, is a plane figure, and the other sides are triangles. The points of the triangular sides join at one point at the top, called the vertex. A pyramid is called triangular, square, etc., according to the form of its base.

QUARRY

(1) A rock bed. (2) A pane of glass cut in the shape of a diamond or a lozenge.

RABBET

(1) A continuous small recess, generally understood as having a right angle included between its sides, especially one whose sides enclose a relatively restricted area. (2) A groove cut in wood along the edge, particularly to receive the edge of another piece of wood and form a rabbet joint. (3) A recess formed by two planes, very narrow as compared with their length, such as the small recess on a door frame, into

which the edge of a door is made to fit; the recess of a brick jamb to receive a window frame; and the like.

RABBET PLANE

A plane used for cutting rabbets on the edges of timber.

RADIUS

The distance from the center of a circle to the outside edge; one-half of the diameter.

RAFTERS

The joists to which the roof-boarding is nailed. *Principal* rafters are the upper timbers in a truss, having the same inclination as the common rafters. The rafters of a flat roof are sometimes called roof joists. *See* also Hip Rafter, Jack Rafter, and Valley Rafter.

RAIL

A piece of metal or timber extending from one post to another, as in fences, balustrades, staircases, etc. In framing and paneling, the horizontal pieces are called rails; the perpendicular, stiles.

RAKE JOINT

Type of mortar joint between bricks. The mortar is raked out of the joint to a certain depth before it sets.

RAKING

Moldings whose arrises are inclined to the horizon.

RAMP

(1) A concavity on the upper side of hand railings formed over risers, made by a sudden rise of the steps above; (2) any concave bend or slope in the cap or upper member of any piece of ascending or descending workmanship.

RANDOM WORK

A term used by stone masons to describe stones fitted together at random without any attempt at laying them in courses. Random coursed work is a term applied to work coursed in horizontal beds when the stones are of any height.

RANGE WORK

Ashlar laid in horizontal courses. This term is synonymous with coursed ashlar.

RASP

A coarse file used mainly for filing rough surfaces. Like files, rasps are classified from rough to smooth.

REBATE

A groove or channel cut in the edge of a board; a rabbet.

RECESS

A depth of some inches in the thickness of a wall, as a niche, etc.

RED LEAD

A paint primer used on metal.

REINFORCED CONCRETE

Concrete that has been strengthened internally by the use of steel bars or heavy wire mesh.

RENDERING

(1) In drawing, finishing a perspective drawing to bring out the spirit and effect of the design. (2) The first coat of plaster on brick or stone work.

REPAIRS

The reconstruction or renewal of any existing part of a building or of its fixtures or appurtenances.

RETAINING WALL
See Wall, Retaining.

RETURN
The continuation of a molding, projection, etc., in an opposite direction.

RETURN HEAD
One that appears both on the face and edge of a work.

REVEAL
The two vertical sides of an aperture, between the front of a wall and the window or door frame.

RIBBON
A narrow board let into the studding to add support to the joists.

RIDGE
The horizontal line at the top of a roof formed by two surfaces rising to an acute angle.

RIDGE-CAP
A wood or metal cap used over roofing at the ridge.

RIDGEPOLE
The highest horizontal timber in a roof. It extends from top to top of the several pairs of rafters of the trusses, and supports the heads of the jack rafters.

RISE
The distance through which anything rises, as the rise of a stair or an inclined plane.

RISE IN INCHES
Of a roof, the number of inches that the roof actually rises for every foot of run. It is determined by multiplying the pitch by the unit of span.

RISER
The vertical board under the tread in stairs; it forms the front of the stair step.

ROOF
The covering or upper part of any building.

ROOFING
The material put on a roof to make it watertight.

ROUGHCAST
A sort of external plastering in which small, sharp stones are mixed. When it is wet it is forcibly thrown or cast from a trowel against the wall, to which it adheres to form a coating of attractive appearance. When done well, the work is sound and durable. The mortar for roughcast work should always have cement mixed with it.

ROUGH LUMBER
Lumber that has not been surfaced or dressed.

R.P.M.
Revolutions per minute.

RUBBLE WORK
Masonry of rough, undressed stones. When only the roughest irregularities are knocked off, it is called scabbled rubble; when the stones in each course are rudely dressed to nearly a uniform height, ranged rubble.

RUN
The shortest horizontal distance that the rafter must cover.

RUST
A reddish coating that forms on iron as the result of oxidation.

RUSTIC OR ROCK WORK
A mode of building in imitation of

nature. This term is applied to those courses of stone work having a jagged face or to those that have been picked to present a rough surface. That work is also called rustic in which the horizontal and vertical channels are cut in the joinings of stones, so that when placed together an angular channel is formed at each joint. *Frosted rustic work* has the margins of the stones reduced to a plane parallel with the plane of the wall, the intermediate parts having an irregular surface. In *vermiculated rustic work* the intermediate parts are so worked as to appear worm-eaten. In *rustic chamfered work* the face of the stones is smooth and parallel to the face of the wall; the angles are beveled to an angle of 135° with the face, so that when two stones come together on the wall the beveling forms an internal right angle.

SADDLE BOARD
Boards nailed along the ridge of a roof.

SAGGING
The bending of a body in the middle by its own weight or by the load upon it.

SANITARY SEWER
A sewer for sewage disposal only, as differentiated from a storm sewer, which is intended for rainfall disposal.

SASH
The framework that moves and holds the panes of glass in a window.

SASH WEIGHT
Metal bar attached to the end of the window sash cord and used to balance the sash.

SCABBLE
To dress off the rougher projections of stones for rubble masonry. This is usually done with a stone axe or a scabbling hammer.

SCANTLING
(1) The width and thickness of a piece of timber. (2) The studding for a partition, when it is under five inches square. (3) Small pieces of dimension lumber. The term is often applied to 2″x4″s and 2″x6″s.

SCARFING
Joining and bolting two pieces of timber together transversely so that the two appear to be one.

SCONCE
A fixed hanging or projecting candlestick.

SCORE
To make notches or incisions along a cutting line.

SCRATCH COAT
The first coat of plaster. It is scratched to afford a bond for the second coat.

SCREEDS
Long, narrow strips of plaster put on horizontally along a wall and carefully faced out of wind. They serve as guides for plastering the wide intervals between them.

SCREEN
(1) A perforated or meshed fabric, usually framed, used to separate finer from coarser parts; a sieve. (2)

A wall or partition which does not reach up to the ceiling. (3) A perforated covering, as a window screen or a fire screen.

SCRIBING

Fitting woodwork to an irregular surface.

SECTION

A drawing showing the internal heights of the various parts of a building. It supposes the building to be cut through entirely, so as to show the walls, the heights of the internal doors and other apertures, the heights of the stories, the thicknesses of the floors, etc.

SERVICE HEAD

A special fitting used where service wires leave the conduit or cable to be attached to power lines; it prevents moisture from entering the conduit or cable.

SETBACK

A flat, plain setoff in a wall. Also, a setting back of the outside wall of a building for some distance from the street.

SETOFF

The horizontal line shown where a wall is reduced in thickness and, consequently, the part of the thicker portion seems to project beyond the thinner. In plinths this is usually simply chamfered. In other parts of the work the setoff is generally concealed by a projecting string.

SHAFT

(1) Any open space, other than a court, that extends through a building for two or more stories. It may be interior or exterior, and it may be for air, light, elevator, dumb-waiter or other purposes. A vent-shaft is one used solely to ventilate or light a water-closet compartment, bathroom, or pantry. (2) Slender columns, standing either alone or in connection with pillars, jambs, vaulting, etc.

SHEATHING

Boards nailed over rafters or studding to serve as a base for roofing or siding.

SHEATHING PAPER

A building material used in wall, floor, and roof construction to resist the passage of air.

SHED ROOF OR LEAN-TO

A roof having only one set of rafters, falling from a higher to a lower wall, like an aisle roof.

SHIM

A strip of material used to fill a small space.

SHINGLES

Roof covering made of wood cut to stock lengths and thicknesses and to random widths.

SHIPLAP

Boards cut along the edge in such a fashion that when nailed alongside one another they form a half-lap joint.

SHOE MOLD OR BASE SHOE

A strip of quarter-round that is nailed across the joint between the floor and the baseboard.

SHORE

A piece of timber placed in an oblique direction to support a building or wall temporarily while it is being repaired or altered.

SHOULDER
A projecting part.

SIDING
Boards used as exterior walls.

SILEX
Finely ground quartz used as a filler.

SILL
(1) Those pieces of timber or stone at the bottoms of doors and windows. (2) The wood portion of a house that rests on the foundations; the timbers on the ground which support the posts and superstructure of a timber building.

SIZE
Glue, varnish, shellac, etc. used to seal pores of material to be painted.

SIZING
A coating applied to plaster or wallboard before paint or paste is put on, to prevent uneven absorption.

SKINTLED BRICKWORK
Irregularly formed brickwork arranged with variations in projections on the outside face-wall. It is usually made of irregularly shaped bricks.

SKIRTING
Trim used between floor and walls; the narrow boards that form a plinth around the margin of a floor. More often called baseboard.

SLEEPER
A piece of timber laid on the ground to receive floor joists.

SMOKE CHAMBER
Portion of a fireplace directly over the damper.

SOFFIT
The lower horizontal face of a part or member of a building.

SOIL PIPE
A cast-iron pipe used for the house sewer line.

SOLDER
An alloy of tin and lead having a low melting point. It is used for joining metal.

SOLDIERS
In brickwork, bricks set on edge.

SOLE OR SOLE PLATE
A horizontal member, usually a 2"x4", on which wall and partition studs rest.

SPACE HEATERS
Small automatic heaters; pipeless furnaces that do not have to be installed in basements.

SPACERS
Wood strips used to hold the sides of a concrete form an equal distance apart at various points.

SPALL
(1) Inferior or broken brick; (2) stone chips.

SPAN
The distance between the supports of a beam, girder, arch, truss, etc.

SPECIFICATION
The designation of the kind, quality, and quantity of work and material that are to go into a building, in conjunction with the working drawings.

SPLAYED
The jamb of a door, or anything else of which one side makes an oblique angle with the other.

S.S. Glass

Single-strength glass, used in ordinary window panes.

Staging

A structure of posts and boards for supporting workmen and materials in building.

Stile

The upright side frames of a panel door.

Stilted

Term used to describe anything raised above its usual level.

Stool

The inside sill of a window frame.

Stoop

A seat before the door; often a porch with a balustrade and seats on the sides.

Story

That portion of a building included between the surface of any floor and the surface of the next floor above. If there is no floor above, it is the space between the floor surface and the ceiling or roof above. A half-story is that portion of any building wholly or partly within the roof framing. In some sections, a basement or cellar is considered as a story if its ceiling is more than five feet above grade.

Strap

An iron plate for connecting two or more timbers, to which it is screwed by bolts. It generally passes around one of the timbers.

Strap Hinge

A heavy hinge used on large doors.

Straightedge

A board with a straight side used for measuring and drawing.

Stretcher

A brick or block of masonry laid lengthwise in a wall.

String Board

A board placed next to the well-hole in wooden stairs, terminating the end of the steps.

String-course

A narrow, vertically faced, slightly projecting course in an elevation. If window sills are made continuous, they form a string-course; but if this course is made thicker or deeper than ordinary window sills, or covers a set-off in the wall, it becomes a blocking-course.

Stringers

The sides of a flight of stairs. Also called carriages.

String Piece

The piece of board put under the treads and risers to form the support of the stair.

Struck Joint

A mortar joint used in brickwork.

Strut

Timber used as a brace or support, such as framing.

Stucco

Any material used to cover walls and the like, put on wet and drying hard and durable. Plaster, when applied to walls in the usual way, is a kind of stucco; the hard finish is almost exactly like fine Roman stucco except that it is applied in one thin coat instead of many. The term is commonly used for outer walls. The practical value of stucco is very great, this material being almost impervious to water. An excellent wall three or more stories high can be built with eight inches of brick on the inner side, four inches of brick on the outer side, an air space of two or four inches across which the outer and inner walls are well tied, and two coats of well-mixed and well-laid stucco on the exterior. The stucco is finally painted with oil paint.

STUDS OR STUDDING
The small timbers used in partitions and outside wooden walls, to which the laths and boards are nailed. The uprights of a wall. The 2″x4″ stock used to frame the sides of a building.

SUB-FLOOR
The rough floor under the finish floor.

SUMMER
A girder or main-beam of a floor. If supported on two-story posts and open below, it is called a brace-summer.

SUMP
A pit, well, or the like in which water or other liquid is collected.

SURFACE LUMBER
Lumber that has been dressed.

SWEATING
The condensation of moisture vapor on a surface.

TAIL BEAM
A relatively short beam or joist supported in a wall on one end and by a header on the other.

TAIL TRIMMER
A trimmer next to the wall, into which the ends of joists are fastened to avoid fires.

TAMP
To pound earth down firmly.

TANG
Portion of metal tool that fits into handle.

TEMPLATE
A pattern cut out of paper, cardboard, or a similar material. Also, a short piece of timber put under a girder or other beam for added strength. A beam over an opening, such as a doorway.

TENON
Tongue or lip cut on a piece of wood to fit into a mortice.

TERRA COTTA
Baked clay of a fine quality. Used for architectural ornaments, statues, vases, etc.

THICKNESS
In lumber, the distance between the two broad surfaces. *See* also Wall Thickness.

T-HINGE
A hinge shaped like the letter T.

THRESHOLD
A piece of wood or metal under a door.

THROAT
(1) Opening at top of fireplace into chimney where damper is located. (2) A channel or groove made on the under side of a string-course, coping, etc., to prevent water from running inward toward the walls.

TIE

A timber, rod, chain, etc., which binds together two bodies that have a tendency to separate or diverge from one another. The *tie-beam* connects the bottom of a pair of principal rafters and prevents them from bursting out the wall.

TILES

Flat pieces of clay burned in kilns, used in place of slates or lead to cover roofs. Also used for floors and wainscoting, about fireplaces, etc. Small squares of marble are also called tiles. Tiles are also made of plastic or metal and often used in these forms to cover walls.

TIN SNIPS

Shears used for cutting thin metal.

T-JOINT

A joint shaped like the letter T.

TOENAIL

To drive a nail in at an angle in order to permit it to penetrate a second member. This makes a stronger joint than does driving the nail straight down.

TONGUE

The part of a board left projecting so that it can be inserted into a groove.

TRANSFORMER

An electrical device used to reduce voltage.

TRANSOM

(1) The horizontal construction that divides a window into heights or stages. (2) A window which is built above a door or other window and is attached to a transom.

TRAVERSE

To plane in a direction across the grain of the wood, as to traverse a floor by planing across the boards.

TREAD

The horizontal part of a step of a stair.

TRELLIS

Latticework of metal or wood for vines to run on.

TRESTLE

A movable frame or support for anything. When made of a cross-piece with four legs, it is called a horse.

TRIM

(1) The finish materials in a building, such as moldings applied around openings (window trim, door trim) or at the floor and ceiling of rooms (baseboard, cornice, picture molding). These are almost always made of wood. (2) Of a door, sometimes used to denote the locks, knobs, and hinges.

TRIMMER

The beam or floor joist to which a header is nailed in the framing for either a chimney, a stairway, or other opening.

TRIMMER ARCH

An arch built in front of a fireplace, in the thickness of the floor, between two trimmers. The bottom of the arch starts from the chimney, and the top presses against the header.

TUCK-POINTING

Marking the joints of brickwork with a narrow, parallel ridge of fine putty.

TURPENTINE, GUM

Liquid used in painting. The distilled gum from yellow pine trees.

TURPENTINE, WOOD

Liquid extracted from pine wood waste by distillation or by solvents.

UNIT OF RUN

The unit of measurement used with a framing square for measuring rafters.

UNIT OF SPAN

Twice the unit of run.

UPSET

To thicken and shorten, as by hammering a heated bar of iron on the end.

VALLEY

The internal angle formed by two inclined sides of a roof.

VALLEY RAFTER

A rafter that forms the intersection of an internal roof angle.

VEHICLE

In painting, the liquid with which the paint pigment is mixed so that it can be brushed on a surface.

VENEER

A thin layer of wood glued to a base made of a cheaper or inferior wood.

VERGE

The edge of the tiling, slate, or shingles projecting over the gable of a roof, that on the horizontal portion being called eaves.

VERGE BOARD OR BARGE BOARD

The board under the verge of gables.

VERMICULATED

Stones and other materials that have been worked so as to have the appearance of being worm-eaten.

VITRIFIED SOIL PIPE

Hard-baked clay pipe used for outside sewer lines.

WAINSCOTING

Wooden lining of the lower portion of an interior wall, generally in panel form.

WALL, BEARING

A wall which supports any vertical load other than its own weight. It may support joists, beams, girders, or the trusses of a floor.

WALLBOARD

Wood pulp, gypsum, or a similar material made into large, rigid sheets that can be fastened to the frame of a building to provide a surface finish.

WALL, CURTAIN

An enclosing wall, built and supported between columns and piers, which sustains no weight other than its own.

WALL, DIVISION

A bearing wall which runs between two exterior walls and subdivides the building into several parts.

WALL, EXTERIOR

An outside wall that serves as a vertical enclosure of a building.

WALL, FIRE

A wall of solid masonry or reinforced concrete which subdivides a building to restrict the spread of fire and which starts at the foundation and extends continuously through all stories to and above the roof.

WALL, FIRE DIVISION

This is the same as a fire wall, except that it is not necessarily continuous through all stories and it does not necessarily extend beyond the roof.

WALL, FOUNDATION

That portion of an enclosing wall below the first tier of floor-joists or beams nearest to and above the grade-line, and that portion of any interior wall or pier below the basement or cellar-floor.

WALL, NON-BEARING

A wall designed to carry only its own weight.

WALL, PARTITION

See Partition.

WALL, PARTY

A wall that is used jointly by two buildings.

WALL PLATES

Pieces of timber placed on top of brick or stone walls in order to support the roof of a building.

WALL, RETAINING

A wall designed to resist lateral pressure. It may resist the lateral pressure of either the adjoining earth or internal loads.

WALL THICKNESS

The minimum thickness required by a building code for the walls between the floors and the ceiling or roof of a structure.

WANE

The natural curvature of a log or of the edge of a board sawed from an unsquared log.

WARPED

Twisted out of shape by seasoning.

WATER TABLE

A molding or slight projection on the outside of a wall. It usually

occurs a few feet above the ground, and it serves as a protection against rain.

WEATHER BOARDING

Boards lapped over each other to prevent rain, etc., from passing through.

WEATHERING

A slight fall on the tops of cornices, window sills, etc., to throw off the rain.

WEEP HOLE

A small hole in a masonry wall. Its function is to permit water to drain through.

WELDING

A method of attaching pieces of metal by means of intense heat.

WET-WALL CONSTRUCTION

See Dry-wall Construction.

WHITE LEAD

A paint pigment.

WIDTH

In lumber, the distance across the grain on the broadest surface.

WIND

A turn or a bend. A wall is said to be out of the wind when it is a perfectly flat surface.

WINDOW FRAME

The portion of the window that holds the sashes.

WINDOW SILL

The bottom of a window frame.

WITHES

The partition between two chimney flues in the same stack.

YARD

An open, unoccupied space on the same lot as the house.

INDEX

*following a page number indicates an illustration.